HUMANITAS

Readings in the Development of the
Medical Humanities

Perspectives in Medical Humanities

Perspectives in Medical Humanities publishes scholarship produced or reviewed under the auspices of the University of California Medical Humanities Consortium, a multi-campus collaborative of faculty, students and trainees in the humanities, medicine, and health sciences. Our series invites scholars from the humanities and health care professions to share narratives and analysis on health, healing, and the contexts of our beliefs and practices that impact biomedical inquiry.

General Editor

Brian Dolan, PhD, Professor of Social Medicine and Medical Humanities, University of California, San Francisco (UCSF)

Recent Titles

Health Citizenship: Essays in Social Medicine and Biomedical Politics
By Dorothy Porter (Winter 2012)

What to Read on Love, Not Sex: Freud, Fiction, and the
Articulation of Truth in Modern Psychological Science
By Edison Miyawaki, MD, Foreword by Harold Bloom (Fall 2012)

Patient Poets: Illness from Inside Out
Marilyn Chandler McEntyre (Fall 2012) (Pedagogy in Medical Humanities series)

Bioethics and Medical Issues in Literature
Mahala Yates Stripling (Fall 2013) (Pedagogy in Medical Humanities series)

Heart Murmurs: What Patients Teach their Doctors
Edited by Sharon Dobie, MD (Fall 2014)

www.UCMedicalHumanitiesPress.com

brian.dolan@ucsf.edu

This series is made possible by the generous support of the Dean of the School of Medicine at UCSF, the Center for Humanities and Health Sciences at UCSF, and a University of California Research Initiative, Grant ID 141374.

HUMANITAS

Readings in the Development of the Medical Humanities

Edited by Brian Dolan

First published in 2015

by the University of California Medical Humanities Press

UCMedicalHumanitiesPress.com

© 2015

University of California

Medical Humanities Consortium

3333 California Street, Suite 485

San Francisco, CA 94143-0850

Designed by Virtuoso Press

Cover photo courtesy of the Wellcome Library, London.

Colour photograph showing an anatomical model advertising a pharmacy in Delhi, India. The model is behind glass and surrounded with bottles. The pharmacist's name, Kaviraj A N Roy, BSc, MASFRMP, is written on a label at the top left of the glass case. A man, the pharmacist, sits reading a book.

Library of Congress Control Number: 2015937544

ISBN: 978-0-9889865-7-2 (Print)

ISBN: 978-0-9889865-9-6 (ePub)

Printed in USA

"Not many students today perceive the value of a rigorous education in the cognitive elements of traditional humanism. Some will perceive them later in life, when medicine itself becomes so routinized as to verge on boredom."
—*Edmund D. Pellegrino, MD*

This book is dedicated to all the students who desire to pursue *humanitas* – education in humanism – to broaden their perspectives on the art and science of healthcare.

Contents

Preface & Acknowledgments

Humanities-based instruction in medical training has a long history. Spanning more than a hundred years of medical education in the United States, a science-driven and clinical-skills oriented curriculum has been integrated with subjects that draw on broader cultural and philosophical perspectives for critical reflection on medical practice. Concerns over the essentials of a well-rounded medical curriculum have yielded enormous amounts of published commentaries, critiques, and recommendations. Along the way, educators have developed new subjects and disciplines of use to future health professionals, have added strength to the concept of a "field" of medical humanities, and have diversified its curricular presence.

The articles reproduced here, which span the period from the early 1900s to 2011, provide a one-stop introductory guide to the major developments in the history of this field. These selections, it is hoped, portray the historical depth and range of articulations, even to those familiar with the medical humanities who have followed recent debates about its uses and outcomes in professional education. From the purported gaps in prerequisite training in the years preceding the Flexner report, to the "moral challenges" of the 1950s and 1960s, to concern over professionalism and communication skills in the 1990s and 2000s, the evolving relationship between the humanities and medicine is a history of reflection on the philosophy of education and the conduct of medical practice. Overall, these articles reveal that humanities subjects in medical education respond not only to alleged problems or lacunae in medical training (whether that is being too technological or disease-centered), but to the changing social context that impacts the form and practice of medicine. Yet despite a history of strategies to bring holism to the education of healthcare professionals, there remain common and persistent challenges to the endeavor that go far back in time. An historical perspective is therefore useful to anyone teaching medical humanities or developing courses within this area.

I started teaching the medical humanities in 2004, soon after it was created as an "Area of Concentration" for fourth-year medical student research projects at the University of California, San Francisco. Dividing my time between teaching graduate courses for PhD students in the history of medicine program and teaching medical students, I struggled at the beginning to find the right balance in the level of scholarship assigned for discussion and measured my expectations of what could be accomplished over the course of one elective term. In the five years I directed that program before it was discontinued by a major curricular reform at the school, my colleagues and I felt that we had finally succeeded in engaging a multi-disciplinary humanities curriculum with medical knowledge and healthcare. The projects the students produced were informative, creative, and often extremely meaningful.

Throughout that time, however, when I was educating myself about all the different approaches that encompass the medical humanities – narrative medicine, literature in/and medicine, readers' theater, and so on – I was tasked with answering regular questions from curricular organizers and committee members about why the medical humanities were important to medical education. These are questions that almost everyone teaching medical humanities in medical schools needs to answer, repeatedly. Perhaps I would have been better prepared with these answers, better equipped to develop courses using diverse approaches, had I known the history of others' attempts and rationales for doing the same. As an historian of science and medicine by training, my instinct has been to comb the literature, looking further and further back, for insights as to how this all came about. Going back to the beginning of the twentieth century, the emphasis here is on historical, primary readings that address the philosophy of medical humanities and the challenge of integration into medical education. It will be easy to criticize all that has been omitted from this volume – particularly among the selections of more recent decades, when the amount of literature expands exponentially. The limitations of copyright permissions and occasional denials of requests to reproduce meant that some important pieces do not appear here, though I refer to some of these in the thematic introduction to the volume.

I would like to make special note of a few titles that should be acknowledged as important sources of information on the state of the art of medical humanities. The *Journal of Medical Humanities* is the first. The history of this journal itself provides interesting insights to the evolution of the field, starting off as *Bioethics Quarterly* in 1979, becoming the *Journal of Medical Humanities and Bioethics* in 1985, and assuming its present title in 1989. The apparent disappearance of bioethics from the realm of medical humanities is a story not presented here ("apparent" because there is not an absolute divide), but since some readers will wonder about the lack of "classic" bioethics articles as part of this volume, I wish just to comment that this is because I decided that bioethics has formed enough of a separate identity to warrant a separate volume. The diversity of disciplines and the coverage of topics in the *Journal of Medical Humanities*, as well as the younger British journal *Medical Humanities* (a joint publication by the Institute of Medical Ethics and the *BMJ*), have been pioneering in advancing the philosophy and logistics of the field.

Another journal that has attempted to connect humanities with medical curricula is *Academic Medicine* (the special issue in 1995, volume 70, number 9, established its commitment to regular reports on the development of the medical humanities). Edited volumes have begun to appear with new scholarship organized thematically and pragmatically: Ronald Carson, Chester Burns, and Thomas Cole's *Practicing the Medical Humanities: Engaging Physicians and Patients* (Hagerstown, MD: University Publishing Group, 2003); Victoria Bates, Alan Bleakley, and Sam Goodman, eds., *Medicine, Health, and the Arts: Approaches to the Medical Humanities* (London: Routledge, 2013); Jerry B. Vannatta and Ronald Schleifer, *Chief Concern of Medicine: The Integration of the Medical Humanities and Narrative Knowledge into Medical Practice* (Ann Arbor: The University of Michigan Press, 2013); Thomas Cole, Nathan Carlin, and Ronald Carson, *Medical Humanities: An Introduction* (Cambridge: Cambridge University Press 2014), are all notable publications.

I'll mention one more recent volume separately: Therese Jones, Delese Wear, and Lester D. Friedman, eds., *Health Humanities Reader* (New Brunswick, NJ: Rutgers University Press, 2014) is a volume edited by pioneers in the field who chose "health humanities" as a title for their book to indicate a wider scope. In the spirit of interprofessional education that is spreading among health science campuses, many feel that the "medical" in medical humanities is interpreted or applied too narrowly to medical schools and the training of physicians. Health humanities includes all healthcare professionals and even patients. I mention this to address the reason that the present volume retains the term "medical humanities." I believe this is warranted because its concern is the historical roots of the field and the articulation with "medical" education, but with the acknowledgement that it could equally refer to other practitioners also involved with medical care.

I would like to acknowledge the advice and encouragement of a number of scholars who have been instrumental in the development and promotion of medical (or health) humanities and took time to consider my bibliographic choices: Felice Aull, Jack Coulehan, Therese Jones, Martin Kohn, Guy Micco, Johanna Shapiro, and Delese Wear. I am grateful to the editorial board at the University of California Medical Humanities Press for their guidance. I regret that not every recommendation could be included. Despite all intentions to be thorough, limitations beyond my control yielded a shorter, more selective, volume.

My colleagues in the Department of Anthropology, History and Social Medicine and the course directors in the School of Medicine provided the wonderful context in which this research and the work of medical humanities takes place at UCSF. I would like to thank Deanne Dunbar at Emory University for her reading of the manuscript and critical comments.

This project would not have been possible without the generous financial support provided by the University of California Office of the President who awarded Grant ID No. 141374 under the University of California Research Initiatives program to fund the UC Medical Humanities Consortium, the publisher for the series. Matching funds for this endeavor were provided by the Dean of the School of Medicine at UCSF. Finally, I wish to thank Professor Dorothy Porter as director of the Center for Humanities and Health Sciences at UCSF for supporting this project and more generally the UC Medical Humanities Press book series.

1

One Hundred Years of Medical Humanities:
A Thematic Overview

Brian Dolan

When pressed to define "medical humanities," it becomes more inclusive than exclusive, thereby resisting conventional disciplinary identity. History of medicine, bioethics, narrative medicine, medicine in literature, creative writing, disability studies, and various social sciences (for example, medical anthropology and sociology) can all be part of medical humanities programs or curricula. However, "it" (*the* medical humanities is often used in the singular, as a unified presence) also embraces the creative arts, so that music, painting, reader's theater, and dance are considered expressive of medical humanities. Anything that touches on "the humanizing process" or "the humanist philosophy" becomes relevant. Medical humanities programs are often conceived as having two functions. First, they service a deficit in medical education by facilitating a wider perspective and reflection on healthcare, broadening the minds and qualitative research skills of students. Second, they promote better healthcare through therapeutic interventions and outreach to patients using literature, art, writing, and other creative media for health recovery and promotion. Recognizing the growth and nourishment that the medical humanities presently enjoys in institutions across many countries, historicizing the humanities in medicine movement allows us to reflect on the degree to which problems with its curricular integration have been solved, and which seem to endure.

Despite a wide array of humanities subjects on offer and varied functions they allegedly serve to educate physicians, throughout the twentieth century there has been marked success in the institutionalization of the medical humanities. The first mention of a specific "Department of Medical Humanities" that I have found was in 1948, in reference to anticipated medical school reforms at New York University.[1] (Though the department never materialized.) The first Department of Humanities in a medical school was established in the Hershey Medical Center at Pennsylvania State University in 1967. In 1988, the Institute for the Medical Humanities at the University of Texas Medical Branch at Galveston was the first program in the United States to offer a PhD degree in the medical humanities.[2] New medical schools are being designed from the beginning with Departments of Medical Humanities. With funding initiatives through bodies such as the Wellcome Trust, new centers and research collaborations are being supported throughout the UK. This is in addition to individual faculty appointments and specialized programs, like the history of medicine programs established at Johns Hopkins in the 1920s or the University of California, San Francisco, in 1930.

It has been often argued that the *raison d'être* of the medical humanities is to remind us that modern medicine should look beyond its technological fixation and reductionism to reconnect with the conditions of disease and the cultural contexts of illness, as well as the myriad ways people cope with them. It is an antidote to the alleged dehumanization of modern medical education that is always on the verge of failing to foster empathic patient care.

Seen as inherently bound to concerns over the human condition, much attention has been given throughout the previous century to the uses of certain humanities subjects for improving medical training and the minds and skills of future physicians. To be sure, what we see throughout the hundred years or so reviewed here are specific examples of how subjects such as history, literature, philosophy, theater, creative writing, and so on, work to enhance fundamental aspects of the education of physicians. "The education of physicians," however, is a different idea than "medical education," and this nuance provides insight to the evolution of the philosophy of collegiate and professional education throughout the period. This thematic overview begins with a look at how the medical humanities, or certain subjects within it, first helped to shape the idea of a liberal medical education. It then looks at the funding and institutional nourishment medical humanities received mid-century through its efforts to promote "human values" in medical education. The concluding sections look at the institutional expansion of medical humanities through the popular literature and medicine movement, and the branching areas of medical humanities that diversify the pedagogical programs.

This account is by no means intended to be an exhaustive literature review, or address every development and definition of medical humanities. It merely identifies certain themes that are also revealed through the selected classic readings reproduced here as a guide to some of the major topics of discussion and events that led us to where we are today.

From Curricular Reform to Character Reform

At the beginning of the twentieth century, prerequisites for admission to medical school were very different from now. As the American Medical Association's Council on Medical Education reported in 1910, in summary of the findings of the "Flexner report," the very definition of a "medical school" itself was variable, with nation-wide differences in educational prerequisites, facilities available, and subjects taught. The report envisioned a new standard modeled on what almost half of the existing medical schools were requiring at the time: "A four-year high school education; a year or two in the university laboratories of chemistry, physics, and biology; four years in the medical school, and a clinical year as an interne in the hospital."[3]

However, as the separate *Report of the Commissioner on Education* for the US Bureau of Education indicated that same year, high school standards were also variable. This meant that educational prerequisites and expectations were poorly defined for doctors in training at the beginning of the twentieth century. With the early reforms in medical education following the Flexner report, discussions emerged regarding what subjects would best prepare physicians for their craft. While the sciences were prominent in these deliberations, other subjects were considered essential (by some) to prepare the student to do research that engaged with an international community, to work with a diverse population of patients, and to run a business. Therefore, the education of a physician was best supported by offering courses in French and German, since many scientific publications emanated from those countries; sociology and history, to understand better the dynamics of the practice of medicine; and economics, to foster understanding of the financial aspects of providing medical services.

Thus, the integration of what might be considered humanities subjects to medical school education was intended to provide foundational knowledge that was otherwise not provided in earlier education. While various subjects and courses were deployed in medical schools to fulfill these needs, early attempts never congealed into a unified "humanities" presence in the curriculum, akin to something like the triad of chemistry, biology, and physics. In the first few decades of the twentieth century, the one subject that stands out as providing an added value to the education of a physician – in terms of the number of schools that identified it as a part of their curriculum – is history of medicine. We will return to that below.

However, as the decades passed, more humanities subjects began to appear as useful in their own ways to the education of physicians. But with intellectual expansion comes a kind of cranial pressure, so to speak. The curriculum reaches a point of maximum capacity, and everything that wants a presence in it jostles for space. With national standards and medical boards driving the requirements for a knowledge base, the challenge became one of justifying what might be perceived as unnecessary expansion for medical degree qualification. If it is not on the exam, why teach it? These challenges will be examined in relation to the various innovations that are made throughout the century by different disciplines, but we here recognize that at certain moments a broader vision of educational reform emerges that recalls the need for "the humanities" writ large to address what are perceived as systemic problems with medical education, returning to the ideal of educating physicians.

If the term "medical humanities" is somewhat vague and its *modus operandi* varied, the results of its pedagogical offerings can be equally indistinct. True, an essay written with the advice of an English professor or an acrylic painting executed under the guidance of an artist can yield a polished product. But unless the intention is to award a dual degree, the function of the medical humanities is usually not to produce independent essayists or artists. The curricular context is not meant to yield specialists but rather, it is said, to improve behavior through liberal education. The result of medical humanities as it was articulated around mid-century was to produce a "humanist physician." But this ideal seemed to blur two ancient concepts, one relating to "good education" and the other to "good feelings." As the eminent physician and ethicist Edmund Pellegrino wrote in 1974, "the meaning of the word *humanitas*, from which 'humanism' was later derived ... is more properly subsumed under the Greek term *paideia* – an educational and cognitive ideal; and the 'good' feeling – what we would call compassion – is more akin to the Greek concept of *philanthropia*."[4] So, onto the shoulders of the humanities was placed the unenviable task of providing a well-rounded, liberal education that at once broadened perspective on the social relations of medical practice *and* enhanced human values. Could such lofty ideals be attained?

In a crowded curriculum, the question became whether the humanities are capable of demonstrating success in providing students with *humanitas* and *philanthropia*. And if could not be demonstrated, was it then worth the time and effort in the context of pressured training, where skill at data collection, diagnosis, and treatment decisions can be more sharply assessed. In the physician-writer Rafael Campo's words, "Can we really expect beleaguered clinicians and medical educators to teach ethical thinking or to nurture compassion to trainees who come to their prospective profession lacking these fundamental personal virtues that more appropriately ought to have been instilled in them by their parents, or by immersion in what should be a healthier, more universally humane society?"[5] In other words, in contrast to the early twentieth-century sentiment that: "we'll do it ourselves if no educational provision existed earlier to train physicians foundational non-medical skills," the mentality entering the second half of the twentieth century in medical schools seemed to be: "is it really our job to do what should be done elsewhere." In some respects the puzzling question about this from a historical perspective is why more consideration and debate was not given to pre-medical curricular requirements where more opportunity exists in systems of liberal education to take humanities courses. Flexner, it seems, was more concerned about the preparatory education of students entering medical school than medical educators a half century later.

As the medical curriculum developed as a system designed by professional educators (who formed their own discipline), the languages used to justify all aspects of the curriculum turned "the education of a physician" into a dimension of "medical education." A subject's curricular presence hinged on its ability to demonstrate utility in answering a needs assessment with measurable outcomes. Are such things as "empathy" and "compassion" capable of being objectively taught? As we will see, this is a debate that is still occurring today. Yet before we examine persisting problems with integrating medical humanities to medical education, let us historicize the notion that the humanities builds character and trace how this function was overshadowed by social ideology as the impetus behind embracing medical humanities. The place of history of medicine in medical education provides a good example.

The History of History in Medical Education

Historical instruction in American medical curricula was prevalent in the first half of the twentieth century.[6] By 1930, two medical schools, Johns Hopkins and the University of California (at San Francisco, now UCSF), established Departments of Medical History. The results of a survey of US medical schools by Henry Sigerist published in 1939 showed that 46 out of all 77 medical schools offered integrated medical history courses (two-thirds of those schools requiring enrollment in the courses).[7] Yet, by this point, medical history in medical schools seemed to have reached its peak. In 1969, the historian Genevieve Miller published the results of a field survey of all existing 85 medical schools reporting that 33 offered course instruction in medical history (11 requiring it).[8] However, the number of dedicated departments or divisions of history of medicine among them had increased to twelve, with six of these offering separate graduate degrees in the subject.[9]

Early twentieth-century writers argued for the practical utility of having students read historical medical texts as part of their medical training. For faculty with a philosophic bent, history taught students hard truths about medical knowledge – namely, that it was unpredictable. In 1904, the physician Eugene Cordell, president of both the Medical and Chirurgical Faulty of Maryland and the Johns Hopkins Hospital Historical Club, expressed concern about the "inexcusable apathy on the part of our medical schools" for teaching medical history.[10] Cordell advised his medical readership that history not only contained a store of valuable yet forgotten knowledge, but lessons about past failures and follies that could induce humility and perspective on the changing nature of medical knowledge. In 1919, Charles Singer, a British medical officer, Oxford University Regius Professor of Medicine, and doyen of history of science and medicine, lamented the provision of medical history in British medical education. He too argued that history was important because it demonstrated how the "presentation of truth" changed through time. Only dogmatists, he expressed, would maintain a vestige of eternal truth or tout the timeless stability of scientific knowledge.[11]

In 1948, the physician and historian of medicine Henry Sigerist opined that medical history books "were read for their practical content, irrespective of the period at which they had been written. Doctors read them in order to learn how to treat their patients, and they thought that they could gain practical knowledge from Hippocrates or from Sydenham."[12] But he also pointed out that the rise of the "new pathology" changed the concept of the relevance of older clinical practices. "The old literature reflected a different concept of disease," he wrote. That concept "knew nothing of new diagnosis, was ignorant of many new treatments, surgical and others."[13] Thus the recourse of using them in modern medical education was to demonstrate the value of documenting change. If many points of practice were rendered useless with the rise of germ theory, at least history of medicine retained value as a way of demonstrating the impact of conceptual revolutions on medical practice.

With the emergence of new ways of conceptualizing disease in the mid-twentieth century came new ways of offering historical insight to the conditions of disease prevalence and propagation. Once disease itself was conceptualized as "social," as the outcome of poverty or disparities in healthcare provision, historical scholarship found new claims to offer practical contributions to medical literature, allied to transformations in medical practice itself. Both in Britain and in the US, the mid-twentieth century saw the creation of social medicine programs bolstered by funding bodies such as the Russell Sage Foundation. Situated to enable medical schools to interact with the world outside laboratory walls, institutes were founded to facilitate interdisciplinary research into the social and economic problems of medical care. Scholars on both sides of the Atlantic, including historically-minded medical educators like Henry Sigerist and George Rosen, promoted the view that physicians must assume leadership in the struggle for the improvement of social welfare.[14] Thus, as a humanities discipline finding a place for itself in medical curricula, history was used first as a mechanism to instill humility among doctors, and then as a tool to advocate for social rights. Its function changed alongside coeval changes in medical epistemology, underscoring the original point about teaching history to medical students that nothing is stable.

While this impacted developments in medical education, the rise of social medicine was more closely tied to social science research than historical or humanities-based research. While Sigerist's own students were taught that "the new physician [of the twentieth century] will be the social physician, protecting the people and guiding them to a happier and healthier life," the agenda for historical research was rearticulated.[15] Although Sigerist was a notable proponent of the history of medicine, historian John Pickstone has observed that "it was through his commitment to teaching the social relations of medicine that Sigerist found a wider mission – turning social history into social medicine."[16] The birth of new disciplines such as medical sociology, anthropology, and other social and behavioral sciences that drew inspiration from the 1970s "biopsychosocial" model of illness seemed to further destabilize the place of history of medicine and provide alternative models for analyzing cultural dynamics in medicine.[17] According to the physician and medical historian Chester Burns in 1975, "just as the social sciences had undermined the eminence of historical studies in collegiate education, they began to do the same for medical history in medical education after 1950."[18]

Tracing the fate of historical instruction in medical schools illustrates the different ways that one subject responded to different, evolving, problems that were considered ripe for humanities-based analysis, from providing depth of perspective on revolutions in medical knowledge to raising social consciousness. What we begin to see are ways that the medical curriculum and its reformations are tied to concerns generated by social ideology.

Humanities and Human Values

Throughout the twentieth century, the very concern to bring "humanities education" into medical training, whether articulated as an intellectual forum for developing individual sensibility or a philosophical contemplation of human values, exposes an irony. When taken as commonplace that human values and humanitarian interests were traditionally considered synonymous with medicine, how could these concerns be in need of attention? While it has often been suggested that humanities foster personal development and, to put it crudely, "makes better doctors," the more engaging debate about the role of humanities in medical education has less to do with humanizing the physician, than in their ability to contribute to an intellectual environment that enhances the vision of what it is to practice medicine and how to build rapport with patients.

"Bringing the humanities into medical education has long been seen as helping to equalize the rigors of rote memorization and to provide engagement with the social milieu that impacts healthcare delivery, patients' beliefs, and physicians' emotional equanimity."

As suggested in the previous section, curricular design is a fundamental issue in the articles reproduced here that argue for a place to teach medical humanities, and the philosophical intention of such educational reform debates often relates to the general welfare, life-balance, and attitudes of idealistic young students. As a student who contributed to the American Medical Association's panel discussion on "The Medical Curriculum and Human Values" in 1969 wrote: "Our immediate goal is to help you to humanize the environment of our training, and to make it more relevant to the preparation that we need to meet the health care problems of our people, so that we will become physicians whose ideals remain oriented toward the improvement of society ...." (see chapter 6 in this volume) Bringing the humanities into medical education has long been seen as helping to equalize the rigors of rote memorization *and* to provide engagement with the social milieu that impacts healthcare delivery, patients' beliefs, and physicians' emotional equanimity.

A discussion of "problems in present day medical practice and their relationship to medical education" among the faculty at the University of California, San Francisco, in 1955 provides insight to the concerns. Dr. Malcolm S. Watts, associate dean of the school of medicine, outlined a report from San Francisco County Medical Society that evaluated modern trends towards "organized medicine" and the feeling that physicians were becoming medical scientists and technicians, losing their spiritual and personal contact with their patients. Five causes of this problem were presented as follows:

- Lessened emphasis on the doctor-patient relationship
- Unwarranted faith in medical science
- Medical economics and the cost of medical care
- Isolation and compartmentalization of physicians
- Cumbersome administrative policies (this however, he said, pertains to medical societies)

Watts felt that these were not best taught to students in a course on the doctor-patient relationship, but that this should be stressed by members of the teaching staff in ward rounds, and in other contacts with patients and students.[19]

As we know, medical schools had for decades built their curricula along lines of scientific research and bedside care experience, but the discussions which began in the 1950s moved toward creating an educational environment that fosters "a consciousness and awareness of societal human values," in Edwin Rosinski words. "Only if students have an opportunity within the educational environment to deal with broad social issues revolving around the health needs of society will they confront problems involving societal human values." This turn toward "human values" is another theme worth a closer look.

In 1968, a volume of essays and roundtable discussions from a meeting sponsored by the Josiah Macy, Jr., Foundation and the National Library of Medicine focused in part, as one contributor put it, on the question of using history for "somehow developing a soul in new medical students or providing therapy for what we consider amiss in contemporary medical education."[20] In an attempt to throw off the yoke of its former logic of practical utility culled from the pages of ancient medical texts, medical history's new lessons were embedded in tales of moral conduct. It was a discourse closely associated with the ecumenical concerns over a "desacralized" society becoming morally adrift in the quest for scientific preeminence. This occurred in a moment of a symbolic passing-of-the-baton when history gave way to the development of a ministerial articulation of how humanities (religio-philosophical subjects and ethics) could aid the cause of healing by providing guidance on the conceptual challenges within medicine that new technologies presented.

The role of the United Ministries in Education was important here. In the late 1950s churches began experimenting with new forms of ministry, looking afresh at the role of academic and university chaplaincies. In medical schools, a new role was considered where instead of primarily supporting the spiritual needs of patients, the ministry would serve students, staff, and faculty struggling with difficult issues in providing care. After preliminary discussions in the early 1960s, the Danforth Foundation sponsored a meeting in New York in 1965. The Foundation funded many projects relating to religion and higher education as part of its "Study of Campus Ministries" (a program that evaluated Protestant churches' work in public schools). A few key individuals spearheaded discussions about "trends and issues in medical education," including Ronald McNeur, PhD, from the Division of Higher Education of the United Presbyterian Church (a board that worked with Presbyterian colleges, seminaries, and groups at non-Presbyterian colleges), Samuel Banks, PhD, Chaplain and Assistant Professor of Psychiatry and Religion at the University of Florida, and George Harrell, MD, Dean of Hersey Medical Center at Penn State University. According to E.A. Vastyan, an Episcopal chaplain at the University of Texas Medical School, Galveston, who later reflected on this event, a core group emerged that called itself the "Committee on Health and Human Values."[21] After further meetings, the United Ministries in Higher Education (established in 1964 from the United Campus Christian Fellowship) provided financial support to establish a Society for Health and Human Values in 1969 (it also received funding from the National Endowment for the Humanities and the Russell Sage Foundation). As an example of their activities, early on the Society received grant support to study the workings of committees on human experimentation in medical centers.

But the Society was also interested in curricular reform and medical education, not just supporting campus counseling and bioethical research. In fact, in 1967 Dr. George Harrell, Dean of Medicine at Hersey Medical Center and founding member of the committee on health and human values established the first department of humanities at a medical center. Institutional developments, however, were not necessarily smooth. In 1968, a conference was held at the Florida Medical School at the University of Florida in Gainesville where a humanities "program" had been established in 1963. The group was told about their efforts to build this program, and were informed that the challenge was selling the notion that physicians and patients would be better off if physicians learned to be more holistic in their approach to patient care. James J. Quinn, a Jesuit counselor at Creighton University School of Medicine in Nebraska, who founded the humanities program there in 1972, recounted the meeting:

> In 1963, a humanities program was introduced to the seniors [fourth year medical students] in the belief that they would be the ones most apt to appreciate the benefits. The seniors rejected all attempts to start a program because for three years no one ever mentioned the need, and they did not want something being added to an entirely crowded curriculum.
>
> The following year the program was introduced to the incoming freshmen, and they accepted it as a worthwhile adjunct to medical education. Each succeeding year to 1968 these same students took humanities courses and lectures, and evaluated them as profitable. However, many faculty in the basic sciences believed the program to be an encroachment upon the scientific preparation of medicine, while many faculty in the clinic believed that humanities should be taught at the bedside by physicians who acted humanely, and not by a faculty trained in the humanities.
>
> So, after five years the Florida Medical School had educated the students and administration to recognize the benefits of a humanities program. The faculty, however, continued to offer strong resistance. Their reactions caused the students to look upon the humanities as an adjunct to medical education and not as an integral part. To overcome this impression, the humanities faculty, which had been an independent unit in the school directly responsible to the dean, allied itself with the Division of Ambulatory Medicine and Community Programs in the Department of Medicine in 1968. This division achieved departmental status in 1971 and was named the Department of Community Health and Family Medicine. In 1974, this department split along divisional lines and the humanities program was under the Division of Social Sciences and Humanities, where it remains today. With this new status the program became an integral part of the medical curriculum.[22]

The Society for Health and Human Values (SHHV) emerged in the context of what Edmund Pellegrino, one of the Society's early presidents, called "the troubled waters of the scientific and moral revolutions" of the twentieth century. "Medicine is in convulsion today because society is in convulsion," he said in a forum of medical educators at the AMA in 1969. Pellegrino, along with colleagues David Thomasma, Eric Cassell, Al Jonsen, and others who formed part of the Christian coalition within medical schools, elaborated a theory of the philosophical basis to medical practice and helped define the place of medical humanities in medical curricula that revolved around bioethical considerations.[23]

At one of the first meetings of humanists and medical educators that the Society sponsored, speakers emphasized that the true measure of humanism in medicine should reference one's humane treatment of those in need. "For a medical school faculty member to teach students to operate most effectively in the community context, he must have a value system in which social issues have a high priority and he must base his behavior on these values."[24] And while service to humanity by practicing medicine might have been guided by Christian values, the right to health was political; maintaining health gave one a shot at overcoming social vulnerabilities. As Pellegrino and Thomasma wrote, "we perceive health as a means toward freedom and other primary values."[25]

It is at this juncture when this branch of medical humanities appears to reunite with some of the developing themes in social medicine, to which we alluded at the conclusion of the previous section. The development of bioethics as a discipline and as part of medical school curricula is specifically not examined in this volume through primary readings (with the feeling that that is another project). However the articles reproduced in this volume relating to the SHHV capture a critical moment early in its life, in 1969, when the debates over human values in medical education were just developing.

The Society itself eventually disappeared with the emergence of new organizations, culminating, through a complicated lineage, with the present American Society for Bioethics and Humanities (ASBH). Today, the ASBH has membership from a wide range of humanities disciplines showing the growth of interest and professionalization of medical humanities over the past four decades. It is to another of these disciplines we now turn.

Literature-and-Medicine (and the trials of interdisciplinarity)

Not long after its foundation, the Society of Health and Human Values initiated a series of meetings to examine the intersection of medicine and medical education with history, the visual arts, religion, and the social sciences. With additional sponsorship from the National Endowment for the Humanities, a series of workshops were held over a two year period for professors of literature, writers, and physicians to meet, read essays and books, and discuss the potential of literature to broaden the perspective of anyone engaged with medicine. Language, it was observed, was a kind of connective tissue between the two subjects. "A primary source for the physician is the personal history of each patient, which may be thought of as the patient's life story or novel," wrote Edmund Pellegrino, chairman of the SHHV. And since a patient's social and medical history follows narrative structure, students were taught to gain some comprehension of what constitutes proper narrative form by ascertaining ways that writers construct stories.

Members of the SHHV were very active in this endeavor, and indeed the Society had just published a path-breaking book by Joanne Trautmann and Carol Pollard called *Literature and Medicine: An Annotated Bibliography* (1975, subsequently republished by University of Pittsburgh Press in 1982). Tellingly, some of the founding members of the SHHV such as Samuel Banks and E.A. Vastyan had been undergraduate majors in literature and came to have an interest in humanities through that route.

According to Joanne Trautmann, a literature professor from the Department of Humanities at the Hershey Medical Center at Penn State and chair of the literature and medicine workshops, things started along swimmingly.

> During our first meeting, the tension usually present at interdisciplinary dialogues was absent. At the personal level there was no inhibiting threat. The people from medicine did not feel themselves in the presence of the keepers of beauty and truth. Nor did the writers and teachers of literature feel they were facing the white knights of action. There was, to be sure, some reverential bowing to each other's direction, but in our imaginations we formed a Round Table – no disputes about precedence among these seekers – and we sought at ease for what our fields shared. All signs pointed toward convergence.

At one gathering, the surgeon and writer Richard Selzer read an essay of his that featured an account of "Joe Riker," a short-order cook who refused surgical treatment to fix a hole in his head caused by cancer.

> "Joe, let's get rid of it," the surgeon in the story says. "Cut out the bad part, put in a metal plate, and you're cured."
> "No operation," says Joe.

Time passes and eventually the surgeon visits Joe to see how he is doing. The cook removes his hat to show that the wound was healed. He told the surgeon he had been cleansing it with a bottle of holy water from Lourdes. The story ends with the surgeon reflecting on how he felt a spiritual dimension to healthcare.

Subsequently published under the title "The Surgeon as Priest," the story was presented as an exploration of how medicine rises above the mundane, a topic of concern to the whole group of workshop participants, which also included a pathologist, a poet, an internist, and a psychologist. Speaking to a pathologist earlier at the conference who was himself despondent about the routines of medicine and looking to literature for enlightenment, Selzer had commented: "We are both engaged in what I would like to think is a priestly business, that is, making sick people who want to live, well."[26] But when the pathologist listened to Selzer's story, he struggled to accept the symbolic and spiritual meaning of the surgeon's experience with the patient's supernatural recovery, and challenged the certainty of the medical diagnosis, since it was ostensibly based on a "true" story.

The ensuing conversation between the surgeon, the pathologist, and the rest of the group was transcribed in the volume that was published following the workshops, which captured the dialogue throughout their meetings.

The Pathologist: You know, pathologists are gadflies. Dick, what was your diagnosis for that skin lesion on the scalp?

The Surgeon-Writer: That it was an epidermal carcinoma. Why?

The Pathologist: Oh, I just wondered. It might have been a keratoacanthoma, which heals itself in six months and looks exactly like a squamous carcinoma clinically and very much like one microscopically.

The Surgeon-Writer: No good will ever come of you for having said that.

The Poet: A tinker's curse!

The Surgeon-Writer: Exactly. But this was based on a true story. And it was a carcinoma. I have the pathology to prove it.

The Pathologist: Uh-huh. That is one of the saddest mistakes made in medicine. I am very serious about this. I'm sorry to be an S.O.B. about it, but this is my business.

The Surgeon-Writer: It doesn't change my diagnosis (but this is all so superficial as to be trivial). I prefer to think of the lesion as a cancer because it serves my purpose in this instance.

The Pathologist: It serves my purpose to point out that it might have been keratoacanthoma, which is benign.

The Surgeon-Writer: You're perfectly within your rights to respond to my writing any way you want. It's just that I . . .

The Literature Professor (breaking in): Now just a minute! What that lesion was matters enormously in some ways, and in some ways it doesn't matter at all. What we are working on is "the healing arts," and it is from that artistic point of view that it doesn't matter.

The Psychiatrist: If I had to choose between the knife and the holy water, much as I hate the knife, I'd choose it over the holy water any day.

The Literature Professor: Of course. But that's irrelevant too.

The Psychiatrist: No, that's the moral impact of what Dick has written; that there is something holier than the mundane physical forms of treatment that are available.

The Surgeon-Writer: I find myself in a very peculiar position.

The Internist: Dick's description of the lesion was in words of truth. What the slide actually shows cannot alter the truthfulness. I think the description was beautiful.

The Poet: "Beauty is truth, truth, beauty."

The Pathologist: It can be beautiful and true and dead wrong.

The Internist: It's not that it's "wrong." It's a matter of supplementary evidence. You can revise the histological diagnosis, but that's another dimension of truth.

The Literature Professor (angry now): That's as irrelevant as revising the story! We have a story, the primary responsibility of which is that it be faithful to language and faithful to the medium in which it works. In the same way, the critic must be faithful to the literature with which he is working; the pathologist must be faithful to the organism with which he is working. If any of them fails, he is being irresponsible, but we can't take the responsibility of the one and transfer it to the other.

The Surgeon-Writer: I am shocked that this is the mode of discussion, though I should be accustomed to being misread.

The Pathologist: You're not being misread – you're being revised. What you've written is very beautiful and very good and I like it. But the question remains as to what you are dealing with in fact. Your story is true insofar as clinical observation goes. But there is another level of truth; that is, What the hell is it?, and that can only be decided by somebody's observations with a microscope.

As Joanne Trautmann observed in her comments on this exchange, there was now a "basic intellectual divergence" among the group, some participants testing the epistemological foundations to the writer's story, looking for reality to emerge, while others embraced its narrative aesthetics.[27]

The vignette also illustrates the challenges that new humanities endeavors faced not just in regard to sharing curricular space with medical education but in sharing intellectual space. Finding a common language to generate true dialogue, and not just having words pass each other, proved more difficult than the group of sympathetic participants anticipated. In the infamous words of one participant who attended only the first workshop, described as a "shadowy, challenging presence:" "You can link anything *and* anything," using the word "and," such as literature *and* medicine, "and pretend for a while that you have a subject, but do you really have one?"[28] For years this comment caused reflection and consideration, leading literary scholar Anne Hudson Jones to point out the uses of writing "literature-and-medicine," with hyphens linking the two, to show "a field that involves a more integral relationship between the two …"[29]

In 1982, the first issue of the journal *Literature and Medicine* appeared. Joanne Trautmann, the first editor, wrote the inaugural essay presenting a "state of the union" of the discipline which now had its own journal, where she surprisingly declared, "it is presently tenuous." Over the course of the previous decade since her own appointment as the first-in-the-world, full-time scholar of "literature and medicine" in a medical school, the future of the field of literature and medicine (and perhaps even the medical humanities) was uncertain. The problem was one that comes with a scholarly commitment to talk across disciplines: "the problem of patina," that is, scholars trained in different disciplinary traditions who assume a veneer of acquaintance with another.[30] Yet, considered another way, new disciplines are born by emerging from such complex interactive processes that develop over time, like chemical reactions.

Anne Hudson Jones, who was appointed to the faculty at the Institute for the Medical Humanities at the University of Texas Medical Branch at Galveston, pointed out how the challenges of being accepted by *either* the discipline of literature or medicine led to the necessary reaction of creating their own space and journal.

> Those of us working in the field [literature-and-medicine] had no formal way of communicating with each other. We had no place to publish the kinds of articles we were beginning to write. It was – and is – enormously important for people who want to be tenured in a medical school to have a refereed journal in which to publish. The standard literary journals, for the most part, were not interested in the kinds of scholarship we were doing. Our articles weren't right for them. Our articles weren't right for the medical

journals, either. We could not reply upon either literary or medical journals for a primary publishing outlet.

In her article "Reflections, Projections, and the Future of Literature-and-Medicine," in *Literature and Medicine: A Claim for a Discipline*, published by the Society for Health and Human Values in 1987, Jones refers to a number of important events that were happening in the early 1980s that gave hope for the future of the field. But behind the scenes, challenges were presenting themselves that may have made things look more discouraging.

The year 1981 marked the tenth anniversary of the funding initiative supported by the Ministers in Medical Education and the grants from the National Endowment for the Humanities to drive the efforts of the Institute on Human Values in Medicine (a funding branch of the SHHV). The decade yielded a million dollars' worth of effort to foster the development of medical humanities programs across the nation, resulting in many new programs and faculty positions within medical schools. But that same year, the national grants and the support from the Presbyterian Church were coming to an end. The Institute was asked to wind-down its activities for lack of future funding and the administrative office space provided for the Institute was being removed owing to reorganization within the United Ministries in Education.[31] To add salt to the wound, an organization called the Association of Teachers of Humanities in Medicine was being formed with little consultation with SHHV and was revealed, in the words of David Thomasma, director of the medical humanities program at Loyola University of Chicago school of medicine and council member of SHHV, as "a *fait d'accompli.*" "It might therefore appear to many that the Society was falling apart," wrote Thomasma in a newsletter statement to the members, "its emphasis on dialogue and synthesis certainly appears to be in jeopardy. Will the future lead only to fission of interest groups from the umbrella of the Society?"[32]

Thomasma warned against quick judgment. What the society was facing was similar to what many medical humanities programs within medical schools, or the emerging discipline of literature-and-medicine, was struggling with, which was finding a way to work collaboratively within a diversifying field of interest groups.

Not only does this point remind us of the persistent challenges of interdisciplinary work and the tendency of disciplinary offspring to emerge through cellular division, but the changing social and political context of the early 1980s also conditioned the view of the future. An "augmented meeting" of the Society for Health and Human Values was held in early 1982 to address further these concerns.

Upon reflecting on the Society's purpose, function, and structure, the context of government trends in supporting the arts and humanities was suggestive. The year Ronald Reagan became president, in 1981, the appropriations for the National Endowment for the Arts and the National Endowment for the Humanities dropped significantly. In 1980, the NEH had a budget of approximately $155,000,000. In 1982, it was approximately $143,000,000, and would not recover its 1980-level of funding for another decade. Taking inflation into account, the cut represented a 50% net loss of its budget appropriation in the 1980s compared to the 1970s.[33] The impact of this on the efforts of the Society which relied heavily on grant support to develop programs within universities was significant.

> During the earliest days of the Society, there was great interest in medical educational circles in introducing explicit consideration of human values issues into medical education, pedagogically emphasizing patient-oriented learning, and on community medicine and primary care. New medical schools and special programs in established institutions were emphasizing innovation towards these ends.
>
> Today, while there has been by no means total closing out of such initiatives and interests, the major preoccupations of medical school administrators and faculty are focused around biomedical science, high technology and sheer survival through income generation. While these emphases in academic medical centers may well have generated moral and ethical issues demanding operational and educational elucidation and attention, the need for development of programs in the medical humanities at any really significant funding level as a high priority is not automatically apparent to the power structures of many traditionally operated medical centers. There has, in short, been a swing towards conservative retrenchment in medical education.[34]

Despite the challenges – financial and intellectual – facing the medical humanities, there was a freshness about the methods and perspectives that the humanities offered clinical practice that gave hope to its endurance. Whereas in the 1960s and 1970s the humanities were asserted as being necessary to service a *deficit* in medical education, the more precarious context of the 1980s and 1990s brought in a more nuanced language where the humanities were *value added* to medical education. As a point of illustration, in 1970, the grant application to the NEH which led to funds that established the Institute for Health and Human Values and funded the previously-discussed workshops, proposed to "identify explicitly the human values that are lacking or inadequately represented in the study and practice of medicine and to begin to remedy the deficit." As Daniel M. Fox, professor of humanities in medicine at SUNY Stony Brook (and later president of the Millbank Memorial Fund) commented in an address presented before the Society in 1984, "This was an extraordinary political statement." The idea that "values" could be precisely identified, measured, and presented was intrepid.

> Yet, it would have made sense to many people in a decade when abstract rights were demanded in the streets and accorded by legislature and the courts. A value, like a right, many people then believed, could be made explicit and the extent of its presence or absence measured in a particular environment, even in the attitudes and behavior of health professionals as individuals or in groups. In the late 1960s, as a result of the antiwar and civil rights movements, relativism and gradualism had become dirty words in American universities and in the national bureaucracies of most of the liberal Protestant denominations.[35]

By the 1980s, following a decade or so of institutionalization of the medical humanities and the evident needs to work alongside and promote "dialogue" rather than "doctor bashing," the methodological and curricular developments were considered more as an adjunct to medical education rather than a panacea. Here enters the renewed proposition that the medical humanities is a utilitarian pursuit, working towards practical ends to improve medical practice and advance healthcare. But during a decade when this reorientation was ameliorating past antagonisms, humanities scholars outside the medical school environment (those in the "parent disciplines") were becoming more theoretical and more disdainful about the notion of having applied ends. (To be sure, a separate discussion about the notion of applied humanities, to address the "crisis" facing the humanities, emerged that examined the role of public history, advocacy, business ethics, and other areas where humanities served practical ends.[36]) This furthered the sense of an identity crisis but one that did not overcome the commitment to public service. As E.A. Vastyan said in an address to the Society as early as 1981, "we most not allow ourselves to pander for the approbation of those in our parent disciplines who have no idea what it means to apply learning in the humanities to real and immediate problems. I believe our energies should go into discovering new kinds of teaching, new forms of service, and new kinds of applied humanities."[37]

And indeed new kinds of teaching and forms of applied humanities did develop. A good example is how the field of literature-and-medicine branched out in the 1990s and into the 2000s. Publications were showing that literary texts were rich sources for helping students and practitioners understand patients' perspectives on health and disease, but they also imparted skills at interpreting clinical charts, a patient's history, and the ways patients express their physical and mental well being. With an interest among professional medical educators to innovate in education, throughout the 1990s increasing numbers of US medical schools

> *"Developing a semiotic approach to clinical texts, Charon dubbed her practice 'narrative medicine' which became a new branch of literature and medicine that demonstrated the application of the humanities to clinical encounters."*

taught literature and medicine. According to the *American Medical College's Curriculum Directory*, in 1998 74% of medical schools taught the subject, with 39% requiring it.[38] Part of the result of this effort went beyond courses or modules for medical students, but opened new avenues for personal and professional development for physicians in practice.

With a notion of utility and an opportunity to use "the other side" of the brain to think both critically and creatively about medical problems, the medical humanities gave legitimacy to advanced training as part of a skill set that would not go to waste. This is a path that the Columbia University physician Dr. Rita Charon took. Having developed an interest in literature and medicine and receiving guidance from Joanne Trautmann and Kathryn Montgomery Hunter, Charon associated clinical effectiveness with a physician's ability to grasp multiple meanings of narrative derived from many sources – the patient's account, test results, other professionals' reports, and even signs from the body itself.[39] As with any literary source, the reader must wade through interpretive options and not suffer from ambiguity, uncertainty, and non-closure. Developing a semiotic approach to clinical texts, Charon dubbed her practice "narrative medicine" which became a new branch of literature and medicine that demonstrated the application of the humanities to clinical encounters.

In an article written for an online literary magazine, Charon reflected on her interests in and efforts to develop narrative medicine:

> After a few years of practice after residency, I realized that what patients paid me to do was to listen very expertly and attentively to extraordinarily complicated narratives – told in words, gestures, silences, tracings, images, and physical findings – and to cohere all these stories into something that made at least provisional sense, enough sense, that is, to be acted on. I was the interpreter of these often contradictory accounts of events that are, by definition, difficult to tell. Pain, suffering, worry, anguish, the sense of something just not being right: these are very hard to nail down in words, and so patients have very demanding "telling" tasks while doctors have very demanding "listening" tasks.
>
> These recognitions sent me over to the English Department of Columbia, figuring that they could help me understand how stories are built and told and understood. My plan was to take a course in English; this became a Master's and, soon enough, a doctoral degree. I couldn't bear to stop my studies in literature, not only because I was powerfully drawn to the study of literature but also because *it made the medicine make more sense.*
>
> I realized that the narrative skills I was learning in my English studies made me a better doctor.[40]

In 2001, Charon published articles in *Annals of Internal Medicine* and in *JAMA* (see chapter 14) that outlined the philosophy of narrative medicine, introducing its term.[41] In 2009 a master's degree program in Narrative Medicine was launched through the School of Continuing Education at Columbia University and it was an instant success. Both the concept of professional utility and the institutional integration of the medical humanities had moved one step further in their evolution.

Broadening Engagement and Debating the Outcomes

The institutional expansion and professionalization of medical humanities at the end of the twentieth century and first decades of the twenty-first century reflect the realization of a century's articulation of its uses to humanize physicians, increase perceptions of medical practice, and sharpen students' cognitive skills. Yet, even after a century's worth of discussion and developments, how these things are best accomplished – or whether they can be accomplished at all – remain matters of debate.

At the beginning of the twentieth century, one concern was whether the medical curriculum (the classroom) was the place to try and humanize physicians, or whether the bedside was better than courses. This question still exists. Referring to the trait of professionalism, there remain allegations of a gap between the classroom descriptions of how physicians *should* behave (empathic, compassionate, socially sensitive) and how they often *do* behave. In his article reproduced in this volume (see chapter 16), Jack Coulehan argues that the disconnect between the humanities' portrayal of the ideal physician in the formal curriculum, and the routine actions of "machine-based medical practice" in the "hidden curriculum" (the tacit knowledge acquired in the wards) shows yet again the lack of a "medical morality."[42] Citing a report by a fellow at the Association of American Medical Colleges, Coulehan reiterates the way that this leads to cynicism among students, and that "additional courses on medical professionalism are unlikely to fundamentally alter this regrettable circumstance. Instead, we will actually have to change our behaviors, our institutions, and ourselves."[43]

Scholars from the humanities have also displayed their skepticism about the ostensible aims that can be achieved through humanities courses. At a forum discussing the "emerging definitions" of medical humanities and its uses, UC Berkeley anthropologist Nancy Scheper-Hughes wondered whether "teaching anthropology to doctors is a way to make them better healers? ... Can you teach empathy? I don't know." Just as important to Scheper-Hughes, however, was questioning whether the definition of a "better doctor" hinged on these characteristics instead of their ability to cure disease. Does the long history of what the profession thinks the ideal physician should be match the desires of what patients want from their physician? Patients, says Scheper-Hughes, "don't always want or expect doctors to answer their existential problems, but they want their pain to be diminished. Leave the shamanic task, leave the answering of these larger existential questions, to other groups or individuals in society, to the priests, to the shamans. Can we really form doctors to be both marvelous technicians as well as philosophers?"[44] And, one could continue, would being philosophers help them to become more marvelous technicians? A 1989 survey asked physicians to reflect on their liberal arts education to assess its impact on their professional lives. The results of this showed that 25% believed that further study of the humanities would have enhanced their ability to work with patients, and 44% agreed that "moral development" was "essential to a medical career."[45] One wonders about those who seemed to disagree that moral development was essential to a medical career.

Humanities scholars are trained to be adept at self-reflection and skepticism. Indeed, this was one of the perceived benefits of presenting history to medical students over a hundred years ago, teaching that what is taken as good knowledge at one moment might not be considered good knowledge the next moment. More recently, as Delese Wear, Joseph Zarconi, and Rebecca Garden have examined, reflective writing exercises have been introduced in medical education as a means of getting students to interrogate their experiences and "attend to how they are becoming physicians."[46] But questions such as those raised by Scheper-Hughes expose a more problematic assertion of why humanities should be brought into medical education, which is whether it is valuable as a part of the learning *process* or whether it is valuable for its end *product*. Are the humanities best seen as a method – a way of conceptualizing and approaching complex problems (and as such as adjunct or complement to a controlled scientific experiment) – or are they best seen as an obligatory passage point to the creation of a character type (a virtuous person, a culturally competent person, etc). This fundamental question has been around for as long as considerations have been given to curricular expansion. It is very similar in idea, if not exact expression, to what Edmund Pellegrino was talking about in the early 1970s in reference to the difference between *humanitas* and *philanthropia* – one is a type of learning, a liberal education, that can be provided; the other is a state of being that may or may not be a result of education.

In the 1990s and early 2000s, curricular standardization and medical education reforms put increased emphasis on the notion of a product of its training – specifically, that a core curriculum would meet standards of professionalism that are subject to pre- and post-education measurement. Interestingly, since the 1990s medical educators have appeared more engaged with what they have termed the "cultural" dimensions of healthcare. In response to the Association of American Medical Colleges' mandate that medical education should better address the needs of a diverse society, medical schools widely implemented training in "cultural competency."[47] Such programs in part adapted insights from ethnographic research conducted by medical anthropologists to raise awareness of varied cultural attitudes and practices that impact patients' experiences with the healthcare system.[48] More recent calls for "social relevance" in medical education that aim to ensure social justice and remedy disparities in access to healthcare are suggesting new ways that social science and humanities research can inform physician training.[49]

This would seem to open the doors wider to medical humanities subjects that have long held claim to be intimately engaged with social and cultural research. Yet with every curricular change comes particular methods of assessment that are meant to mirror the "evidence-based" practices that guide medicine itself. What is relevant here are related opinions about what is expected of different disciplines with regard to the performance of their students and how we measure the outcomes of educational interventions. In 2010, a review of 245 articles that discuss the impact of medical humanities programs showed a lack of demonstrable, empirical evidence of their effectiveness.[50] But again, the results sought here relate to a product and not the articulation of a process. It is easy to assess whether a student has learned the techniques of historical investigation, the tenets of literary analysis, or the protocols of qualitative research. It can be extremely difficult to prove that someone equipped with such skills and knowledge becomes more humanistic (however one chooses to define that). As Rita Charon opined in reply to the 2010 study, "One can and ought to wonder whether it is beside the point to try to measure, through reductive processes of evaluation, that aspect of learning which is meant as an antidote to the reductiveness of the curriculum itself."[51] In terms of the history of the curricular integration of medical humanities, it is important to note these concerns about assessment not least because of the amount of publications addressing this trend for metrics in medical education. But it also begs the question of what should be measured, further reminding us of the much older consideration about medical humanities broadening ways of thinking as opposed to delivering values to students.

While the uses or even the possibility of measuring outcomes from humanities courses is debatable, scholars in these fields regularly employ reflexive analysis and solicit feedback to find areas where teaching can be more effective. In the article reproduced here (see chapter 18), Johanna Shapiro, Jack Coulehan, Delese Wear, and Martha Montello shifted away from the concern of medical educators and administrators about outcomes to first inquire what students themselves thought about the medical humanities. What they found was that students resist, if not resent, the "widget-fashion" attempt to form character and "produce" humanistic attributes, but they do value diversity in educational opportunities. This has allowed the medical humanities to grow in the first decades of the twenty-first century despite unanswered questions about its results.

The place of the humanities in medical education has historically been seen as an intellectual pursuit juxtaposed to scientific training. Placed in an offensive role (so to speak), referring to its fight against dogma and reductionism, it was originally predicated on problems with the content of the existing curriculum. However in many ways what is going on with making the curriculum more diverse is not to stage a dialectical opposition or antagonism between types of education and practice, but to create complementary and more complete opportunities to explore the human condition. To be sure, the tenets of the sciences and humanities have long been seen as fundamentally concerned with two different goals. The sciences are historically seen as striving to move from the particular to the general, to formulate universal laws. The humanities are often seen as aspiring to capture individual expression and diversity. A successful scientific finding is replicable in other labs and contexts, and in this manner presented as a fact. A successful humanities project stands alone as a work of individual achievement and is not replicated by others as a means of establishing its value. A breakthrough in science – while itself can be attributed to an outstanding individual achievement – becomes part of the operational tools and the epistemological "paradigm" for scientists. A breakthrough (say, a bestseller) in the humanities can be imitated but stands as a distinction against which other accomplishments will be measured. To put this in biological terms, a disease may be scientifically understood to have certain universal traits (such as viral structure) but each person infected is understood in the tradition of the humanities to experience and cope with the disease in a unique way.

Now, all of this is generalization and somewhat arbitrary categorization. It can also be argued that the sciences are equally concerned with novelty and anomalies in order to expose the limitations of "universal" claims. The humanities can be seen as striving to articulate universal human values and experiences – reaching the essence of "human nature" – through works like Dostoyevsky's *Crime and Punishment* that expose the mental anguish and moral dilemmas of wrongful acts. The point is, neither the sciences nor the humanities can be characterized as serving functions, having goals, or indoctrinating students in ways that are always opposed or different from each other. It is much more beneficial to see scientific and humanities investigations as complementary, each adding value to the approach the other takes at any particular moment. A complementary approach to studying biological and healthcare problems – a dialogue rather than dialectic – provides better coverage for all avenues of interpretation and cooperative action than parsing differences in approach.

The final essays in this volume present a sampling of some of the newer approaches to integrating humanities to medical education by branching out from the familiar subjects of history and literature to include theater, art, poetry, and disability studies. But with every new innovation or adaptation of the humanities to enhance medical education comes the need to reflect on how the diversity of disciplinary perspectives and multiplicity of theoretical frameworks relate to each other. As Tod Chambers said in 2009, having just ended his tenure as president of the American Society for Bioethics and the Humanities, while thinking about all the disciplines now represented in the *Journal of Medical Humanities*, it is easy to claim a stake for oneself by saying that medicine *is like* a text, or medicine (anatomy or radiology) *is like* art, or medicine *is like* ritual, or medicine *is like* theater, and so on. But in appreciating each individual approach, does it make sense anymore to refer to "the medical humanities," suggesting a unified counter-approach to medical training?

It is possible that the increased emphasis on "interprofessional education" that has begun to break down silos separating healthcare professionals will render disciplinary perspectives less distinguishable from each other. Where students training to become physicians, nurses, dentists, pharmacists, and social workers, share common courses and clinical experiences, a teamwork and multi-faceted approach to examining healthcare problems from the cellular to social level will become commonplace. Perhaps the notion of curricular integration itself will be radically redefined in the coming decades and training will take on a more problem-based learning approach that already appears in many medical schools and that allows greater flexibility in bringing in pieces of relevant research to address problems. Perhaps shifting medical education away from pedagogic programs that emphasize disciplinary understandings of patients toward a "structural competency" approach that develops "extra-clinical languages" of deeply rooted healthcare inequalities will eliminate the need to label methodological approaches at all.[52] Only a volume far in the future that reviews another hundred years of curricular innovations will tell, and at that time it will be interesting to see if the challenges that persisted throughout the last hundred years endure or disappear.

References

1   George Rosen, "The Place of History in Medical Education," *Bulletin of the History of Medicine* 22 (1948), 594-629.

2   A.H. Jones and R.A. Carson, "Medical Humanities at the University of Texas Medical Branch at Galveston," *Academic Medicine* 78 (2003), 1006-1009.

3   Abraham Flexner, *Medical Education in the United States and Canada: A Report to the Carnegie Foundation for the Advancement of Teaching* (New York: The Carnegie Foundation, 1910); see the *Report of the Commissioner of Education for the Year*

Ended June 30, 1910, Vol. 1 (Washington, D.C.: Government Printing Office, 1910), p. 117.

4   Edmund Pellegrino, "Educating the Humanist Physician: An Ancient Ideal Reconsidered," *JAMA* 227: 11 (1974), 1288-1294.

5   Rafael Campo, "'The Medical Humanities,' for Lack of a Better Term," *JAMA* 294: 9 (2005), 1009-1111, p. 1010.

6   Some of the content for this section is derived from my expanded discussion of this in Brian Dolan, "History, Medical Humanities and Medical Education," *Social History of Medicine* 23:2 (2010), 393-405.

7   Henry Sigerist, "Medical History in the Medical Schools of the United States," *Bulletin of the History of Medicine* 7 (1939), 627-662.

8   Genevieve Miller, "The Teaching of Medical History in the United States and Canada – Report of a Field Survey," *Bulletin of the History of Medicine* 43 (1969), 259-267, 344-375, 553-586.

9   Johns Hopkins*, UCSF*, Loma Linda University, University of Wisconsin*, Yale*, University of Kansas, University of Washington*, University of Oklahoma, UCLA*, University of Minnesota, Chicago Medical School, University of Texas Medical Branch at Galveston. Asterisk indicates those with graduate degree programs.

10   Eugene Cordell, "The Importance of the Study of the History of Medicine," *Medical Library and Historical Journal* 2 (1904), 268-282, p. 273.

11   Charles Singer, "The Teaching of Medical History," *British Medical Journal* 2 (1919), 141-142.

12   Henry Sigerist, "Medical History in the United States – Past, Present, Future," *Bulletin of the History of Medicine* 22 (1948), 46-60, p. 48.

13   Sigerist (1948) (op. cit), p. 49.

14   Dorothy Porter, "The Social Contract of Health in the Twentieth and Twenty-First Centuries: Individuals, Corporations, and the State," in S.G. Soloman, L. Murard, and P. Zylberman, eds, *Shifting Boundaries in Public Health: Europe in the Twentieth Century* (Rochester: University of Rochester Press, 2008), 45-62. Elizabeth Fee, "Henry E. Sigerist: From the Social Production of Disease to Medical Management and Scientific Socialism," *The Millbank Quarterly* 67 (1989), 127-150.

15   Sigerist (1948) (op. cit.), p. 48.

16   John Pickstone, "Medical History as a Way of Life," *Social History of Medicine* 18 (2005), 307-323, p. 312.

17   Arthur Kleinman, Leon Eisenberg, and Byron Good, "Culture, Illness, and Care: Clinical Lessons from Anthropologic and Cross-Cultural Research," *Annals of Internal Medicine* 88 (1978), 251-258.

18   Chester Burns, "History in Medical Education: The Development of Current Trends in the United States," *Bulletin of the New York Academy of Medicine* 51 (1975), 851-869, p. 859.

19   UCSF Archives and Special Collections, Minutes of School of Medicine faculty meeting: November 1955: AR 24.2 Box 3. SOM Faculty Minutes, 1945-1958.

20   J. Blake, ed., *Education in the History of Medicine* (New York and London: Hafner Publishing, 1968), p. 41.

21   E.A. Vastyan, "Healing and the Wounded Healer," a public oration given at a meeting of the Society for Health and Human Values, November 1, 1981. Typescript at University of Texas Medical Branch, Moody Medical Library, History of Medicine Collections, MS 59, "Society for Health and Human Values Records (1970-1977), Folder 1.

22   James J. Quinn, "Humanities in Medical Education – the Past Ten Years," *Transactions of the Nebraska Academy of Sciences and Affiliated Societies* 7 (1979), 131-135. Quinn cites T.K. McElhinney, ed., *Human Values Teaching Programs for Health Professionals: Self-Description Reports from Twenty-Nine Schools* (Philadelphia: Institute on Human Values in Medicine, 1976).

23   T.K. McElhinney and E. Pellegrino, "The Institute on Human Values in Medicine: Its Role and Influence on the Conception and Evolution of Bioethics," *Theoretical Medicine* 22 (2001), 291-317; Albert Jonsen, *The Birth of Bioethics* (Oxford: Oxford University Press, 1998).

24   L.A. Falk, B. Page and W. Vesper, "Human Values and Medical Education from the Perspective of Health Care Delivery," *Journal of Medical Education* 48 (1973), 152-157, p. 153.

25   E. Pellegrino and D. Thomasma, *A Philosophical Basis of Medical Practice* (Oxford: Oxford University Press, 1981), p. 4.

26   Joanne Trautmann, ed., *Healing Arts in Dialogue: Literature and Medicine* (Carbondale: Southern Illinois University Press, 1982), p. 4.

27   The account is transcribed and published in Trautmann, *Healing Arts in Dialogue* as well as recounted with commentary in her introductory essay to the first issue of *Literature and Medicine*: J. Trautmann, "Can We Resurrect Apollo?" *Literature and Medicine* 1 (1982), 1-18, pp. 3-6.

28   This is quoted in Trautmann, *Healing Arts in Dialogue* (1981) (op. cit.), p. xvi; Trautmann, "Resurrect Apollo?" (1982), p. 1 (with a slightly differently phrased quotation but same message); and Jones, "Reflections" (1987) (op. cit.), p. 40.

29   Anne Hudson Jones, "Reflections, Projections, and the Future of Literature-and-Medicine," in Delese Wear, Martin Kohn, and Susan Stocker, eds., *Literature and Medicine: A Claim for a Discipline* (McClean, VA: Society for Health and Human Values, 1987), 29-40, p 40.

30   Trautmann, "Resurrect Apollo?" (1982), p. 1.

31   David Thomasma, "The Society for Health and Human Values: Fission or
     Fusion?" Typescript in the University of Texas Medical Branch, Moody Medical
     Library, History of Medicine Collections, MS 59, "Society for Health and Hu-
     man Values Records (1970-1977), Folder 1. Also, "Report of the Augmented
     Meeting of the Council, Society for Health and Human Values, Dallas, Texas,
     February 17-18, 1982," University of Texas Medical Branch, Moody Medical Li-
     brary, History of Medicine Collections, MS 59, "Society for Health and Human
     Values Records (1970-1977), Folder 1.

32   Thomasma, "Fission" (op. cit.), p. 1.

33   www.neh.gov. See Cynthia Koch, "The Contest for American Culture: A
     Leadership Case Study on the National Endowment for the Arts and National
     Endowment for the Humanities Funding Crisis," *Public Talk: An Online Journal
     of Discourse Leadership*, www.upenn.edu/pnc.

34   "Report of the Augmented Meeting of the Council," Society for Health and
     Human Values, Dallas, Texas, February 17-18, 1982. Typescript at University
     of Texas Medical Branch, Moody Medical Library, History of Medicine Col-
     lections, MS 59, "Society for Health and Human Values Records (1970-1977),
     Folder 1.

35   Daniel M. Fox, "Who We Are: The Political Origins of the Medical Humani-
     ties," *Theoretical Medicine* 6 (1985), 327-342, pp. 334-335.

36   Daniel Callahan, Arthur Caplan, and Bruce Jennings, eds., *Applying the Humani-
     ties* {The Hastings Center, Institute of Society, Ethics, and the Life Sciences)
     (New York: Plenum Press, 1985).

37   E.A. Vastyan, "Healing and the Wounded Healer," Public Oration, Society for
     Health and Human Values, Novemner 1, 1981. Typescript at University of Tex-
     as Medical Branch, Moody Medical Library, History of Medicine Collections,
     MS 59, "Society for Health and Human Values Records (1970-1977), Folder 1.

38   Rita Charon, "Literature and Medicine: Origins and Destinies," *Academic Medi-
     cine* 75 (2000), 23-27, p. 23.

39   R. Charon, J.T. Banks, J.E. Connelly, A.H. Hawkins, K.M. Hunter, A.H. Jones,
     M. Montello, and S. Poirier, "Literature and Medicine: Contributions to Clinical
     Practice," *Annals of Internal Medicine* 122 (1995), 599-606.

40   http://www.litsite.org/index.cfm?section=Narrative-and- Healing&page=Pers
     pectives&viewpost=2&ContentId=985. Accessed July 27, 2014.

41   Rita Charon, "Narrative Medicine: Form, Function, and Ethics," *Annals of
     Internal Medicine* 134 (2001), 83-87. Rita Charon, "Narrative Medicine: A Model
     for Empathy, Reflection, Profession, and Trust," *JAMA* 286 (2001), 1897-1902.

42   Jack Coulehan, "Today's Professionalism: Engaging the Mind but not the Heart," *Academic Medicine* 80: 10 (2005), 892-898. See also: D. Wear, "On White Coats and Professional Development: The Formal and Hidden Curricula," *Annals of Internal Medicine* 129 (1998), 734-737.

43   T.S. Inui, *Flag in the Wind: Educating for Professionalism in Medicine* (Washington, D.C.: Association of American Medical Colleges, 2003), cited in Coulehan, "Today's Professionalism" (op. cit.), p. 895.

44   Scheper-Hughes quoted in Christina Gillis, "Medicine and Humanities: Voicing Connections," *Journal of Medical Humanities* 29 (2008), 5-14, pp. 9-10.

45   D.W. Fraser and L.J. Smith, "Unmet Needs and Unused Skills: Physicians' Reflections on their Liberal Arts Education," *Academic Medicine* 64 (1989), 532-537; quoted in Aaron Manson, "The Fate of Idealism in Modern Medicine," *Journal of Medical Humanities* 15:3 (1994), 153-162, p. 159.

46   Delese Wear, Joseph Zarconi, and Rebecca Garden, "Reflection in/and Writing: Pedagogy and Practice in Medical Education," *Academic Medicine* 87: 5 (2012), 603-609.

47   S.J. Crandall, G. George, G.S. Marion, and S. Davis, "Applying Theory to the Design of Cultural Competency Training for Medical Students: A Case Study," *Academic Medicine* 78 (2003), 588-594.

48   A. Kleinman, L. Eisenberg, and B. Good, "Culture, Illness and Care: Clinical Lessons from Anthropologic and Cross-Cultural Research," *Annals of Internal Medicine* 88 (1978), 251-258.

49   A.K. Kumagai and M.L. Lypson, "Beyond Cultural Competence: Critical Consciousness, Social Justice, and Multicultural Education," *Academic Medicine* 84 (2009), 787-787.

50   J. Ousager and H. Johannessen, "Humanities in Undergraduate Medical Education: A Literature Review," *Academic Medicine* 85: 6 (2010), 988-998.

51   Rita Charon, "Calculating the Contributions of Humanities to Medical Practice – Motives, Methods, and Metrics," *Academic Medicine* 85: 6 (2010), 935-937.

52   Jonathan Metzl and Helena Hansen, "Structural Competency: Theorizing a New Medical Engagement with Stigma and Inequality," *Social Science and Medicine* 103 (2014), 126-133.

E. Cordell, "The Importance of the Study of the History of Medicine,"
Medical Library and Medical Journal 2 (1904), 268-282

Eugene F. Cordell (1843-1913) received his medical degree from the University of Maryland in 1868. In addition to his role as attending physician to the Good Samaritan Hospital in Baltimore and a founder of at least three convalescent facilities, he was president of the Johns Hopkins Hospital Historical Club from 1902 until 1904, and after that appointed honorary professor of history of medicine and university librarian of the University of Maryland faculty of physic.

In 1882 he was one of the founders of the Women's Medical College of Baltimore, where, between 1896 and 1904, he held a professorship in the principles and practice of medicine. He delivered an inaugural address to the college in 1883, titled "Women as a Physician: Illustrious Examples from History" (published in the *Maryland Medical Journal*). Having worked on historical atlases including his tome *Medical Annals of Maryland, 1790-1899* (1903), and works on the history of the School of Medicine of the University of Maryland, his address to the Women's Medical College echoed other publications that articulated his philosophy of the importance of the study of history to medical education. As in the case of the article reprinted here, Cordell believed that past medical achievements, as embodied in the efforts of illustrious individuals, create exemplars of professional conduct and personal creativity that should inspire budding medical scientists to more humane care. Bucking a trend toward mechanical reductionism which concerned him, history and medical biography, Cordell maintained, helped build character. "Now, I would ask," writes Cordell, "are our young students to be deprived of all the benefits of a knowledge of these, our medical heroes? ... Is education to be for them merely a mastering of the dry details of anatomy, physiology, practice?"

Finding his own examples of physician-historian educators among his friends, including the "most helpful and inspiring" William Osler, Cordell implored his readers to consider the fact that history, as a disciplined method of enquiry, had by the turn of the nineteenth century reached a respectable status, worthy of professional consideration. Historical study now turned "undigested" myths and chaffs that propagated misleading views of the past into critically reexamined records of human achievement that provide depth of perspective and accumulated wisdom to guide modern pursuits. Somewhat hagiographic in tone, Cordell here cites insights and observations of a number of canonical medical practitioners, such as Hippocrates, Galen, and Harvey, which betray his amazement that the past is packed with precedents for modern practice. But do these examples from the annals of medical history and biography change or improve practices now? Does recognizing precedent actually produce a better or more humane physician? Other than applauding those whose shoulders the profession stands on, what function for medical education does studying the past serve?

To be fair to Cordell's article and his philosophy, he did articulate deeper meaning and impact that the humanities bring to medical education. His article suggests six "advantages" to the study of history for medical students, ranging from pragmatic lessons for clinical skills (such as the Hippocratic procedure for correcting clubfoot) to professional self-fashioning. Overall, his argument subtly presents a balance between seeing the past as a repository of useful (that is, utilitarian) knowledge, as well as a pool of reflection to help instill deeper ideals of professionalism that enhance medical morality.

See also:

Bernard Christian Steiner, Lynn Roby Meekins, David Henry Carroll, Thomas G. Boggs, *Men of Mark in Maryland: Biographies of Leading Men of the State*, Volume 2 (Baltimore: B.F. Johnson, 1910), pp. 246-248.

The Importance of the Study of the History of Medicine

Eugene F. Cordell, M.D.

B etween ancient and modern historians two essential points of difference are readily observable. While the former make no use of critical research and confine themselves chiefly to contemporary events, to what they themselves have seen, perhaps participated in, or at least learned from eye-witnesses, with the latter research work is a conspicuous and essential feature, and there is no limit as to the period dealt with. Nothing does so much credit to modern culture, or has been so fruitful of results, as the improvement seen in the methods of historical study. Until a comparatively quite recent period, it was true that under the name of history was accepted almost everything that had been handed down from earlier times, no matter how contradictory to sense and reason it might be. The same absurdities – such, for instance, as the suckling of Romulus and Remus by a wolf – were repeated generation after generation, and everyone accepted implicitly and literally the story of the Garden of Eden. From this undigested mass our historical iconoclasts have sifted out all such chaff and subjected the remainder to the most searching and critical study, with the result that we may feel reasonably certain that what remains represents actual occurrences. By the careful study of original authorities, of manuscripts, inscriptions, tablets, excavations, etc., they have gotten as near as possible to contemporary sources; that is, to the events themselves. And while we must acknowledge our limitations and feel that all human knowledge is in the nature of the case fallible, even that which we acquire from eye witnesses, and still more so that which is handed down through many ages, the thought that we have exhausted all available sources of information and removed all obvious error places the subject upon a much higher plane, and gives us a sense of confidence and mental repose which is a very gratifying exchange for that blind belief in everything which formerly prevailed among the unlearned, or that distrust and disbelief which characterized the mental condition of the few who were real scholars. History may, therefore, now be said to have assumed something of the attitude of an exact science, and we are warranted in accepting it as the basis for philosophical deductions.

Now, since history is ever repeating itself, it is manifestly the part of wisdom to make it the object of our closest study, that we may profit by its lessons, both of success and of failure; for what others have done or have failed to do should point the way to their successors, whether in search of individual, social or national guidance. And what is true of history in general must be equally true of it in particular; the principles of the one are no less applicable to the other, of the whole to the part. The same evolution is seen in both; there is the same devious, uncertain path of human progress—now a sudden leap forward, now a halt, now an attempt to surmount or to find a way around some opposing hill, now a purposeless wandering hither and thither over the plain, now actually a retrogression. "It is, unfortunately, but too certain," says the learned Adams[1] "that there is a tendency in the human mind at certain times to retrograde, as well as in others to advance, both in knowledge and virtue." May not a study of the chart of progress teach us, or at least give us hints, how to make these leaps, to avoid these arrests, to surmount these obstructions, to escape this purposeless wandering, or to shun the greater humiliation of actual loss of ground?

It is a remarkable fact that the great Father of Medicine, 2,400 years ago, almost at the very beginning laid down the only true principles of progress – principles that, under the name "inductive method," were falsely claimed for Lord Bacon 2,000 years later – and that all real advance has been coincident with their observance. When that profession has gone astray or fallen back it was in consequence of their neglect, and more than once our art has been revived by restoring them to their place as our guides. It seems to be an imperative condition of our life and progress that we should be ever impressing upon ourselves that there is no royal road to knowledge, medical or other, and that he who would attain to its hidden treasure must be satisfied to dig deep into the ever lasting hills without other guide than the uncertain chart left by those who in still greater darkness have previously delved therein. Everyone who has studied the history of medicine to any extent must realize the importance of this precaution.

Now, if I am justified in claiming that medical history is but a part of general history and, as such, entitled to the same consideration, it certainly must strike us as strange that the two should be held in such different estimation in our system of education. No subject is considered of more importance in the literary courses of our universities. As evidence of this, I find from the register of students attending the present session of the Johns Hopkins University,

---

1   *The Genuine Works of Hippocrates.* Trans. by Francis Adams, London, 1849. Vol 2, p. 521.

which I presume may be considered as representative, that, the number of those pursuing historical study is exceeded in only two other departments, *i.e.,* English and Chemistry, while it exceeds, and mostly far exceeds, those taking Mathematics, Physics, Geology, Zoology, Latin, Greek, Romance Languages, Sanskrit, Political Economy and Philosophy. On the other hand, it is rare to find the subject even mentioned in the curricula of the medical schools.

I have been at some pains to ascertain to what extent the history of medicine is taught in this country, and with this object in view, have written the Deans of fourteen of our leading universities which have medical departments for information. I append a table made up from the meager replies received from the following: Harvard, Yale, Cornell, Buffalo, Columbia, New York, Pennsylvania, Johns Hopkins, Maryland, Virginia, Tulane, Chicago, Michigan and Minnesota. From this it appears that a full course of lectures, fourteen to sixteen in number, is attempted in but three, viz. Universities of Pennsylvania, Maryland and Minnesota. There are four "lectureships," one just established and still without an incumbent, and another held jointly with a "Clinical Professorship of Dermatology." One of the "courses" consists of three lectures! There is but one professorship, and that an "honorary" one. In two institutions "some" instruction is given by the Professor of Therapeutics and the Assistants in Surgery, respectively; in the latter case only in surgery. In one, and that one, strange to say, Harvard, lectures were attempted, but "no great interest was shown" and they were discontinued. There is no uniformity in those receiving instruction; sometimes it is the sophomores, sometimes the juniors or seniors, and some times any that *choose* to attend. In but one is the claim made that the course is compulsory. In none is there any examination. One can readily imagine what the attendance must be under such circumstances, and the experience of Harvard is instructive. However, according to the table, in three cases it is "good," "one-half of the class" and "poor," respectively. The table gives the size of the medical libraries attached to the universities. And, finally, I would call your attention to that very useful auxiliary, the medico-historical society. There are two of these, but as one is limited to a dozen graduates, is not attended by the students and takes no part in their instruction, it does not concern us here. The other is the excellent Historical Club of the Johns Hopkins Hospital, founded in 1890 upon a very broad basis, and which has exercised a profound influence not only locally, but throughout the entire country. Many able papers have been read before it, and there are few who have any claims to distinction in this field in the United States who have not been its guests.

Let me, in passing, point out the error of a statement by Prof. Roswell

NAME	ARE LECTURES DELIVERED	BY WHOM	TO WHOM	CHARACTER OF THE COURSE	IS IT COMPULSORY	WHEN BEGUN	IS THERE A MEDICO-HISTORICAL SOCIETY	IS THERE A MEDICAL LIBRARY	ATTENDANCE AT LECTURE COURSE
Harvard	No.						No.		Course attempted, no interest shown; abandoned.
Yale	Yes.	Prof. of Therapeutics.	Junior Class.	5 or 6 lectures.	No.		No.	10,000*	
Cornell	No.						Yes.	Yes	
New York	No.						No.	No.	
Columbia	No.						No.		
Pennsylvania	Yes.	Lecturer on Hist. of Med.	4th Year Class	16; 1 Weekly for half session.	Yes.	1892	Yes †	14,100	Well attended. No examination.
Virginia	No.						No.	1,500 1,800	
Chicago	Yes.	Lecturer on Hist. of Med.	Jun. and Sen. Classes.		No.		No.	10,796	Just founded. Course not yet begun.
Michigan	No.				No.		No.	10,000	
Tulane	No.						No.	12,000 Over	
Johns Hopkins	Yes.	Lecturer on Hist.	Students Generally	3 lectures.	No.	1893	Yes.	3,500 8,000	Historical society largely attended by students.
Maryland	Yes.	Prof. of Hist. of Med.	Students Generally	14 lectures.	No.	1903	No.	4,500	Small attendance.
Buffalo	Yes.	Assistants in Surgery.	Sophmore Class	More or less, on Hist. of Surg.	No.		No.	6,255	
Minnesota	Yes.	Lecturer on Hist. of Med.	Senior Class	16 lectures.	No.	1897	No.	3,500	Attended by one-half the class.

* Part of the University Library.
† Small, and limited to graduates.

Park of Buffalo, the author of a very interesting course of historical lectures delivered before the University of Buffalo and published in 1897, viz., that his was "the first attempt in the medical schools of this country to give systematic instruction in the history of the science."[2] For, over three-quarters of a century ago the far-seeing "Sage of Monticello" provided for the teaching of the history of medicine in his great University (Virginia) and the course of lectures there delivered by the late Prof. Robley Dunglison was published in 1872.[3] As appears from the table, there is no course on the subject at that institution at the present time.

Now, I do not believe that anyone who possesses a broad and genuine culture, and whose opinion is, therefore, worth considering, will hesitate for a moment to acknowledge that the facts above given indicate a shocking neglect, an inexcusable apathy on the part of our medical schools. Where is our boasted intelligence and superiority, that we do not perceive the folly and danger of such a course; folly in that we are willing to deprive our young *"The fact is, we of this age are too much carried away with the rage for novelty. Nothing is esteemed of consequence but that which contains something new. But in catching at the new how often we risk losing that which is old, well grounded and far better."* graduates of the accumulated wisdom and experience of all the ages; danger in that we turn them loose without the salutary checks and restraints that such studies afford? "No man," says Lord Macaulay,[4] "who is correctly informed as to the past will be disposed to take a morose or desponding view of the present." The fact is, we of this age are too much carried away with the rage for novelty. Nothing is esteemed of consequence but that which contains something new. But in catching at the new how often we risk losing that which is old, well grounded and far better. Haste is stamped on everything, and this

2   Dedication of his: *An Epitome of the History of Medicine*, Phil., 1897.
3   *History of Medicine from the Earliest Ages to the Commencement of the Nineteenth Century*. By Rodney Dunglison, M.D., LL.D. Arranged and Edited by Richard J. Dunglison, M.D. Phil., 1872.
4   *History of England*, Vol. 1, Page 2.

is particularly true of Americans. We scarcely attain to one point of vantage when, without rest, we rush on to the next. We allow ourselves no enjoyment of anything; indeed, scarcely time for reflection. We seem to be drifting more and more into mere machines, mere worshipers of physical science. Yet, hear the warning words of Prof. Du Bois-Reymond: "Where physical science reigns exclusively, the intellect becomes poor in ideas, the fancy in images, the soul in sensibility, and the result is a narrow, hard and dry disposition, forsaken of the Muses and Graces; and not only so, but physical science leads down by imperceptible gradations from the highest efforts of human intellect to mere mechanical work that looks at nothing beyond gain."[5] Without doubt, we need constant infusions of what the Germans call "the science of antiquity," as a corrective to this mechanical tendency. Here is an opportunity for some *laudator temporis acti*. We must not permit ourselves to be severed from the high ideals and the inspiration that come from a contemplation of the examples, the lives, the achievements, of the great men of the past.

Especially do we need to take deep and frequent draughts from the writings of the great Father, to whose genius we owe an everlasting debt. What a sublime figure he offers to our view! In an age of theory, how free from theorizing! Though one of the priestly caste, how untainted by superstition! Familiar with the natural course of diseases, he was in a position to gauge the true value of remedies, and acquired a wonderful prevision of results. Not content with general impressions, he closely observed and carefully recorded individual diseases at the bedside, and relied only on such experience to direct him to the proper management of his cases. Conscious of the limitations of his knowledge and of the tendency of the human mind to err, he wisely confined himself to the guidance of each case and to the relief of symptoms. Above all things, he was cautious to do no harm. And scarcely less inspiring are the work and lives of his successors. What an anachronism and an oasis in the anatomical desert seems the story of those old Alexandrians, Herophilus and Erasistratus, with their human dissections and vivisections! With what fine judgment and choice language Celsus sums up the knowledge of his day, and what a concise and admirable enumeration he gives of the qualifications demanded of the surgeon! How we linger over his descriptions of lithotomy (the "Celsian operation"), alopecia ("*area*" and "*kerion Celsi*"), and ligation of the arteries! What learning and literary fecundity are exhibited by Galen, "the first experimental physiologist," and what a high conception of professional

---

5   Quoted in: *Essays and Studies*. By Basil L. Gildersleeve. Baltimore, 1890.

morals he possessed!

What graphic and inimitable picture of disease Aretaeus, the Cappadocian, has drawn! What surprises await us in the work of the first gynecologist, Soranus of Ephesus! What a strange work that is of the great Byzantine surgeon and obstetrician, Paul of AEgina, in the seventh century, when his genius alone lit up the darkness of his age! What romance there is about the days of the Arabian cithern player of Bagdad, Abú Becr Mohammed Ibn Zacaríyá Ar-Rází, commonly known among us as Rhazes, who gave that famous description of smallpox! What a fine delineation of the surgeon is that given by old Guy de Chauliac, "the earliest herald of the modern surgery," in 1363, and with what surprise we learn that so high an ideal could be upheld in an age which we are accustomed to look upon as so barbarous! I cannot refrain from giving it to you: "Let the surgeon," he says, "be well educated, skillful, ready and courteous. Let him be bold in those things that are safe, fearful in those things that are dangerous; avoiding all evil methods and practices. Let him be tender with the sick, honorable to men of his profession, wise in his predictions, chaste, sober, pitiful, merciful; not covetous or extortionate, but rather let him take his wages in moderation, according to his work, and the wealth of his patient, and the issue of the disease and his own worth."[6]

How few realize that picture, even in our own far more enlightened day! What an interesting story that is of the great barber surgeon, Ambroise Paré, of how, in 1552, he was led to substitute the ligature for the cautery in amputation, and of the glorious fight he made against the pouring of that horrible boiling oil into the poor soldiers' wounds! And who does not shudder to recall Michael Servetus, the discoverer of the pulmonary circulation, burning at the stake, and strangely, by the hands of a fellow protestant? And what a grand role is that of Vesalius who, while Francis and Charles were turning the world upside down with their wars, was quietly turning anatomy upside down with his scalpel! And how familiar to every student are the names of Eustachius, Fallopius, Arantius, Varolius, Sylvius, Fabricius ab Aquapendente and Caesalpinus! And how many of us are aware that the great astronomer Copernicus, and Rabelais, the greatest wit of that most witty nation, the French, were practicing physicians?

And not long after these there came the greatest of them all. Harvey, whose name is imperishably connected with the discovery of the circulation. It is not so well known, perhaps, that he established also the truth of the doctrine of

6   Paget (S). *Life of Paré*, 1897. Page 2.

the origin of all animals from the egg—"*Ovum esse primordium commune omni bus animalibus.*"[7] I shall have something further to say of the first of these presently. Listen to some well-known names of the same century: Havers, Naboth, Pacchioni, Cowper, Bartholin, de Graaff, Malpighi, Meibomius, Wirsung, Aselli, Highmore, Steno, Glisson, Nuck, Spigelius, Brunner, Wharton, Peyer, Willis and Vieussens, all incorporated into our anatomical nomenclature. Then there were: Borelli, who explained all physiology on mechanical principles; Sanctorius, who weighed himself in a balance for thirty years, and thus determined the amount of the insensible perspiration; Mauriceau, the first great obstetrician; Morel, the discoverer of the tourniquet; Baglivi, the author of the celebrated saying, "He who diagnosticates well, cures well;" Sydenham, the "English Hippocrates," who refused to be bound by the theories of his day; Locke, the philosopher; and the sublime writer, Sir Thomas Browne.

Boerhaave is preeminent in the next century, the creator of no school, but selecting from all sources those things that appealed most to his reason and intelligence; a man of tireless industry, who held his priority as much, perhaps, through his high character as his exalted talents. We must single out also the name of Jenner, at the close of the century, as that of one of the world's greatest benefactors. And are not the following names in our mouths every day: Basedow, Valsalva, Santorini, Winslow, Soemmering, Levret, Gimbernat, Scarpa, Galvini, Goulard, Meckel, Monro, Pott, Anel, Tenon, Petit, Dover, Heberden, Lieberkuhn, Portal, Reil, Gasser, Descemet, Belloc and Chopart? Prominent, also, were Stephen Hales, the experimental investigator; Haller, the author of the doctrine of irritability; John Hunter, the founder of modern scientific surgery; Morgagni, the founder of pathological anatomy; Auenbrugger, the inventor of percussion; Bichat, the founder of general anatomy; James Currie, of cold water fame; Sprengel and Freind, historians; Oliver Goldsmith, poet; and the American, Rush.

And what a great period that was for progress and research, which has just closed, the nineteenth century, which we would fain believe to be the greatest of them all! No longer now do the anatomists predominate, but there is development in many directions. The specialties all come to the front. Clinical teaching and work are conspicuous. More exact methods and instrumental aids of all sorts are introduced. All the sciences are called on to contribute. Auscultation and percussion, improved microscopes, the ophthalmoscope, laryngoscope, endoscope, and specula of various sorts, the thermometer,

7   *Exercitationes de Generatione Animalium.*

electricity, the X-ray apparatus. etc., open new fields to our vision and multiply our diagnostic resources. With the discovery of anesthesia, surgery takes a great bound forward, acquiring a further acceleration of speed upon the discovery of antisepsis. Pathology and histology are cultivated with increasing success, and the new science of bacteriology is created. What an array of names one can call up—Corvisart, Lrennec, Louis, Bright, Addison, Hodgkin, Bennet, Wunderlich, Skoda, Trousseau, McDowell, Mott, Astley Cooper, Esmarch, Wells, Paget, Langenbeck, Billroth, Strohmeyer, Lister, Simpson, Re camier, Sims, Semmelweis, Hebra, Magendie, Broca, Bernard, Charles Bell, Marshall Hall, Charcot, Helmholtz, Beer, Donders, Graefe, Pinel, Griesinger, Erb, Weir Mitchell, Czermak, Türck, Bayle, Virchow, Cohnheim, Klebs, Rokitansky, Koch, Laveran, Walter Reed, Pasteur!

In this rapid survey my only object has been to show you at a glance, as it were, how rich our past has been in example and inspiration. I have thrown but a few pictures upon the historical canvas. I might have increased the number to a thousand, but these are sufficient for my purpose. Now, I would ask, are our young students to be deprived of all the benefits of a knowledge of these, our medical heroes—these men who, as Plato said, have: "handed on the torch of life from generation to generation?" Is there nothing in such lives for them—nothing that will help them onward and upward in their professional career? Is education to be for them merely a mastering of the dry details of anatomy, physiology, and practice? Is there to be no attempt to direct motives, to strengthen conscience, to build up character? I tell you again there is danger in such a course.

There are two other thoughts suggested by this survey. One is that there has been no degeneration in these latter days. Where do we find higher patterns of all that is noble and inspiring than in Pasteur, Virchow, or Lister? Nay, we do not have to go beyond the limits of our own city to find those who are the peers of any whom I have named, great leaders in medical progress, beacon lights among us for all time to come.

Another thought is the solidarity of our art. Although differing in importance, each age has contributed something of permanent value to it; each stage of progress is indissolubly bound to all other stages. "What we know and what we think," says Foster,[8] "is not a new fountain gushing fresh from the barren rock of the unknown at the stroke of the rod of our own intellect; it is a stream which flows by us and through us, fed by the far-off rivulets of long

8   *Lectures in the History of Physiology.* Cambridge, 1901.

ago." In the house that we are building each stone, each brick, each arch, has its place, contributing to the strength and symmetry of the structure. Nor because we are living on the sixth floor can we be indifferent to what is going on in the first or second. We stand, as it were, upon the shoulders of our predecessors, and it would be very little to our credit if we did not see further than they; but to imagine, as some appear to do, that they were blind and saw nothing, indicates a very shallow knowledge, and a judgment warped by the greater relative size of near objects. It would be interesting to know whether posterity will assign to us the precedence that we think is our due.

"It would be very little to our credit if we did not see further than they; but to imagine, as some appear to do, that they were blind and saw nothing, indicates a very shallow knowledge, and a judgment warped by the greater relative size of near objects."

But not only do we profit by the high ideals and the inspiration of great lives which we derive from the past, but it is of the greatest practical benefit to trace the history of great researches. Let us review for a few moments that which led to the discovery of the circulation of the blood.

Before the days of Harvey – in the previous century – the lesser or pulmonary circulation had been clearly enunciated by Servetus and Realdus Columbus, and both lesser and greater circulations had been described by Caesalpinus. But these views seem to have been purely theoretical; there is no evidence that they were based upon direct observation or experiment, and they made no impression on contemporary sentiment. The old Galenic doctrine was still held by Harvey's teacher, the great anatomist of Padua, Fabricius ab Apuapendente, at the beginning of the seventeenth century. The blood was still supposed to pass in part by invisible pores through the septum of the ventricles, and this was the only connection acknowledged between the venous and the arterial blood. There were, in fact, two distinct and independent circulations: the venous blood, with its natural spirits derived from the liver, passing out from the right ventricle along the veins to the tissues, and the thin arterial blood, containing the innate heat of the heart and the vital spirits derived from the lungs, in like manner proceeding from the left ventricle, both by a to and fro movement. The idea held of the action of the heart was just the reverse of the truth. The active period (the systole) corresponding with the impulse was supposed to be that of dilatation, when the air and blood were assumed to be drawn into the left and right ventricles, respectively, by the suction force thereby exerted. Harvey did away entirely with the "spirits," because he could find no evidence of their existence in his researches. He denied the pores in the septum of the heart for the same reason, and taught that all the blood passes through the lungs. He ascertained the action of the auricles and ventricles, with their respective valves. He realized that the active period of the heart was that of contraction upon its contents, and that the blood was thereby driven into the arteries, producing the pulse. He calculated carefully the amount of this blood passing out from the heart at each systole, and thus found that in a few minutes as much must pass as is contained in the whole body; that is, that all the blood passes through the heart. It was also obvious that the amount was far greater than that which is absorbed by the veins from the food and drink, previously considered its sole source, and that the far greater part must be blood which has passed from the arteries to the veins in the tissues, in some such hidden manner as it does in the lungs. Harvey never saw the capillaries, either in the lungs or elsewhere; he had only a logical evidence of their existence. Their discovery was reserved for Malpighi and the microscope.

Fact after fact arose to confirm Harvey's views: that the heart was emptied when the vena cava was tied, and filled to distention when the aorta was tied; that a moderate ligation of a limb made it swell with venous blood, but a tight one kept the blood from entering by compressing the arteries; that the whole of the blood in the body could be drained away by opening a vein; that the valves of the veins (discovered by his master, Fabricius, but misinterpreted by him) were designed to prevent reflux of blood in its passage onward to the heart. Harvey's solution of the circulation was a purely mechanical one, based on patient anatomical examination and comparison of various animals, on the adoption of some explanation for what he saw, and the confirmation of this explanation by repeated dissection, vivisection and experiment—in other words, on true Hippocratic principles.[9] Who will say that it is a matter of indifference whether such a work be brought to the attention of students or not?

Again, medical literature is a mine of neglected and overlooked discoveries. Take, for example, club foot, both the true nature and successful treatment of which were known to Hippocrates, but were lost for many ages after his

9   See Foster, *Loc. cit.*

death. Says Adams:[10] "In all the works on ancient surgery, I verily believe there is not a more wonderful chapter than the one which relates to club-foot. In it he has not only stated correctly the true nature of this malformation. but he has also given very sensible directions for rectifying the deformity in early life. Now, it appears to me a lamentable reflection, as proving that valuable knowledge, after being discovered, may be lost again to the world for many ages, that not only did subsequent authorities, down to a very recent period, not add anything to the stock of valuable information which he had given on the subject, but the important knowledge which he had revealed to the profession came to be disregarded and lost sight of, so that, until these last few years" [he refers to the introduction of tenotomy by Strohmeyer and Delpech] "talipes was regarded as one of the *opprobia medicinae*" Hippocrates was also acquainted with dislocation of the acromial end of the clavicle, the knowledge of which was entirely lost until within the eighteenth century.[11] According to Celsus, lithotripsy, which held so prominent a place in the surgery of the latter part of the last century, was invented and practiced by Ammonius of Alexandria, about B. C. 230.[12] Heliodorus, about A.D. 100, was well acquainted with torsion of arteries, a particular mode of operating for the radical cure of hernia by excision of the sac, and excision of stricture of the urethra—all of which have been proclaimed as marvelous discoveries in later days.[13] You all remember the statement of the late Dr. T. Gaillard Thomas, which formed the theme of my predecessor's Presidential Address last year, that more had been done for the advancement and growth of medicine in the last half of the last century than in all the preceding ages from the days of Hippocrates. Yet hear the acknowledgment of the author of the statement in his well-known work on "The Diseases of Women;"[14] "Some of the most valuable contributions to modern gynecology will be found to be foreshadowed, or even plainly noticed, by the writers of a past age, and afterward entirely overlooked;" and he cites as examples the use of the uterine sound, sponge-tents, dilatation of the constricted cervix, and even the speculum itself. The history of the last-

---

10 *Loc. cit.* Vol. 2, page 559.

11 Baas (J.H.): *Outlines of the History of Medicine.* Trans. by H.E. Handerson. New York, 1889.

12 Celsus. De Medicina, vii, 26.

13 Billings (J.S.). In: *System of Surgery.* Edit. by F.S. Dennis. Phil., 1895. Vol I, page 30.

14 Thomas (T.G.). *A Practical Treatise on the Diseases of Women.* 6 Ed. Phil., 1891. Page 17.

named instrument, upon which modern gynecology is based, is exceedingly instructive. Employed habitually by Paul of AEgina in the latter half of the seventh century, A.D., and furnishing him with an excellent knowledge of diseases of the uterus, it was forgotten by his successors until rediscovered by Recamier and introduced to the profession in 1818.

But it is probable that we may learn equally as much from the follies, omissions and failures of the past as from its successes and achievements. Experience will always be fallacious and judgment difficult, and it is not likely that error can ever be avoided. It is well for us to realize that the future may pluck many a feather from even our ambitious wings, who plume ourselves on our attainments. It is not impossible that some Praxagoras of Cos may hereafter open the abdomen for the relief of obstruction of the bowels 2,200 years before men shall think the example worth following; that some Celsus may confound veins and arteries, although this same Praxagoras shall have known of their differences 400 years earlier; that some Aretreus shall have heard a "bruit" in heart disease, but the hint lie dormant many centuries; that this same close observer shall describe the crossing of the nerves and its effects 1,400 years before a Willis appears to beat it into men's brains; that men shall believe that arteries contain only air, although experience be continually teaching that they contain blood; that they shall believe that there are pores in the septa of the heart, although the utmost effort of vision fail to detect them; that some Massaria shall rather be wrong with Galen than right with anyone else; that men shall have practiced ligation of arteries for hemorrhage for centuries before a Paré teach them to apply it in amputation; that surgery shall be turned over to the barbers; that mesmerism and hypnotism shall have another periodic discovery under some new name; that some Sylvius shall teach that the whole art of medicine consists in the administration of acids and alkalies, some Cullen that all pathology is referable to spasm, some Broussais that we must seek it only in inflammation; that some Auenbrugger's epoch making discovery of percussion shall have to wait for the coming of a Corvisart; that some Brown shall slay his thousands with whiskey and opium, some Rasori his ten thousands with the lancet and tartar emetic; that those will be found to combat blindly the unanswerable logic of the germ theory, and even to persist in their opposition when the germs themselves shall be placed before their eyes; that they shall fight against the obstetrical forceps, cinchona and antiseptics. We may smile at the suggestion of such possibilities, the list of which could be very much lengthened, yet some of them have actually occurred not so very long ago; and what has been, or its like, will with certainty of fate be again. He only is wise who realizes this fact, listens to the wholesome confessions of the past and is ever on his guard.

Let us now sum up some of the advantages of the study of medical history that have been pointed out in this address:

1. It teaches what and how to investigate.

2. It is the best antidote we know against egotism, error and despondency.

3. It increases knowledge, gratifies natural and laudable curiosity, broadens the view and strengthens the judgment.

4. It is a rich mine from which may be brought to light many neglected or overlooked discoveries of value.

5. It furnishes the stimulus of high ideals which we poor, weak mortals need to have ever before us; it teaches our students to venerate what is good, to cherish our best traditions, and strengthens the common bond of the profession.

6. It is the fulfillment of a duty—that of cherishing the memories, the virtues, the achievements, of a class which has benefited the world as no other has, and of which we may feel proud that we are members.

Having now shown the value – nay, I should rather say the necessity – of the study of medical history, I shall conclude with a few words regarding its teaching. So important a branch should receive the highest consideration. It should be taught in no desultory fashion, but as thoroughly as any other. There should be a full chair of the history of medicine in every university. A systematic course of reading should be required in addition to the lectures, which should be not less than sixteen to twenty in number. It should be made a subject of examination, for all experience proves that in no way can the attendance of the students be enforced. The time is near at hand when the standing of universities will be judged by their attitude to this branch, and when it will be assigned a front rank in the curriculum.

3

Christian A. Herter, "Imagination and Idealism in the Medical Sciences," *The Journal of the American Medical Association* 54: 6 (1910), 423-430.

Christian Archibald Herter (1865-1910) received his medical degree from the College of Physicians and Surgeons at Columbia University in 1883. Following graduation he studied pathology under William Henry Welch at Johns Hopkins University, who himself was a devotee of the history of science and medicine. Herter started his clinical career as a neurologist, publishing *The Diagnosis of Diseases of the Nervous System* (1892), but left practice to pursue research in biological chemistry in his private home laboratory in New York. He was appointed professor of pathological chemistry at University and Bellevue Hospital Medical College in 1897, and then Professor of Pharmacology at Columbia University in 1903, the year he established the "Christian A. Herter Lecture Series" which exists today and is organized by the Department of Biochemistry at New York University School of Medicine.

Having co-founded and then becoming the first editor of the *Journal of Biological Chemistry* in 1905, and being noted for his research in celiac disease, it could be considered surprising that his colleagues, writing his obituary in *Biochemical Journal*, described him in the title as "one who championed the cause of imagination and idealism in the medical sciences." Though, if such an assumptive bias exists, it might be owing to more current sentiments about reductionism in science than Herter and his colleagues possessed. Similar to Eugene Cordell in the previous chapter, in the article reproduced here Herter impresses upon his readers the importance of realizing that medicine is built on a history of changing ideas, making it a dynamic pursuit, not a set of fixed facts. Having students understand that medical knowledge is built on a shifting and growing foundation of experimental findings helps allay his concern that future practitioners will have minds "statical in conception," as he says—that is, an intellect that is stuck in stasis.

In "Imagination and Idealism," Herter was simultaneously showcasing the achievements of scientists whose work he himself found particularly inspirational (the connection between Claude Bernard, Louis Pasteur, and Hermann von Helmholtz and his own work on gastrointestinal disorders is suggestive), while also arguing that a roaming intellect – an investigator with wide interests – is a model of behavior for successful outcomes in science. While the general style of Herter's writing is celebratory of what he sometimes refers to as "lofty intellects" (possessed by the "noblest of men"), his message is ultimately more about the process of intellectual investigation rather than the notion that one has to be a genius in order to succeed.

At the heart of his article is his concern with methodology in science, with the very ways that broad thinking and traits of character inform and inspire possibilities of scientific inquiry. Warning against an overt obsession with utility as a driving motive for research, Herter's biographical studies are intended to illustrate that revolutionary outcomes are often products of questions that "promised to be intellectually satisfying." What do discovery stories – such as Bernard's findings relative to the glycogenic function of the liver, or Helmholtz's construction of the ophthalmoscope – teach students? For Herter, they show students ways that great outcomes are the result of framing questions in ways that absorb one's attention, driven by curiosity. As he says, "The history of medical discovery is a long chain of imaginative experiences whose links have been welded and fixed by passing through the fiery ordeal of appeal to experimental tests." As a contribution to a philosophy of medical education, Herter hoped that the history of science would prove that research is far from a "dry and painful task" and, when pursued with ideals and imagination, engulfed in "the vicissitudes of hope and despair, success and failure" – all part of the baffling mysteries of human life and the pursuit of alleviating human suffering.

Imagination and Idealism in the Medical Sciences

Christian A. Herter, M.D.

The presidential invitation in response to which I am about to address you to-day was welcome to me because it offered a rare chance to express some views of medical progress which I think are too seldom presented to the student. I have in mind the influence of imagination and idealism on the growth of medical discovery. Vividly recalling, as I do, the experiences of my own student days, more than a quarter century past, I fancy you as coming to the acquisition of the myriad facts of medicine with little to tell you of the intellectual forces and historical sequences by which those facts have emerged. If this surmise be correct, it follows that you incline to take a static rather than a dynamic view of the nature of scientific medicine, in the sense that you regard medical lore as something much more fixed than is actually the case. In reality, our science is fortunately plastic, constantly subject to revision of its facts, and ever ready to welcome new interpretations of old facts as well as new discoveries, both great and small. This very plasticity it is that makes progress attainable and fascinates our minds. But our text-books and our lectures are necessarily conservative and dispose us strongly to the notion of fixity of facts, making our minds statical in conception. I would like to dispel, in a measure, this retarding conception by telling you something of the ways in which gifted and trained minds have enriched the medical sciences by significant discoveries. And of the qualities underlying such discoveries I would emphasize especially the rôle of imagination and idealism.

The fine humanitarian aim of medicine always has been and always will be one of the features that make men love to practice the art. And the idealism that delights in the relief of human suffering and disability will remain alive so long as the healing art itself. But we must not blind ourselves to the fact that this very attitude of eager desire to help our fellows in distress is a source of weakness as well as a pillar of strength. For he who would answer the calls of the sick must resort to direct methods and must generally tread the paths of the obvious. He has not time to turn aside to the indirect ways of winning the citadel, nor, indeed, is he likely to be in that frame of mind which urges to such an approach; he is preoccupied with the crying needs of the suffering or dying man committed to his charge. Yet it is growing every day clearer that the progress of the medical sciences depends in a remarkable degree on discoveries made by indirect methods—that is, by methods not looking to the immediate relief of disease. These discoveries are made chiefly by men who, while in deep sympathy with the humanitarian aims of medicine, nevertheless find time to turn aside to studies and experiments from which the active practitioners are, in general, excluded, by the circumstances of their lives and the intensely practical nature of their vocation. There was a time when the alert physician or surgeon, with little or no training in the experimental method, might make important contributions to knowledge by following rather evident suggestions derived from the study of patients. The Romans, operating for stone in the bladder; Paré, using the ligature to check hemorrhage on the field of battle; McDowell, successfully removing ovarian tumors, give us examples of great advances along rather obvious lines of development. To-day the chances for significant progress in such evident directions, although not exhausted, are far less frequent. The golden nuggets at or near the surface of things have been for the greater part discovered, it seems safe to say. We must dig deeper to find new ones of equal value, and we must often dig circuitously, with mere hints for guides. Our most effective tools are to be found in the experimental laboratory, where the fundamental sciences, physics and chemistry, come to the aid of physiology, biology, pathology and psychology. I should like to tell you of some of the many instances in which these sciences have come to the succor of medicine and have brought her riches of knowledge unattainable had she been limited to resources belonging to the accumulated experience which makes up the accepted material of medical teaching. If I incidentally say something of the personality of the men who have been the living instruments of this progress, it is in order to give you occasional glimpses into the workings of some of the most original and productive of minds.

I like to think of medicine in our day as an ever broadening and deepening river, fed by the limpid streams of pure science. The river at its borders has its eddies and currents, expressive of certain doubts and errors that fringe all progress; but it makes continuous advances on the way to the ocean of its destiny. Very gradual has been the progress of its widening and deepening, for it is a product of human ingenuity and artifice, and only skilled engineers could direct the isolated currents of science into the somewhat sluggish stream of medical utility. The names of some of the greatest of these engineers are familiar to you—Vesalius, Harvey, Malpighi, John Hunter, Claude Bernard, Helmholtz, Virchow, Metchnikoff, Pasteur, Lister, Koch, Behring,

Ehrlich, Emil Fischer, Weigert, Wright, Theobald Smith, Flexner. Different as have been the achievements of these men, there are some qualities of mind and of heart which nearly all of them have shown in ample measure, and of such qualities none are more evident than imagination, or play of fancy, and personal idealism, using the latter term to mean a readiness to make sacrifices for the sake of lofty achievement. And I think we are quite safe in making the generalization that the discoveries for which we hold these thinkers in honor would have been impossible but for the exercise of these qualities. If this be true, the fact furnishes us with a clue to present tendencies in medicine and shows us to what sorts of gifts we have to look for the significant advances of the future. I, therefore, hope to make good my generalizations by a series of examples.

If we look over any list of the names of the makers of modern medicine, we shall find that they may be classed in two main and definite groups, according to the intellectual trend for which they stand. One group holds the men who look at the problems of medical science largely from the standpoint of structure and arrangement. They have the instincts and interests of the morphologists. They represent anatomy, embryology, pathological anatomy and histology. They have usually been men of powerful and logical minds, craving the positive, the definite and the attainable, either shunning somewhat the speculative aspects of science, or moving uncomfortably in the midst of ill-defined or challengeable facts. In this list belong Vesalius, von Baer, Bichat, Virchow and Weigert, who represent with maximal distinction the group of investigators with dominant morphological tendencies.

In sharp contrast with this definite type stands the second group, made up of men whose interests lie in the study of function, rather than structure, and whose minds, far from being dismayed by the speculative aspects of their studies, invite such speculation so long as it is severely controlled by frequent appeals to facts won by experiment. The members of this small group are dynamically minded, highly imaginative, delighting in the play of forces. They are essentially experimentalists, and their thoughts in leisure hours, as in the hours of work, turn always restlessly and uncontrollably in the same direction—to the planning of new experiments designed to answer the questions uppermost in consciousness, questions having nearly always to do with the phenomena of living beings. Claude Bernard, Helmholtz, Pasteur and Ehrlich are the unexcelled prototypes of investigators of life-phenomena in medicine, and we shall not go far astray if we fancy them as spirits inspired by

"All that is great and all that is strange
In the boundless realm of unending change."

We have also, I think, to recognize an intermediate group of great investigators who, while highly trained in a morphological way, have shown also a deep and productive interest in the functional aspects of organized nature, without, however, attaining the highest levels of achievement in thought on the dynamical side of medical research. In this category we may place Harvey, Malpighi, John Hunter, Johannes Müller, Cohnheim and Robert Koch. And I think we may safely add that most modern investigators, educated under the influence of the strong trend to physiological thought, belong in this intermediate position.

The examples of medical discovery which I shall first bring to your notice I shall select from the first and intermediate groups of workers, reserving the illustrations from the second group for later consideration.

The first great morphologist of modern times is Vesalius, whose claims to recognition rest not merely on his masterly and precise description of the parts of the human body, but also on his abrupt departure from the Galenic traditions and teachings, forced on him by the objectivity and sincerity of his studies. While we must regard the work of Vesalius as evidence of intellectual and logical power, it would be an error to credit him with the highest type of imagination or with elaborate esthetic reactions. The self-willed, clear-thinking man won his triumphs more by force of character and unswerving purpose than by creative intellect; and we see this type of worker repeated in some of our greatest modern anatomists, as also in some fields in which the experimental method is prominent.

The gain in scientific method, initiated by Vesalius, was fixed and established in England by the spirited, penetrating and imaginative William Harvey, whose monumental work proved that all the blood in the body travels in a circuit impelled by the beating of the heart. That a hugely skilled anatomist should have made this physiological discovery is significant evidence that studies in structure may stimulate a labile mind to serious investigation of the functional side of organic nature. Probably the work which Harvey did with his master, Fabricius, at Padua in the anatomy of the vascular system stimulated his interest in the discovery of experimental methods which should expose the true uses of this elaborate mechanism.

The lofty intellect of Harvey was linked with a generous and idealistic nature. His portraits show a formation of head and face that reminds us of representations of Shakespeare. Like Hunter and Darwin, he had the virtue of being extremely slow in publishing. He forgave his many antagonists, notwithstanding the troubles they brought into his life. He says:

> I would not charge with wilful falsehood any one who was sincerely anxious for truth, nor lay it to any one's door as a crime that he had fallen into error. I am, myself, the partisan of truth alone; and I can indeed say that I have used all my endeavors, bestowed all my pains on an attempt to produce something that should be agreeable to the good, profitable to the learned, and useful to letters.

More than a hundred years after the death of Harvey there emerged from obscurity a Scotchman, John Hunter, of such power and versatility as to make him a worthy intellectual successor of the great Englishman. We may take him as our second example of an investigator of our intermediate group, combining the interests of morphologist and physiologist. One example – a celebrated instance – will illustrate the point I wish to make. It was in Richmond Park that Hunter saw the deer whose growing antlers awakened in his mind a singularly fruitful physiological question. What would happen if he shut off the blood-supply of the antler on one side by tying the corresponding carotid artery? Experiment showed that the antler lost its warmth and ceased to grow; but for a short time only was there this check to growth. After a time the horn warmed again and grew. Had he failed to really obstruct the blood flow in the artery? No. Examination showed the carotid to have been securely ligated. Whence, then, came the blood essential for the antler's growth? Through the neighboring arteries that had grown distended, through what we now call the collateral circulation. So was the fact of the collateral circulation revealed. The thoughtful and logical mind of the practical surgeon soon found an important application of this discovery to human pathology. No one had dared to treat aneurism by ligation for fear of causing gangrene. But the existence of a collateral circulation held out a prospect of keeping the parts alive despite the ligation of an important artery. The first trial of the new method on a popliteal aneurism was successful, and the Hunterian operation, as you know it in surgery today, came into assured existence. An unimaginative man could not have made this discovery in this manner. Yet Hunter belongs to the logical, independent, matter-of-fact type with fancy well controlled, rather than to the dreamers and poets of science. He was a rough diamond, with an intensely objective nature, and he had corresponding limitations. He is said to have rebelled against the classical teachings of Oxford. "Why, they wanted me to study Greek. They wanted to make an old woman of me!" And when twitted with his lack of knowledge of the "dead languages" he said of his critic: "I could teach him that in the dead body which he never knew in any language, living or dead." The idealism of Hunter showed itself in devotion to work and in fortitude in the adversity of ill health.

I wish now to invite your attention to our second type of investigator—the essentially dynamical or physiological discoverer. The group, as I see it, is a small one. It includes Claude Bernard, Louis Pasteur, Hermann von Helmholtz and Paul Ehrlich.

An admirer said sententiously of Bernard: "He is not merely a physiologist; he is physiology itself;" and the saying has the merit of reminding us of the breadth and depth and originality of his researches. With equal skill he worked at the physical and chemical bases of physiology; and we owe to him our knowledge of the glycogenic function of the liver, the enzymes of the pancreatic juice, the vasomotor system of nerves, diabetes from puncture of the fourth ventricle, besides many minor discoveries and researches and a masterly correlation of the general facts of animal and plant life. Bernard was one of the founders of modern pharmacology. He also foreshadowed in a singular manner and under singular circumstances the modern conception of soluble ferments in micro-organisms, a view which unfortunately brought him into an unpleasant antagonism with his life-long friend, Pasteur.

The research that most fully shows the controlled imagination of Bernard is that which, extending over years, culminated in the discovery of the glycogenic function of the liver, a discovery of the very first significance to physiology and pathology. We know the steps which led him to this discovery, and in retracing these steps we get an edifying glimpse of the workings of Bernard's fertile mind. His ambition was to follow the three great classes of foodstuffs, carbohydrates, fats and proteids, through the organism. He soon felt the necessity of limiting himself to the fate of the carbohydrates, which, besides seeming relatively simple to study, especially attracted him on account of their mysterious relation to diabetes. The first step in the research brought out the fact that cane-sugar, when acted on by gastric juice, undergoes a transformation which adapts it for absorption and utilization by the tissues—namely, a change into dextrose (glucose). He knew from the experiments of Tiedemann that starch is changed into dextrose in the digestive tract before absorption. Bernard asked himself what was the fate of this dextrose. He proposed to trace the course of the sugar from the digestive tract, along the portal vein to the liver, from the liver to the lungs by way of the right heart, and finally from the lungs through the left heart to the various tissues. His idea was that at one of these stations the dextrose disappears, is destroyed or in some manner changed. "If I am able," said he, "to suppress the activity of this station, sugar will accumulate in the blood and a condition of diabetes will be brought about." Here, then, was a highly interesting enterprise. The first thing to do was to feed a dog freely on carbohydrates, kill it at the height of digestion and examine the blood leaving the liver by the hepatic veins to see if any sugar were lost in the liver. Please note that Bernard was helped in this search for sugar in the blood and tissues by the cupric sulphate test for dextrose, just introduced by his friend, Barreswill—a very material help. Sugar was found in abundance in the blood of the hepatic veins; therefore, the liver was not the looked-for place of disappearance of dextrose. "But how do I know," thought Bernard, "that the sugar which I thus find in the hepatic vein is the same sugar as that which I introduced into the portal blood through the food?" To get an answer, Bernard fed a dog on meat only, knowing by experiment that no dextrose would then be present either in the digestive tract or in the portal blood. Then he examined the blood of the hepatic vein for sugar. Great was his surprise to find it loaded with dextrose. His keen intelligence at once drew the correct inference—that the liver is a sugar-making organ and makes sugar out of something which is not sugar, and, furthermore, that within the liver lies the secret of diabetes. Bernard now made a variety of experiments to test the correctness of his inferences. He soon found that sugar was contained in a simple decoction of the liver and that this sugar was dextrose, capable of fermentation and responding to all the known tests. But Bernard did not stop here. His fancy urged him to seek the substance in the liver from which the sugar is produced—the "glycogenic substance" whose existence was inferred from experiment. And in time he isolated the substance which we know to-day as glycogen.

Here, then, was a great triumph of the experimental method in the hands of an imaginative, critical and highly skilled technical worker. The completeness with which the discovery of the glycogenic function of the liver was worked out makes it a model of physiological research for all time. Moreover, the facts elicited by Bernard in this research possess a very broad bearing. They show that the liver has a function as important as, but far less obvious than, the secretion of bile—the first example of an internal secretion. And they prove that animals as well as plants can build up carbohydrate material – glycogen – by means of their own tissues. Finally Bernard very clearly showed that, while the production of glycogen from sugar is a vital act, in the sense of occurring only under conditions of life, the converse process, namely, the formation of sugar from glycogen, is independent of living tissues and may occur as the result of the action of a ferment in the blood. As Sir Michael

Foster said most aptly:

> It is in the putting forth of the hypothesis that the true man of science shows the creative power which makes him and the poets brothers. His must be a sensitive soul, ready to vibrate to Nature's touches. Before the dull eye of the ordinary mind facts pass one after the other in long procession, but pass without effect, awakening nothing. In the eye of the man of genius, be he poet or man of science, the same facts light up an illumination, in the one of beauty, in the other of truth; each possesses a responsive imagination. Such had Bernard, and the responses which in his youth found expression in verses, in his maturer and trained mind took the form of scientific hypothesis.

That Bernard well understood the value of imagination in research and also its dangers is well shown by his admirable and memorable advice to his pupils:

> Put off your imagination as you take off your overcoat when you enter the laboratory; but put it on again, as you do your overcoat, when you leave the laboratory. Before the experiment and between whiles, let your imagination wrap you round; put it right away from yourself during the experiment itself, lest it hinder your observing power.

Let us now bring to your attention some features of the mental life of another great physiologist, Hermann von Helmholtz, representing a very different phase of physiology from that developed by Bernard. Bernard, though accomplished as a morphologist and skilled in mechanical physiology, leaned strongly to the chemical side. He was essentially the animal experimentalist. Mathematics played only the most simple rôle in his researches. Helmholtz, on the other hand, approached physiology on its physical side, and, one may remark in passing, with a quality and amplitude of success unequalled before or since. He used the higher mathematics constantly and they proved keen tools in his hands. Although an experimentalist of the very first order, Helmholtz was not an animal experimenter except in a very limited way, the nature of his themes making vivisection for the most part unnecessary.

Even as a child the mind of Helmholtz was unconventional and inquiring, bent on understanding what was going on about him. The boy cut his own path through the mazes of unassimilable educational offerings. His tastes were definite. He obtained notions of geometry from the blocks with which he played, surprised his mother by experimenting on her linen with acids, made telescopes with spectacle lenses, read books on physics and enjoyed greatly his walks in the country. At the university he assimilated ideas with great ease and showed an increasing interest in physics, which he wished to follow as a profession. But his prudent father urged him to study medicine as a surer means of livelihood. And most fortunate it was for medical science that the gifted young man was willing to take up medical studies, for there arose in him a deep interest in the problems of physiology, destined to bear rich fruit. Tire duties of an army surgeon took only part of his time and the rest he gave to physics. His original researches began at the age of 21 and continued through a long lifetime, covering an extraordinary range of topics in an original and masterly way. Helmholtz contributes to minute anatomy, lays the foundations of physiological optics and acoustics (with all that this means for esthetics, psychology and metaphysics), gives to medicine the specific and golden gift of the ophthalmoscope, enriches physics with an imperishable statement of the doctrine of the conservation of energy and with original studies on vortex motion, on hydrodynamics, on electrodynamics, on dynamics, on meteorological physics. He broadens chemical theory by the influence of his vortex motion hypothesis and, in a somewhat incidental way, brings new theoretical conceptions into the realm of pure mathematics. As students of the psychical forces that have fertilized modern medicine it is interesting for us to note that Helmholtz disclaimed any intention to be practical in his work. If the themes that happened to absorb his attention led to practical and humanely useful results, he was pleased; but he seldom pursued a practical aim simply because of its utility. He chose his themes because they promised to be intellectually satisfying, giving little heed to the nature of the probable outcome. He framed his experiments so that Nature would have to answer "Yes" or "No" to his questions, thus furnishing him with definite results.

The story of the invention of the ophthalmoscope illustrates the mental processes of Helmholtz in working out an idea. He did not set out to devise an instrument for studying the retina and the ocular refraction, but as he proceeded these important possibilities ripened into definite objects. He says:

> I was endeavoring to explain to my pupils the emission of reflected light from the eye, a discovery made by Brücke, who would have invented the ophthalmoscope had he only asked himself how an optical image is formed by the light returning from the eye. In his research it was not necessary to ask it, but had he asked it, he was just the man to answer it as quickly as I did, and to invent the instrument. I turned the problem over and over to ascertain the simplest way in which to demonstrate the phenomenon to my students. It was also a reminiscence of my days of medical study, that ophthalmologists

had great difficulty in dealing with certain cases of eye disease, then known as black cataract. The first model was constructed of pasteboard, eye lenses, and cover-glasses used in the microscopic work. It was at first so difficult to use that I doubt if I should have persevered, unless I had felt that it must succeed; but in eight days I had the great joy of being the first who saw before him a human retina.

The basis for this invention was Helmholtz's knowledge of the anatomy of the eye, his mastery of physiological optics, his experimental ability, and, as stated in his own language, his wish to devise an improved method of demonstrating a somewhat obscure phenomenon to his students. Modesty and generous impulse made Helmholtz say that Brücke could equally well have invented the ophthalmoscope had he only asked himself how an optical image is formed by the light returning from the eye. I doubt if it could be successfully contended that Brücke's actual information about the eye was less than Helmholtz's. Helmholtz himself says that Brücke "was just the man" to make the invention, and by this he must refer to equipment in knowledge. In what, then, did Helmholtz excel Brücke? I would answer, in creative fancy, in imagination. The controlled play of fancy, using the facts of the case for its playground, is what made Helmholtz see the possibilities and see them so clearly as also to make it appear worth while to put energy into the effort to see the retina.

It would be easy to multiply examples of the almost playful way in which Helmholtz utilized the children of his rich fancy to extend the bounds of scientific knowledge. The ease with which he made his intellectual progress is one of the most striking features of his wonderfully creative career. Often on solitary walks in the country he experienced ideas that seemed to clarify refractory problems. From the great wealth of his impressions and associated ideas, arising through the operation of active fancy or imagination, there seems to have been a process of controlled selection and rejection by which the finished products, the great ideas, were built up—a conscious selection not without analogies to natural selection in the upbuilding of the physical machinery. In the entire list of the masters of medicine I think there has been only one mind that can be regarded as belonging on the same lofty level as that of Helmholtz, in respect to controlled yet expansive powers of imagination combined with the energy of performance and the technical training necessary to apply those powers. The intellect of Pasteur, and his alone, has revealed associative power and logical sequences of thought culminating in discoveries fairly comparable to those of Helmholtz in respect to the depth of their psychical basis. And it is probably no accident that the two greatest minds in medicine have entered it on the streams of pure science, Helmholtz as the biological physicist, Pasteur as the biological chemist.

As a human being Helmholtz takes rank with the noblest of men. Considerateness for others and a willingness to help worthy persons were prominent characteristics. He had a calm self-control which still left him natural and simple in human relations, although this fine dignity served as a check to the approaches of shallow and trivial people. Helmholtz was an idealist of the purest type, and never permitted personal interest to interfere with his best aims as a student of science. His was a poetic nature, apt in versification and in music, yet with an intellect so searching that he was not entirely satisfied by esthetic feeling and phantasy, but sought also to understand them. Modesty was one of his greatest charms, and this quality was attractively seen in the sentiment which he expressed on being awarded the von Graefe medal in recognition of his services to medicine through the invention of the ophthalmoscope:

> Let us suppose that up to the time of Phidias nobody has had a chisel sufficiently hard to work on marble. Up to that time they would only mold clay or carve wood. But a clever smith discovers how a chisel can be tempered. Phidias rejoices over the improved tools, fashions with them his god-like statues and manipulates the marble as no one has ever before done. He is honored and rewarded. But great geniuses are modest just in that in which they most excel others. That very thing is so easy for them that they can hardly understand why others cannot do it. But there is always associated with high endowments a correspondingly great sensitiveness for the defects of one's own work. Thus, says Phidias to the smith, "Without your aid I could have done nothing of that; the honor and glory belong to you." But the smith can only answer him, "But I could not have done it even with my chisels, whereas you, without my chisels, could at least have molded your wonderful works in clay; therefore I must decline the honor and glory, if I will remain an honorable man." But now Phidias is taken away, and there remain his friends and pupils—Praxiteles, Paionios, and others. They all use the chisel of the smith. The world is filled with their work and their fame. They determine to honor the memory of the deceased with a garland which he shall receive who has done the most for the art, and in the art, of statuary. The beloved master has often praised the smith as the author of their great success, and they finally decide to award the garland to him. "Well," answers the smith, "I consent; you are many, and among you are clever people. I am but a single man. You assert that I singly have been of service to many of

you, and that many places teem with sculptors who have decked the temples with divine statutes, which, without the tools that I have given you, would have been very imperfectly fashioned. I must believe you, as I have never chiseled marble, and I accept thankfully what you award to me, but I myself would have given my vote to Praxiteles or Paionios."

If we turn now to Helmholtz's great contemporary, Louis Pasteur, we discern many points of resemblance in the mental endowments and in the careers of these two superlatively eminent masters of medical science. Pasteur, like Helmholtz, was greatly helped in early life by the patient guidance of earnest and capable parents, and, like him, showed a strong interest in poetry and art, the portraits made by Pasteur during his teens showing unmistakable artistic talent. Pasteur's considerable aptitude for mathematics developed later than that of Helmholtz and was of a less original sort, yet served him well, especially in his earlier researches. Both men were endowed with phantasy and associative power of the highest order, but, while Helmholtz seldom departed from the path of strict logical development of his ideas, Pasteur, with his more impetuous nature, sometimes permitted himself to make speculative excursions of a more random kind. Both found their greatest enjoyment in dealing with the development of general ideas, but Pasteur, on realizing his power to help mankind through his discoveries, deliberately turned his rare gifts to the solution of practical problems in medicine, whereas Helmholtz was satisfied to continue to build the foundations for the physiology of the sense organs and for a better psychology and metaphysics. It is very noteworthy that both Helmholtz and Pasteur were deeply influenced in their outlook by certain conceptions of wide applicability. On the other hand, Pasteur's scientific and philosophical thought was influenced definitely and profoundly by the conception of molecular asymmetry in nature. His interest in this subject was awakened by the study of the salts of tartaric acid, which culminated in 1848 with the famous discovery that the optically indifferent or racemic tartaric acid crystallizes into equal quantities of the ordinary dextrorotary tartaric acid and of the newly recognized levorotary tartaric acid. It was Pasteur's interest in the problem of molecular asymmetry, and especially certain theoretical notions on which we need not linger here, that induced him to experiment on the action of micro-organisms on racemic ammonium tartrate, with the striking result that the living beings converted the optically indifferent solution of salts into a levorotary solution. This showed that the dextrorotary constituent of the indifferent racemic tartrate had been assimilated by the micro-organisms, while the levorotary constituent was unaffected. I emphasize these studies of Pasteur's because they were what excited his interest in the then obscure problem of fermentation, which in turn led him to take up those studies of the causation of disease by micro-organisms and those researches on immunity which have revolutionized the entire science and art of medicine. To do anything like justice to these extraordinarily fertile and original researches of Pasteur is wholly out of question here. I can merely direct your attention to the researches which in the fullest way exemplify Pasteur's gift of imagination and power of experimental control. There are six studies or groups of studies whose histories exhibit Pasteur's genius at its best—the research on the tartrates, the investigations on fermentation, the inquiry into the causes of the silkworm disease, and the methods of its eradication, the research on chicken cholera and immunity to it, the research on anthrax, with the extraordinarily dramatic scenes attending the public test of the immunization methods, and finally the masterly researches on hydrophobia.

In all these different groups of researches were displayed the most active powers of associative thought and phantasy, the most admirable capacity for self-criticism. As Pasteur made his publications in a terse, compact style, we cannot always reconstruct his logical processes by reading them. His method of thought and procedure were, however, well known to his colleagues, with whom he loved to discuss his ideas and plans of experiments. They found him spirited, fertile and imaginative in his conceptions, frankly communicative, generous in giving help and wholly absorbed in his work. Like many intensely serious men, Pasteur lacked somewhat the sense of humor. His feelings of partisanship were so strong that he could never overcome his resentment toward Germany, and he permitted this to color even his relations with German scientific workers. Yet one should dwell but lightly on these slight imperfections in a nature of such great gifts and such lofty and unselfish purpose.

At the time when Pasteur was beginning his research on anthrax, a young student of medicine at the University of Strassburg, Paul Ehrlich, was laying the foundations for that uniquely fertile and versatile career of medical research which has made him the most original and picturesque of living investigators of medical science. Although at this time Ehrlich was especially under the direction of the anatomist, Waldeyer, he rapidly developed a capacity for chemistry which was a surprise both to himself and to the chemist, Adolf von Beyer, whose lectures had been systematically cut by the gifted but unconventional student. For unconventional he then was and ever has been, neglecting what he did not like and throwing himself with fervor and intense energy into the solution of the themes that attracted him. From the outset it was clear that Ehrlich would make a career as an experimental investigator.

Much of the time he was supposed to spend in taking the usual medical courses he devoted to experiment. When Robert Koch was shown through the laboratory at Breslau by one of the professors his attention was called to a young student working at a desk covered with bottles of dyestuffs. "There is our little Ehrlich," said the professor; "he is a first-rate stainer of tissues, but he will never pass his examinations." The prediction about the examinations came perilously near fulfilment; Ehrlich made bad flunks and it is hinted that he would never have received his degree had not he made a discovery—namely, the existence of the peculiar type of leucocyte which is known to us as the "plasma-cell." The faculty reasoned that it would be improper to keep so promising and original a worker indefinitely in an undergraduate position, and it is suspected that they mitigated the rigor of the examinations in order to relieve their own embarrassment.

A noteworthy example of Ehrlich's free-lance method is seen in his peculiar way of working at chemical problems. Though a highly accomplished organic chemist, both as to theory and a singularly rich acquaintance with the properties of substances, Ehrlich rarely uses any but the simplest methods and quite refuses to work quantitatively. His personal experiments are almost exclusively test-tube experiments, most ingeniously contrived to yield a rich fund of knowledge. He says:

> For the pure chemist, who proceeds analytically or synthetically, my way is only an unending *pons asinorum*. The chemist starts from two substances, a and b, both of which he knows, and by synthesis derives substance c. Through this procedure a sure insight into the nature of the process becomes possible. This is exactly as if one drew a circle with the calipers. On the other hand, one may define a circle by means of a large number of tangents, and the chemistry which I practice is a kind of tangent chemistry. Through my schooling in this tangent chemistry I have had a great advantage in dealing with immunity problems. If one cannot define chemically the components entering into action, as is frequently the case in immunity problems (for example toxin and antitoxin) one cannot draw the circle in the usual chemical way and the nature of the reaction process must remain a closed book. But for one who has worked for decades, as I have done, at tangent chemistry, the task is no longer so difficult; and I think that in this way, through the recognition of toxoids and their quantitative formation from toxins, I have succeeded incorrectly bringing out the two functional groups, the toxophore and the haptophore, which indeed furnish us with the key to the entire doctrine of immunity.

Ehrlich's dominant interests during the student days were histology and chemistry, but his attitude toward these subjects was even then highly individual, original and laden with the dynamic spirit—the spirit that seeks to gain a conception of what goes on in the living cells. Throughout his career Ehrlich has sought to use his knowledge of histology and of chemistry to gain light on the processes of life. The clarity of his visual perceptions and the tenacity of his visual memories have enabled him to cultivate a sort of chemistry peculiarly suited to this aim. Ehrlich early recognized that he had a peculiar gift of being able to recall and represent mentally the constitution of a large variety of substances and with little effort to picture vividly their interactions. He definitely states that he considers this chemicoplastic memory his greatest scientific endowment, and it is clear that the long line of his investigations is founded on this faculty and on his taste for rational therapeutics. Like Helmholtz and Pasteur, Ehrlich has been guided in his experiments by certain well-defined general conceptions. The most important of these in Ehrlich's case is the idea that the living cells have many different kinds of definite chemical affinities, by virtue of which they are able to enter into combination with some compounds and not with others. This idea is at the foundation of Ehrlich's well-known researches on the basophilic, acidophilic and neutrophilic leucocytes, on the distribution of dyestuffs in the so-called "intravital" staining, on the cell affinities of the different alkaloids, on the side-chain theory of immunity and the measurement of the strength of antitoxin, and on the organic chemical compounds of arsenic in relation to the trypanosomes of the sleeping-sickness.

The recital of Ehrlich's achievements in medicine would demand a voluminous space, for his activities have been intense and varied. The pharmacological studies, the work on immunity in its different phases (including the action of hemolysins), the experimental studies on carcinoma—each of these deserve the most careful study, not merely because of actual results gleaned, but on account of the luminous ingenuity of the methods employed. It is in the field of immunity that Ehrlich has won his brightest laurels. The discovery that vegetable poisons like abrin and ricin excite antitoxicity, the development of a method of measuring the activity of the diphtheria antitoxin – a standard method the world over – the extremely ingenious studies of hemolysins, the recognition of the laws of transmission of immunity from mother to child, and the discovery of immunity in trypanosomes exposed to the action of arsenical poisons, are all contributions of far-reaching import. And cementing all Ehrlich's special investigations of immunity, relating them also with his work on the distribution of dyestuffs, alkaloids and nutritive materials generally, stands the famous "side-chain" theory. This bold, elaborate and refined hypothesis of the nature of immunity, this offspring of rich phantasy and fertile experimentation, was long the source of discord and strife among bacteriologists and pharmacological theorists. At the height of the controversy Ehrlich once remarked: "They are shooting into my antitoxin tower and I will reply vigorously." To-day a welcome peace – perhaps merely a truce – has succeeded the sometimes heated contest, and only an occasional stray shot is heard. However widely the rival camps may disagree on certain points, there seems now to be a common ground. The centrally emergent conception in immunity appears to be the existence of a specific binding or anchoring avidity between the immunity-excitant or antigen and certain substances belonging to the living cell—the so-called receptors. This conception and the extensions that follow from it – including, for example, the now familiar view that the antitoxin freed in the blood represents excessively multiplied receptors disengaged from the stimulated cells – are peculiarly original with Ehrlich. His mind reached this central idea, because it is a mind beset by chemical phantasy, a mind seeking to explain all biological phenomena in medicine by means of chemical principles. In the special case of the side-chain theory, Ehrlich's intimate knowledge of the chemical and biological properties of the dyestuff splayed a very large part, and it should be noted that the theory is in this sense a hybrid, that it originates not from a purely chemical conception, but from a chemical and a biological idea. Slowly that theory grew to its present full proportions and its somewhat bewildering intricacies of superstructure. In this elaborate form there is doubtless much in the hypothesis that can be criticized if we turn to it in the hope of learning the absolute truth in respect to immunity. It is perhaps just to say that the value of the theory lies largely in the fact that it expresses relationships. Time and experiment will doubtless mold it anew. But whatever changes in form it may suffer, the data collected by Ehrlich and correlated by him will long remain a monument to his experimental genius and creative imagination. And the fair-minded critic will remember the great practical services which this theory has rendered and is still rendering to medicine, in enabling investigators to pursue their experiments in new territories of research in immunity by giving them points of attack and lines of advance. It is stated by Wassermann, the discoverer of the serum reaction of syphilis, that he could never have worked out this biological reaction had he not possessed the side-chain hypothesis as a guide. It seems clear, too, that the intelligent use of this hypothesis is destined to aid us greatly in learning something of the seat and mode of action of many drugs of which we now know but little. And, again, there are unmistakable signs that the side-chain conception will give many a clue to the understanding of the nutrition of cells.

Ehrlich's mind is singularly labile, playful and restless. It passes quickly and casually from one subject to another, yet without the least confusion. It is always on the alert, ready to dally with a new fact or a new idea, in the hope that it will illumine one of the many experimental interests with which consciousness ever teems. Ehrlich reads medical literature rapaciously but selectively, ignoring all but the themes in which he has a special interest, as one reads who reads for his pleasure and not for duty's sake. This unusual method is extremely effective and gives a highly serviceable command of facts likely to be helpful in extracting from Nature new facts by experiment. Even during holiday seasons, this spirituelle, penetrating mind knows no real rest, for the time is beguiled by the reading of detective stories, even second-rate ones, in the hope of finding some new and complicated situation, for which an ingenious solution can be invented.

It is a cheering sign of the times that the cultivated classes are beginning to recognize the essential rôle of imagination in the progress of the biological and medical sciences. President Eliot remarks that the nineteenth century has taught us that, on the whole, the scientific imagination is quite as productive for human service as the literary or poetic imagination. "The imagination of Darwin or Pasteur, for example, is as high and productive a form of imagination as that of Dante, or Goethe, or even Shakespeare, if we regard the human uses which result from the exercise of imaginative powers and mean by human uses not merely meat and drink, clothes and shelter, but also the satisfaction of mental and spiritual needs." The history of medical discovery is a long chain of imaginative experiences whose links have been welded and fixed by passing through the fiery ordeal of appeal to experimental tests. And could we but set forth, in fitting language, the true story of these mental experiences, with all their vicissitudes of hope and despair, success and failure, we should certainly dispel for all time the wide-spread notion that medical research is a dry and painful task, to which only an unimaginative mind can turn with satisfaction.

There is a phase of imaginative thought and feeling which expresses itself in a strong desire to pursue ideal ends, even at the cost of the ordinary prizes of life, wealth, material power and physical comfort. This idealism has been a very pronounced attribute of the great masters of medicine. In a noteworthy degree they have all possessed it and some, like Helmholtz and Pasteur, have led lives of unpretentious, simple self sacrifice in admirable harmony with the illustrious and superlative service they have rendered mankind. This idealism, while clearly a moral trait in the conventional sense, seems to be the offspring of the creative intellectual attitude and especially of an absorption in work, which leaves the mind neither time nor inclination to seek the petty advantages for which most men at sometime in their lives find themselves struggling. For these reasons, indifference to vulgar aims and aloofness from commonplace interests are apt to be found where there is preoccupation in productive work of a high order, whether this be concerned with science or not. But in the medical sciences the rewards are so great, in the sense of personal satisfaction from superior achievement, that there is an especial and peculiarly potent incentive to repress those exaggerations of the self-preservative instinct which show so insistently in the selfish conduct of commonplace persons.

There is a special quality pertaining to the greatest masters of medicine which arrests our attention when we survey their life work. This is the wonderful variety and number of their discoveries. We are struck with this quality of productivity in the works of Hunter, Malpighi, Johannes Midler, Claude Bernard, Helmholtz, Pasteur, Koch and Ehrlich. In some instances the range of topics is relatively narrow, as in the case of Koch, or extraordinarily wide, as in the case of Helmholtz, but in nearly all instances the great masters have been repeatedly productive, and this varied productivity on a high plane is an unfailing mark of genius. On the other hand, it is necessary to recognize that very important discoveries in medicine have been made by men who once in their lives, and once only, have attained a high level of achievement. There are two examples of this singularity in discovery which I would bring particularly to your notice—one the discovery and development of the antiseptic method by Lister and the discovery of general anesthesia by Morton.

When Lister visited Pasteur in 1865 he was much impressed by the attitude of the great master in regard to the wide part played by micro-organisms in fermentation and disease. As a surgeon he had a deep interest in the diseases of wounds, and the idea established itself in his mind that such diseases might be due to a kind of fermentation which might be checked or prevented by the use of antiseptics. This idea, worked out by Lister with the utmost patience and superior intelligence, gave the wonderfully far-reaching results with which we are all familiar. The important results of Lister's methods are not limited to the surgical diseases of human beings. By making it possible to experiment on animals in wholly new ways, these methods have placed in the hands of the physiologist a powerful instrument for the extension of medical and biological knowledge along most significant lines of progress. We have, therefore, to concede that Lister's discovery is one of such rich fertility as to make it rank among the great discoveries of medicine. Yet it cannot be claimed that Lister was a great scientist. In training, in originality, in versatility and in imagination he is far from being the peer of the great masters of whom we have spoken. And we see here, again, that the practical import of a discovery is no arbitrary measure of the scientific attainments of the discoverer.

Hardly less valuable an asset of practical medicine is the discovery of general anesthesia, but it appears that the qualities of mind revealed by Morton belong to a level less high than those of Lister. Morton was an alert, enterprising young dentist in Boston, who, while educating himself in medicine, successfully practiced his calling and invented an improved system of dental plates. The use of this system required the free removal of carious and otherwise diseased teeth, and this caused great pain. To relieve this pain, Morton pertinaciously sought an efficient anesthetic. After many unsatisfactory trials with different substances, he with experimented sulphuric ether, given him by Jackson, the professor of chemistry in the Harvard Medical School. In 1846 he succeeded in demonstrating the efficacy of sulphuric ether as a general anesthetic and thus gave to mankind a precious, almost unequalled boon.

This great discovery cannot be reckoned as one of high fertility, since, aside from anesthesia, it has not opened new lines of thought or practical service. Neither can it be said to have sprung from a scientific mind of exalted qualities and attainments. It has the earmarks of a child of empiricism. Morton's scientific knowledge was slight, and his mind had a strong commercial bent. The singularity of his discovery, the only one of his life, points neither to fertility of resource nor to lofty imagination, but to the fortunate combination of conditions under which he insistently exercised his ingenuity.

Having told you something of the qualities distinguishing the modern masters of medicine, I now ask your permission to speak of certain aspects of these qualities as they seem related to the career of the thoughtful student of medicine. And first of all I would correct in your minds any impression I may have made of a discouraging nature. Having drawn our examples of medical advance so largely from the work of supremely gifted men, workers in laboratories, many of whom have not been practitioners of medicine, or have only casually practiced, it may possibly appear that you are confronted with the paradox that an essential condition of the loftiest success in medical science is to abstain from the practice of medicine. There is, indeed, a measure of truth in this, for, as I have already tried to show you, entire absorption in the practical problems of medicine unfits men to pursue with the highest success the career of discovery. In this there is naught of real discouragement, but only a sign that the problems of disease, as we meet them by the bedside, are far too complex to permit solution there. There was a time when all medical discovery was based directly on observation at the bedside. Then, with the growth of anatomy, the invention of the microscope and the coming of the twin hand-maids of medicine, physics and chemistry, the laboratories spring into existence. Much there was that could be discovered only by laboratory methods, and so it happened that some men were justified in working at medicine, and able to become masters of medicine, though they scarcely left their laboratories. But I would have you note well that we have now entered on a time when the clinics and the laboratories must work more and more closely together, aiding each other at every step to bridge the wide chasms of our ignorance. And just here lies one of the greatest opportunities for the alert student of medicine, undergraduate and postgraduate to do something worth while. For the problems are so many, so varied and so widely graded as to difficulties that for almost every earnest student there is at hand a theme suited to his powers and training.

I have intimated my belief that the powerful and controlled imagination is generally associated with a strong vein of idealism. The explanation is not remote; the imagination separates the wheat from the chaff in the realm of ideals, picturing vividly what will yield enduring

"There is no surer road to hopeless mediocrity than that which leads the young physician to assume an active practice before he is ripe for it."

satisfaction. In persons of average capacity and imagination, idealism is more halting because the perceptions of what is permanently worth while are less definite and carry less firm conviction. Hence in such persons idealism of conduct is less spontaneous and calls for conscious effort to sustain it. It is, indeed, a quality which may be deliberately cultivated if the germ exists in the character.

What I would like particularly to impress on your minds is that without idealism of purpose, without the willingness to make sacrifices of material comfort and much that the world overprizes, the career of the student and practitioner of medicine is almost certain to be pitifully limited and mediocre. He will do well who has the character to run his course in a strong spirit of independence, satisfied during the long years of professional preparation with the slender means that permit the prolongation of some phase of the student life long after graduation from the medical school. There is no surer road to hopeless mediocrity than that which leads the young physician to assume an active practice before he is ripe for it. On the other hand, the student physician who waits patiently, year by year, to strengthen his intellectual grip on the processes of disease, if possible under the guidance of some master of medicine, is laying the unshakable foundations of a telling and distinguished career. He need have no anxiety as to the future either on the score of professional recognition or the ability to earn a sufficient income. For the world needs and must ever seek the serious, well-trained, idealistic physician whose first thought is to render a high grade of service. The superior type of student will not dread the long years of preparation in laboratory and clinic. He will eagerly seek them and will count it the greatest privilege of his life to be able to utilize and develop his powers. The fascinating interest of his problem and the elevation of his ideals will keep him buoyant under circumstances of discouragement. If he be blest with a fair share of imagination and idealism he will never falter in the struggle to make a worthy career, for he will know that he is treading in the footsteps of the great masters of medical science and that in doing so he is helping to assuage human suffering, perhaps also to illuminate some of the dark problems in the baffling mystery of life. And in this consciousness will he find ample compensation for the self-abnegation which such a career must necessarily exact from its votaries.

4

Erwin H. Ackerknecht, "The Role of Medical History in Medical Education,"
Bulletin of the History of Medicine 21: 2 (1947), 135-145.

Erwin H. Ackerknecht (1906-1988) was born in Germany and studied medicine, along with a number of other subjects including economics and literature, at various universities, graduating from Leipzig in 1931 having written a dissertation on nineteenth-century German medical reform, under the supervision of Henry E. Sigerist. Politically active, Ackerknecht later left Nazi Germany and eventually moved to Paris where he studied ethnology at the Musee de l'Homme and the Sorbonne. He moved to the United States in 1941 and obtained a fellowship at the Institute for the History of Medicine at Johns Hopkins, now under the direction of Sigerist. In 1947 Ackerknecht was appointed the first professor in the history of medicine at the University of Wisconsin.

Ackerknecht is considered a pioneer historian of medicine in part because of his commitment to demonstrating that medical theory could be analyzed through political actions, historicizing social medicine and demonstrating that medicine was ideological. Through a number of influential articles and books, Ackerknecht established himself as one of the leading scholars that defined the agenda for the growing discipline of medical history. The article reprinted here is of interest in part because, as his inaugural lecture in the history of medicine presented to the University of Wisconsin School of Medicine, he reflects on the status of the profession and its changing relationship to, and usefulness for, medical training.

Ackerknecht reflects on the "age of specialization" and the propagation of the professional historian of medicine appearing in more universities post-World War II. At the same time, medical science – through its own specializing tendencies – was losing interest in medical history, leaving the field open to scholars with more philological and bibliographic interests to write its history, yielding work that was, in

Ackerknecht's articulation, "of no immediate appeal to the average medical man." Echoing sentiments expressed by writers decades earlier (discussed in earlier articles in this volume) regarding the utility of intellectual pursuits and changing cultural values surrounding a liberal education, Ackerknecht here suggests that the history of medicine best tread carefully as it matures or suffer being the victim of its own success. In essence, Ackerknecht is warning against a professionalization of medical history that isolates itself through specialized language and analyses of minutiae at the expense of engaging with the broader development and impact of theoretical and practical elements that define medicine. As he writes, "studying medicine in connection with its cultural, that is spiritual and social, background tends to promote and uphold the consciousness of the totality of medicine and its students."

While in part admonishing his fellow historians of medicine not to lose sight of the broader impact that history can bring to medical education – underscoring the etiological relation between humanities and humility – he is also addressing medical students, instructing them not to lose sight of the fact that medicine is not only a biological science, but a social science as well.

See also

Owsei Temkin, "In Memoriam: Erwin H. Ackerknecht (1906-1988)," *Bulletin of the History of Medicine* 65 (1989), 273-275.
Paul Cranefield, "Erwin H. Ackerknecht (1906-1988): Some Memories," *Journal of the History of Medicine and Allied Sciences* 45: 2 (1990), 145-149.

The Role of Medical History in Medical Education

Erwin H. Ackerknecht

A regular chair for the History of Medicine in the University of Wisconsin is certainly something new. But neither the teaching nor the pursuit of medical history is anything new on our campus; in a way such activities are even older than our medical school. In 1909 the late William Snow Miller (1858-1939), who was internationally known for his work on the anatomy of the lungs, and taught anatomy in this University from 1892 to 1925, started medico-historical work with a circle of students and young medical teachers in a seminar. This seminar has somewhat changed its character since the retirement of Dr. Miller, being now composed exclusively of faculty members, but it is functioning in full vigor up to this day, and, I hope, will do so for many years to come. Since 1913 the papers delivered by the members of the seminar have been collected, and in the early volumes we find papers by such eminent alumni or members of ourfaculty as Herbert Gasser, Dr. Meek, Dr. Middlleton, Dr. Bast, Dr. Erwin Schmidt or Dr. Clark. Many among the hundreds of papers given in the course of years have been published, many more would have deserved publication. Dr. Miller's excellent collection of old medical books, now one of the cherished treasures of our library, furnished the raw material for a great many of these studies. Though Dr. Miller was perhaps sometimes a hard taskmaster, we remember him gratefully today for having sown the seed, for having inspired so many excellent students of medical history, and for having kept alive with rare perseverance during 30 years in this University the interest and enthusiasm in our field. For a number of years Dr. Ch. Leake, Dr. Bunting and Dr. Meek gave an elective course in medical history.

Though one might regret that, in our age of specialization, even medical history has become a specialty, it seems to me that with the help of all those who in our school have so faithfully and successfully cultivated the subject, the new arrangement will allow us to envisage a far more extensive teaching and research activity. Appreciating fully the great honour that has been bestowed upon me in entrusting me with this chair, I will do my utmost to realize such expectations. A particularly encouraging fact is that our University shows a unique and very promising feature: we already have on the campus an Institute of the History of Pharmacy under the direction of Dr. Urdang and a Department of the History of Science in the College of Letters and Science. I have no doubt that we all will greatly profit from collaboration with these disciplines that have so much in common with medical history.

Right now the knowledge of the history of medicine and science among the average practitioners and general public seems at a low ebb as a few random examples might show. In an "educational" advertisement in the New York subways the public is being "taught" that the great 18th century French chemist Lavoisier was executed because of his opinions on human metabolism. A medical journal can seriously argue that the great German poet, Schiller (originally a military surgeon), left his country because of social legislation that actually was introduced 80 years after his death by Bismarck. Medical books still inform us that the Spanish physician Servetus was burned at the stake by Calvin because of his opinions on the circulation of the blood. [*Ed. note*: see p. 39 in this volume] That all this and an enormous number of similar stupidities can be poured out daily by the radio, press, and in books without any reaction from the profession, are very disquieting symptoms.

The causes for this situation seem manifold. Probably the majority of medico-historical documents is written in Greek, Latin, Arabic or a non-English modern language. While this fact was rather irrelevant during the 19th century, it has now created a barrier between medical history and the profession at large which it is hard to conquer. Though we still proudly exhibit the medieval title of "Doctor" (learned man), the knowledge of languages has become rarer and rarer among us in an age where everybody is forced to know more and more about less and less.

Still more important seems to me the fact that the medical classics were up to the middle of the 19th century not purely historical phenomena, but of great practical importance for every medical man—in 1804 Laennec, the father of the stethoscope, still wrote his thesis on the doctrine of Hippocrates in its relation to practical medicine. The enormous development of modern science relegated all earlier data into the realm of the not immediately practical and useful; in a society that has the fatal tendency to disregard all values which are not immediately practical and useful this meant that, for a while at least, medical history fell into almost total oblivion.

Eventually the medical historians themselves are not entirely free from blame in this situation. When the majority of the medical profession abandoned medical history, our discipline was mainly cultivated by philologists, bibliographers, and medical men who were primarily interested in philology and bibliography. I am convinced that the work of these men will at the day of last judgment not contain more worthless elements than the mountains of contemporary biological literature, and that as a whole it is of great importance and value. Yet it must be admitted that this literature is of no immediate appeal to the average medical man, and that in the ivory tower of our philologist-bibliographers this "common man" of medicine was rarely remembered. Those who nevertheless wanted information concerning medical history were too often left in the careless hands of the so-called "popular writer," the literary quack of our age.

A small elite of medical men has never followed the general trend of abandoning medical history. I have already mentioned examples from our own school. I could add for this country, in speaking only of those who are dead, the names of men like William Osler, Halsted, Welch, Kelly, Cushing, David Riesman, who were medical leaders as well as enthusiastic and accomplished medical historians. The mere fact that these men felt it worthwhile to devote so much of their time to medical history

"Whether a physician is conscious of the fact or not, his actions will always be influenced by his picture of the past."

shows that *medical history, like history in general, is most decidedly not a luxury, but of vital importance.* Whether a physician is conscious of the fact or not, his actions will always be influenced by his picture of the past. As Abraham Jacobi, the father of American pediatrics and a German refugee of 1848, said in 1905 to the students of the Washington University Medical Department of St. Louis: "For as without the knowledge of the history of your country. you cannot understand its structure, or without that of the embryo the full development of the body, so without that of your science and art you will not be a citizen in your profession." It is one of the many historical paradoxes that of all professions the one could become estranged from its own history which daily in taking "case histories" pays its tribute to the enormous clarifying value that a knowledge of the past holds for the present and future.

The end of the first World War may be regarded as the turning of the tide. Nations as a whole and special disciplines in particular made very incomplete but sincere attempts to change a passive attitude towards general and special developments that had born such bitter fruits. In the field of medicine it was realized that, in spite of the great triumphs of modern scientific medicine on the battle field, not everything was above criticism and beyond the need of improvement. The necessity to humanize medicine again through medical history was sharply felt all over Europe, and new chairs of medical history sprang up in war-torn Poland, Germany and Italy. The greater emphasis on the history of medicine in its turn produced new, more medically minded tendencies in its own ranks. The general trend of our time, which ran across the lines of peaceful reform and endeavors, has destroyed all those earlier efforts.

When we are trying today to build a better future after a second and far worse catastrophe, it is no accident that medical history is again called upon, and that such efforts are now centered mainly in the United States. Continental Europe seems to be destroyed and weakened this time to a point where not much hope is left for a return to the old levels of civilization. This leaves us with an entirely new situation. In the concert of Western civilization, we had made it to a certain degree our specialty to develop in a practical way and on a very large scale clues coming from poorer and less streamlined countries. Now it has become for us a moral obligation, as well as a practical necessity to cultivate a number of so called "non-practical" fields, because nobody else will be able or willing to develop them any longer; and yet normal functioning and progress in our Western civilization depends just as much on the cultivation of these fields as it depends on cultivation of the strictly useful ones. These necessities have been foreseen by clear-minded leaders long before the second World War; they seem to be recognized more and more, and they offer new possibilities of realization to those who have worked for many years for a more extensive and intensive cultivation of medical history in our schools and universities.

It seems to me that everybody who starts the study of scientific medicine must be tremendously impressed by the enormous number of known facts and techniques. To the newcomer all those data appear, of course, to be of very recent vintage. These feelings are whipped up in the general public by certain writers and radio propagandists to an almost criminal feeling of pride and security. In the due course of years we are likely to become more modest as through experience we learn more about the limits of our knowledge and abilities. It seems to me that an early contact with medical history could shorten considerably this undirected progress of the medical pilgrim. It could help to avoid certain undesirable side effects of this premature pride. Out of disappointment the practitioner might sometimes develop a kind of cynical nihilism, while the general public still, in too many cases, turns back to quacks of all sorts. We should know not only the history of our accomplishments but also the history of our failures. The future scientist in particular should know how many hours and lives are spent in vain for one simple positive result. *History shows us our science and science in general in proper perspective.* It gives us the proper mixture of pride and humility which should be our attitude. There is no doubt that medical progress during the last 100 and particularly during the last 50 years as reflected in our greatly increased life expectancy has been stupendous, and that we have every reason to be proud of this. But there is also little doubt that much of this progress is due to fundamental search done patiently and often under great difficulties during preceding centuries. Modern scientific medicine would be practically inexistent without the work culminating in the discoveries of men like Vesalius, Harvey, Malpighi, Robert Boyle, Lavoisier, Spallanzani, Morgagni, Pinel and others, not to speak of work done during the 19th century. In some problems we have made almost no progress or have gone around in circles, and at best are today at the point where the Greek classics were, more than 2,000 years ago (e.g. epilepsy). Some of the difficulties which we have more or less overcome now, for in stance in the field of infectious diseases, we have first produced ourselves through the blind development of our society. Some, like those connected with the increased life expectancy, we are only beginning to tackle. You see, there is still enough left for coming generations to do.

In learning from history that our modern medicine grew out of a new departure in anatomy, we become conscious of the fact that our medicine in this respect differs radically from e.g. Sydenham's or from classic Greek medicine; or for that matter from any other medicine in any other period or country; and is for the better or the worse based on an anatomical approach.

> *"What disease is, is by no means a foregone conclusion, even if we eliminate all supernaturalistic explanations. Actually opinions about the nature of disease have greatly changed during the last 100 years and are still changing."*

What disease is, is by no means a foregone conclusion, even if we eliminate all supernaturalistic explanations. Actually opinions about the nature of disease have greatly changed during the last 100 years and are still changing. *Consciousness of such fundamentals is awakened by the study of medical history.* Such consciousness is necessary for those who want to understand what they are doing, and particularly for those who want to make new discoveries, and to start new developments.

The fact that medical history deals to a large extent with past theories and philosophies is, in my mind, not a disadvantage but an asset of our discipline. The so-called practical men tend to look down on theories and philosophy. They proudly show that many philosophies and theories have become obsolete, and forget that nevertheless everybody works on the basis of a certain phlosophy and of certain theoretical assumptions. This can be shown for even the most empirical and "positive" scientist—as my colleague Temkin did recently for the famous French experimentalist and physiologist Magendie. The fact that with many of these practical men such assumptions are more or less unconscious or undigested does by no means improve their situation. Philosophy is not necessarily sterile scholasticism. Philosophy has sometimes stifled science, but sometimes also it has stimulated science tremendously. As theories are just as vital for our scientific thought as facts, it seems wiser to face the situation, and to acquire some of the old art of thinking and the thinking about fundamentals, instead of discarding it entirely. Study of past theories is an excellent preventive against an unhealthy conservatism, to which man seems to tend naturally. Closer examination of past theories like Galen's theory of blood "circulation," of "malaria," or phlogiston shows that people accepted them not out of sheer inertia and stupidity, but because they did explain the greater number of the then known facts and because our forerunners were just as much limited by the total knowledge and attitude of their times as we are. The history of old theories reminds the scientist of the fundamental truth that his own theories are bound to be superseded by new and better theories just as were those of his predecessors.

The development of modern science has created such technical conditions that we are all almost forced into specialization if we want to accomplish something. Specialization is also economically at a premium. These trends are all the more paradoxical since all our modern discoveries in all sciences, social and natural, have rather emphasized the mutual interdependence of all phenomena.

The negative effects of specialization are so obvious and have been exposed so often during the last decades that I need not go into detail here. One of the worst consequences of scientific specialization seems to be that it tends to produce more and more technicians instead of scholars and well rounded personalities. Medical history, conscious for instance of the damage done to medicine through the rigid separation of surgery and internal medicine that lasted from the 12th to the end of the 18th century, is particularly sensitive to this situation. *It prides itself on being a specialty which to a certain extent tends to counterbalance the negative effects of specialization.* Medical history, in surveying the whole history of all those theoretical and practical, human and non-human elements that form eventually medicine; in studying medicine in connection with its cultural, that is spiritual and social, background tends to promote and uphold the consciousness of the totality of medicine in its students.

I think it is legitimate to define disease roughly as a process of disintegration on three levels: the physical, the mental, and the social. Medicine is therefore a biological as well as a psychological and social science. While we are very conscious of the first element and becoming increasingly conscious – sometimes over-conscious – of the second, the third, the social element, is only gradually becoming recognized, and yet factual proof of its existence is overwhelming, as soon as we look for it. Social considerations, for instance, have deeply influenced the recognition of the contagious character of disease; social factors play a role in localization and occurrence of cancer. It is noteworthy in this connection that a hundred years ago Rudolph Virchow, the man who with his cellular pathology laid the foundations of modern pathological anatomy, stated at the same time that "medicine is a social science." Part of his apparently silly opposition to bacteriology can be better understood when we realize that to him epidemics were not primarily climatic catastrophies, as they had been to all his forerunners, nor the exclusive work of bacteria as they were to his contemporaries, but the consequences of social disequilibrium. We have come around to this point of view, and today for instance base prognostication of malaria epidemics on a combined study of rainfall cycles, changes in immunity, and the economic situation. Disease and its treatment arc only in the abstract purely biological processes. Actually such facts as whether a person gets sick at all, what kind of disease he acquires, and what kind of treatment he receives, depend largely on social factors. Medicine's practical goal is not primarily a biological one, but that of social adjustment in a given society. I have been particularly impressed in the course of my anthropological and historical studies by the degree to which even the notion of disease itself depends rather on the decisions of society than on objective facts. This is particularly obvious in, but not limited to the field of mental disease. The mentally "normal" of other cultures and periods appears abnormal to us—and the "normal" of our culture and period appears pathological to other cultures and periods. Pinto (clyschromic spirochetosis), a skin disease, is so common among many South American tribes that the few healthy men that are not suffering from pinto, are regarded as pathological to the point of being excluded from marriage. The crippled feet of the traditional Chinese woman, diseased to us, were, of course, normal to the Chinese. Intestinal worms among the African Thongas are not at all regarded as pathological. They are thought to be necessary for digestion. But we need not go either to South America, Africa or Asia in order to encounter our phenomenon. When malaria, called also ague at the time, was at its peak in the Mississippi Valley, Wisconsin included, around the middle of the last century, people used to say: "He is not sick he's only got the ague" and as Timothy Flint puts it, the patient "was not allowed to claim the immunities of sickness."

"Medicine's practical goal is not primarily a biological one, but that of social adjustment in a given society."

Medical history, being a social science insofar as it is history, seems *therefore one of those disciplines which are best suited to make us acquainted with the social science aspects of medicine.* Medical history is therefore also able to make a definite contribution in the field of social sciences, under the condition that it remains scientific, that is detached from the more emotional attitude of the politician.

It might be understandable that when there are so many problems to be explored and so few workers in the field, we professional medical historians sometimes get somewhat impatient with the amount of time that is spent on the writing of biographies of great doctors. Seen from the educational angle we are somewhat unfair, because there is no doubt about the great stimulating and purifying value that the story of these exemplary lives has for the young doctor. Medical biography is even quite useful in a minor way as an aid for remembering all these eponymics which follow us throughout our professional career.

Medical history can give us even more than proper perspective, consciousness of our fundamental notions, understanding of the role of theory and of the social element in medicine. Medical history can be valuable in a more specific way and it can really be a part of medicine as well as just history. The old books and documents, and for that matter the traditions of the tribal medicine man, which are our raw material contain more than the errors and the recognized discoveries of the past. They contain a number of clinical and therapeutic observations which might be very suggestive if we are open-minded enough to recognize them. Unfortunately, these data are in general rediscovered only after the modern "discovery" has been made. You will find numerous examples for this in every medico-historical textbook. Let me mention a few of the less known like the correct observation of Benjamin Rush that malaria does not occur among those dwelling in stables—a fact which we can now explain through the zoophily of many malaria-carrying anopheles mosquitoes. We find mention of the beneficial effect of malaria on certain mental diseases in the old records of Bloomingdale Hospital, New York, about 80 years before Wagner Jauregg. When, during World War II, the Russians did some interesting work on the salutary effect of onion extracts in battle burns, Dr. Henry E. Sigerist of Baltimore could point to the fact that already old Ambroise Paré had reported good results with onions in burns. Ephedrine, isolated first by Dr. K. K. Chen (by the way, also once a member of Dr. Miller's seminar), comes right out of the classic Chinese pharmacopoeia.

The history and geography of disease have to be studied together in order to be meaningful. Both subjects form essential parts of the history of medicine: they had been sadly neglected for about 60 years. When World War II broke out, the practical shortcomings of this omission became painfully obvious, and a whole section of the Surgeon General's Office was mobilized to do an accelerated job on the subject. Medical historians should remember once more the words of Daremberg: "Dans l'histoire de la medecine les veritables personnages ce sont les maladies." They should use the new peace to do more thorough work on a subject which offers the promise of furthering the solution of very practical problems. It is extremely interesting to see how careful historical work, for instance by Greenwald on goiter, puts doubts on answers which seemed firmly established.

All these reflections on the advisability of studying and teaching medical history assume that medicine is a science. It certainly is becoming one to an ever-increasing degree. *And yet, medicine still remains at the same time an art,* differing thus from pure sciences like chemistry, physics, botany, etc. In this respect there lies some deep relationship between the two fields of history and medicine insofar as history too tends to be a science and yet remains an art, unlike younger social sciences like sociology or linguistics. Because of the particular object of its endeavor which is man, medicine is very likely to remain an art at least for a very long time, and at least for the larger part of the profession which still deals with individual patients. Science is primarily analytical, art primarily synthetical. In practical life, we are dealing with patients, that is, whole human beings, not disordered metabolisms, specific infections, or neoplasms. In the interest of the patient – and after all, medicine is made for man, and not man for medicine – it is extremely important that the doctor remains mindful of this art aspect of his calling, that he never loses the consciousness of dealing with human beings, that he develops himself into a well rounded human being instead of a mere technician, and remains one instead of becoming a mere man of routine. It is my conviction that the history of medicine, which is bound to emphasize the character of medicine as an art, can contribute considerably towards forming the humanistic physician who is the ideal of all of us.

I have given you some abstract reasons why I believe that medical history should be given a legitimate place in the medical school. I gratefully remember at this time my colleagues and teachers in the Institutes of the History of Medicine at Leipzig and Baltimore where these concepts were cultivated, and in particular my former teacher, Dr. Henry E. Sigerist, to whom I owe so much. I hope that through active collaboration we will be able here to realize at least a few of these rather ambitious goals, though I have to claim your indulgence. As our master, Hippocrates, says in his first aphorism: "The art is long and the life is short, occasion fleeting, experience fallacious, and judgment difficult."

5

Henry Borsook, "The Humanities in Medicine," *American Journal of Cardiology* 1: 1 (1958), 121-131.

Henry Borsook (1897-1984) was a British-born, Canadian-raised scientist-physician with a PhD in biochemistry and MD from the University of Toronto. In 1929 he was appointed to a faculty position in Tracy Hunt Morgan's newly established biochemistry division at California Institute of Technology (Caltech) where he remained until his retirement in 1968. After that he continued research until 1977 as an emeritus professor at Berkeley. An expert in the biochemistry of protein synthesis, his interests grew to include the science of nutrition, and later partnered with the philanthropist Clifford Clinton, owner of Clifton Cafeteria Line in Los Angeles, to produce and distribute a soybean-based Multi-Purpose food for impoverished populations around the world. Diverse in his interests, he was founder of the Anaximandrian Society at Caltech, where students came to Borsook's house monthly to discuss research papers in the history of biology. Borsook's own career is an interesting case-study of the correspondence between humanitarianism and biochemical medical research, especially when linked to his philosophical engagement with the topic "The Humanities in Medicine."

In 1957, Borsook delivered the Franz Groedel Memorial Lecture to the American College of Cardiology. Groedel, a pioneer in electrocardiography and founder of the American College of Cardiology, endowed the series to "serve as a yearly reminder of our humanistic obligations" as clinicians and medical researchers. Thus, as Borsook observed, the same stream of funding that brought the instruments of physics into biology labs and clinics left as a further legacy of Groedel's success a titled lecture series intent to bring the humanities into medical consciousness.

Published in the first issue and first number of the *American Journal of Cardiology* (1958), Borsook's article continues a theme raised in previous articles reproduced here relating to the development of ideals among medical graduates. The ideal, argues Borsook, is to embrace a holistic view of disease that does not reduce a suffering patient (one with dis-ease) to broken parts that focus a physician's attention. Holism – an ancient concept that saw a philosophical revival in the interwar years – gives rise to the epitome of humane treatment; holistic views see the disease as the *essence*, in the Platonic and Hippocratic sense, of a suffering patient, which differ in kind but, like tables that are shaped and assembled differently, are essentially the same.

Borsook points out that "the humanities in medicine" is not a phrase interchangeable with "humane medicine" – the former provides tools to create conditions for the latter. What is notable about Borsook's article is the very way he historicizes and contextualizes "the humanities," showing the range of disciplinary learning to be a product of a traditional "liberal education," where liberal amounts to a freedom of intellectual inquiry, as opposed to learning through rote memorization or uncritical catechism. What Borsook argues here, and illustrates through historical, literary, and philosophical references, is that medical students (and indeed all professionals under continual self-improvement) would instill values and ideals of humane care by embracing philosophical liberalism over the prevailing dogma of medical training.

Borsook's article is subtle and smart. While using a multitude of historical anecdotes to illustrate the pioneering work of earlier scientists, he is careful to point out the necessity of understanding that social values themselves change through time, so that it is important to see things in context and "to apprehend the different systems of values by which men lived." This suggests a relativist historical perspective. He is also prescient in his concerns about the technologization of medicine, repeatedly warning against seeing patients as mere statistics. "It will be sad," he writes, "if medicine ever ceases to be an art and becomes only science, solely a matter of test, technic, and prescription by IBM machine."

This article thus begins to articulate concepts developing mid-century in humanities disciplines that reflect a critical engagement with social thought and methodological maturity. His article also represents an important contribution to the philosophy of medical education by adhering to the principle that students' sympathies – what we probably today prefer to call empathy – toward patients can be taught and shaped through study of the humanities. A final note of interest here is Borsook's suggestion that such study should be interdisciplinary, embracing anthropology as well as the literary, philosophical, and historical disciplines he previously discusses.

See also

Norman H. Horowitz, "Henry Borsook, 1897-1984." *Engineering and Science* 47: 5 (1984), p. 24.

The Humanities in Medicine

Henry Borsook, M.D.

I am deeply moved by the honor and privilege of delivering the Franz Groedel Memorial Lecture this year I ask you to accept my sincere thanks. It is interesting, indeed noteworthy, that the late William G. Kerckhoff, who gave Dr. Franz M. Groedel, whom this lectureship commemorates, funds to build at Bad Nauheim a laboratory to be devoted to research in cardiovascular disease, also gave the California Institute of Technology in Pasadena funds to build the William G. Kerckhoff Laboratories of the Biological Sciences, of whose staff I am a member. Franz Groedel sought, from the beginning of his career, to use the methods and instruments of physics in medicine; he was one of the pioneers of clinical electrocardiography. The Kerckhoff Laboratories of Biology were built at Pasadena to bring to biology the methods and ideas of physics, chemistry, and mathematics. The title of the Groedel Lecture is "The Humanities in Medicine." It is to "serve as a yearly reminder of our humanistic obligations." The hope was expressed that it may "inspire us to take an active role in shaping the motivations of the medical student and the ideals of the graduate." The title implies that there are problems such as how to bring together the humanities and medical science, how medical practice may be scientific and yet kept consonant with the patient as a person. Both kinds of problems are related. It is a matter of mixing vinegar and oil. In medicine, as a science, the proper manner is objectivity, rigor, and un-excusing logic. Eloquence, personal warmth, sympathy, and temperament are eccentricities in science; they are the life blood of the humanities.

There is a danger that we may be using the term "the humanities" as if it meant the same as "humane." My old Webster's Collegiate Dictionary defines "humane" as

Having feelings and inclinations creditable to man; benevolent. Synonyms: kind, merciful, compassionate, sympathetic, tenderhearted, lenient, clement, forgiving.

"The humanities" the same dictionary designates as an archaic term referring to "branches of polite learning, especially the ancient classics." Nowadays the term "the humanities" is broadened to mean nonscientific learning: history, literature, and philosophy; but there is still in its meaning something of its classical ontogeny. Even then, the terms "the humanities" and "humane" have directly in common only that they both pertain to humans. When the Greek and Roman classics were written society was not humane; there was slavery, there was cruelty everywhere, in war, in law, in sport. Thoughtful, educated men could be only pessimistic about the realities of the world in which they lived. The Epicurean philosophy taught that if you do not attract the notice of the world it will not hurt you; wisdom is to withdraw to a quiet private life with a few friends. For the Stoic all is predetermined; virtue is to choose in accordance with the divine plan, and if you do not choose you will have to anyway; nothing but this grim, if noble, virtue is of any value. Both philsophies rejected the world; both were philosophies of escape. The centuries and countries of the revival of the classical learning were not notably humane. Humanitarianism became the mode in society only in the nineteenth century, with the rise of liberalism, at a time when the classical learning and the obligatory study of the nonclassical humanities were in their decline.

It is hoped the Medical Humanities will "inspire us to take an active role in shaping the motivations of the medical student and the ideals of the graduate."

Yet who of us has not hankered after the polite learning! If only our art of medicine were not so long and life so short! If only we had time for both! Our present-day notion of "liberal," as in a liberal education, is a Greek idea, connoting what is to be expected of a free man. Plato in the Laws distinguishes between two kinds of doctors, one a slave, the other a freeman.

> The slave doctors run about and cure the slaves, or wait for them in the dispensaries—practitioners of this sort never talk to their patients individually or let them talk about their own individual complaints. The slave doctor prescribes what mere experience suggests as if he had exact knowledge; and when he has given his orders, like a tyrant, he rushes off with equal assurance to some other servant who is ill; . . . But the other doctor, who is a freeman, attends and practices upon freemen; and he carries his enquiries

far back, and goes into the nature of the disorder; he enters into discourse with the patient and with his friends, and is at once getting information from the sick man, and also instructing him as far as he is able, and he will not prescribe for him until he has first convinced him; at last, when he has brought the patient more and more under his persuasive influences and set him on the road to health, he attempts to effect a cure.

The latter is a philosopher's ideal physician. But this is based on physicians as they were to the degree that Greek statue represented a man as he actually looked.

Medicine of the Greeks

The Greek physicians of 430-400 B.C. were the fathers of modern medicine. It is only decent piety to try to understand them. There were two chief medical schools. Neither was in the great capital, Athens, but in the provinces, at Cnidos on the coast of Asia Minor, and at Cos off that coast. The physicians worked for a living; they could not have been rich, or an apprentice taking the Hippocratic Oath would not have sworn,

> To hold my teacher in this art equal to my own parents; to make him partner in my livelihood; when he is in need of money to share mine with him.

Greek medicine was the first intellectual discipline, and this was in the fifth century B.C., to abjure, not only superstition, but also general philosophic postulates and systematizing. The Coan author (430-420 B.C.) of "Ancient Medicine" began,

> All who, on attempting to speak or to write on medicine, have assumed for themselves a postulate as a basis for their discussion – heat, cold, moisture, dryness, or anything else they may fancy – obviously blunder . . . . Wherefore I have deemed that [medicine] has no need of an empty postulate as do insoluble mysteries, about which any exponent must use a postulate, for example things in the sky or below the earth. . . . For there is no test the application of which would give certainty. But medicine has long had all its means to hand, and has discovered both a principle and a method.

It was the Golden Age of Greece, the wonderful fifth century of boundless confidence and optimism that was soon to disappear from the Mediterranean for four centuries. Both schools based their teaching on direct observation of cases and case histories. It is unfortunate and unfair that nearly all we know of the Cnidian school is from the criticism of it by its rival, the Hippocratic school at Cos. The author of the "Regimen in Acute Diseases," who may have been Hippocrates himself, begins:

> The authors of the work entitled Cnidian Sentences have correctly described the experiences of patients in individual diseases and the issues of some of them. So much even a layman could correctly describe by carefully inquiring from each patient the nature of his experiences. But much of what the physician should know besides, without the patient's telling him, they have omitted; . . . And whenever they interpret symptoms with a view to determining the right method of treatment in each case . . . I censure them because the remedies they used were top few in number—purges and to drink whey and milk . . . .

> The many phases and subdivisions of each disease were not unknown to some; . . . but their account was incorrect. For the number will be almost incalculable if a patient's disease be diagnosed as different whenever there is a difference in symptoms, while a mere variety of name is supposed to constitute a variety of illness.

The Cnidians emphasized diagnosis, and carried differentiation to absurd lengths. They used few remedies, which was certainly better at that time for their patients. One may imagine them as practical, unphilosophic, middle-class men, diligently comparing observations and puzzling over them, as one does when there is not to hand a workable hypothesis. The Cnidians, we may surmise, insisted on sticking to the facts of observation, nothing but the facts, and all the facts. They were on the straight road of science, but over two thousand years back.

The Hippocratic school was not so purely scientific. And it was the nonscientific impurity, probably, that has made its reputation throughout the centuries. Like the school of Cnidos, the school of Cos brushed superstition aside, and based itself on direct observation and the recording of case histories; but whereas the Cnidians emphasized the differences, i.e., diagnosis, at Cos they taught the unity in disease, they described the natural history of disease, as a pathologist today might write about inflammation in general. Their case histories show a close observation of signs and symptoms and their sequence, of the sputum and urine; these are recorded baldly, without inference. In their textbooks, as it were, they taught that diseases have a natural course, which the physician must know thoroughly in order to treat the patient properly and to be able to decide beforehand whether the patient will get well or die. For purposes of treatment and prognosis they did not, apparently, think it necessary to go further in diagnosis than to distinguish chest complaints, most commonly tuberculosis, and different kinds of malarial fevers. Diseases, they taught, are caused by a disturbance in the composition of the constituents of the body, by imbalance, disharmony. Nature tries to restore the balance, the harmony, which is health. *Vis medicatrix naturae* was the central Hippocratic doctrine. Nature may succeed or fail. All the physician can do for the patient is to remove by regimen all that may hinder Nature in her beneficent work of combating the disease. The notion of the crisis, the very word, was brought into medicine by Hippocrates.

For all their criticism that the Cnidians used too few remedies, the Hippocratics. used hardly any more. They were fussier: the barley gruel had to be prepared just so; more or less fluid for the disease in this stage or that; there were rules about bathing, and so on. Both the patient and his family no doubt benefited from the exactly detailed care that was prescribed. Hippocrates stressed prognosis:

> I hold that it is an excellent thing for a physician to practise forecasting. For if he discover and declare without being told, by the side of his patients, the present, the past and the future, and fill in the account in the gaps given by the sick, he will be the more believed to understand the cases, so that men will confidently entrust themselves to him for treatment. Furthermore, he will carry out the treatment best if he know beforehand from the present symptoms what will take place.

The case histories show, Plato's description of the ideal physician notwithstanding, that Hippocrates attended slaves as well as their masters; the case histories of both are recorded in the same manner. Hippocrates took into account the mental state of the patient:

> She was silent and did not converse at all. Depression, the patient despaired of herself. There was also some inherited tendency to consumption. It was no longer possible to do her any good, and she died.

> In Thasos a woman of gloomy temperament, after a grief with a reason, without taking to bed, lost sleep and appetite, and suffered thirst and nausea.

As night began there were fears, much rambling, depression and slight fever-
ishness. Early in the morning frequent convulsions; whenever these frequent
convulsions intermitted, she wandered and uttered obscenities; many pains,
severe and continuous.

As one reads Hippocrates' case histories and his teaching, one feels a mind
probing ceaselessly for correlations. One must take account (he insists) of the
patient's symptoms, of course, but also the climate, the season, the weather,
the sex, age, and diet. The temptation of a correlation is to believe it. Hippocrates believed some of his: that there are critical days in a disease, these are
a fixed number, in some cases odd, in others even, when the battle between
Nature and the disease reaches a climax—the crisis; diseases are connected
with the seasons and the winds, and it is chiefly the change itself in the season
which produces disease.

Where the Cnidians abjured all philosophy and dealt only with diseases,
the Coans were distinguished by their philosophy, which was that of Nature,
and this led them to a doctrine of health. Health was Nature's way, disease was
violence which Nature combated. Hippocrates taught what we call Hygiene,
a regimen that preserved health: one must take account, not only of the kind
of man a person is, but of what he eats and drinks, how he lives, and how
the climate and seasons affect him. Hippocrates was the father of preventive
medicine.

To Plato and Aristotle, Hippocrates was "Mr. Medicine"; it was through
them that his fame was perpetuated. Plato used the Hippocratic emphasis on
"disease" rather than on "diseases" as a powerful example in his doctrine of
essences, of the idea of a thing. The Ionian philosophers, Hippocrates' predecessors, had conceived the universal whole as Nature. Hippocrates brought
it down to earth in his idea of Nature in a man's body. Nature was health: the
right proportion, the right mixture, the right balance of opposites (Heraclitus).
The doctrine appealed because it was optimistic: Nature was on our side: *Vis
medicatrix naturae*—she would cure if given a chance. It was optimistic also
because Nature's way was no dark secret, we could learn it. To Plato the physician was the model for the philosopher. For the Greeks, for whom culture of
the body was an integral part of culture as a whole, it was an easy step from
the special case of the health of the body to the general idea of spiritual
health: harmony, the balance of opposites, hence symmetry, was Nature's way.
Hippocrates' idea had still an additional appeal to the Greek philosophers.
For them law was so wonderful an idea, it must be divine. Nature's way in the
body, as Hippocrates saw it, was its purpose, its law. So from medicine, from

our own most direct, personal experience we could learn Nature's law. From Hippocrates, Plato drew the Greek ideal of the golden mean, of proportion, which is health in mind, in body, in all things.

It is a noble philosophy. It was medicine's glory and a catastrophe for over 2,000 years; because medicine became inextricable from philosophy. From then until the end of the eighteenth century medicine was taught as some system, some dogma or other. It was as important, or more important, to be versed in rhetoric – a Sophist art – than to know the facts of medicine. There were few facts and many philosophies.

From the Greeks to the 18th Century

The centuries resounded with the arguments of contending dogmas of the schools. The Alexandrians surpassed the Greeks in anatomy, and some, drawing on their newer anatomic knowledge, insisted on nothing but mechanical explanations for all symptoms. Others, from the study of anatomy, and with no physiology, taught that it was useless to inquire into the causes of things; it is better to observe the facts and then do what one can; but observation of the facts and doing what one can was to juggle with analogies. No wonder a Pliny could brag that for 600 years the Romans got along very well without doctors. The drugs which they used were also superstitions. Galen's pre-eminence came from having read everything. He gave every phenomenon its name, every medical problem its solution. Drugs pertained to the hot, cold, moist, or dry, and one cured by opposites.

The medicine of the Arabs was little more than a retrograde gloss on Galen. Their real advance was in pharmacy and the therapeutic use of drugs; theirs was the first pharmacopoeia; they established the first apothecaries' shops. But their pharmacology was tainted with alchemy, and when it passed into the hands of the Europeans, it was mixed with witchcraft and magic.

Medicine then was book learning; educated laymen knew the names of famous physicians of the past and had a smattering of their doctrines. From the lay literature we can see how little medicine changed century after century. In the prologue to the Canterbury Tales we are told of the doctor

... being grounded in astronomy,
He watched his patient's favorable star
And, by his natural magic, knew what
Are the lucky hours and plantary degrees
For making charms and magic effigies.

The cause of every malady you'd got.
He knew, whether dry, cold, moist or hot;
He knew their seat, their humor and condition.
He was a perfect practicing physician . . .

He was well versed in Esculapius too
and what Hippocrates and Rufus knew
And Dioscorides, now dead and gone,
Galen and Rhazes, Hali, Serapion,
Averroes, Avicenna, Constantine,
Scotch Bernard, John of Goddesden, Gilbertine
. . . he was rather close as to expenses
And kept the gold he won in pestilences.
Gold stimulates the heart, or so we're told,
He therefore had a special love of gold.

Chaucer's dates are 1340 to 1400. Sir Thomas Browne (1605-1682), some 250 years later, wrote

the substance of gold was invincible by the powerful action of natural heat; and that not only ali-mentally in a substantial mutation, but also medica-mentally in any corporeal conversion.

The thirty-seventh chapter of Montaigne's second book of essays has been an armory of assault weapons on medicine century after century down to Bernard Shaw. Montaigne was a sufferer of the stone when he wrote it; it was published in 1580.

"I see no kind of men," he wrote, "so soone sick, nor so late cured, as those who under the jurisdiction of Physicke . . ."
"No man unless he be a foole ought to undertake (purges). Cause a purgation to be prepared for your braine; it will be better employed under it than to your stomacke."
"A sick man was asked by his physician how he was. 'I have sweat much,' he said. 'That is good,' replied the physician. Another time the patient said he had a great cold and quivered much. 'That is very well,' said the physician again. On a third occasion the patient said he swelled and puffed up as if he had dropsy. 'It is not amiss,' the physician said. The patient exclaimed, 'I die with being too, too well.'"

"How many debates, doubts and controversies have they among themselves about the interpretation of urine."

Yet Montaigne protests that his best friends were physicians. "It is not them I blame, but their art."

In 1673 Molière's "Le Malade Imaginaire" appeared. Molière (1622-1673) was a dying man when he played in the first performances. The patient, Argan, has been imagining that he is ill, and wants his daughter to marry a physician so as to have a doctor in the family. Beralde, the brother of the invalid, is remonstrating with him :

Beralde: He would dispatch you with the most implicit faith; and he would in killing you, only do what he has done to his wife and children, and what, if there were any need, he would do to himself.

Argan: What must we do then, when we are ill?

Beralde: Nothing, brother. Nothing. We must remain quiet. If we leave nature alone, she recovers gently from the disorder into which she has fallen. It is our anxiety, our impatience, which spoils all; and nearly all men die of their remedies, not of their dis-eases. [Montaigne]

Argan: But you must admit, brother, that this nature may be assisted by certain things.

Beralde: Good Heavens! brother, these are mere ideas with which we love to beguile ourselves. When a physician speaks to you of aiding, assisting, and supporting nature, to take away from her what is hurtful and to give her that which she wants, to reestablish her and to put her in the full possession of her functions: when he speaks to you of rectifying the blood, of regulating the bowels and the brain, of relieving the spleen, of putting the chest to rights, of mending the liver, of strengthening the heart, of renewing and preserving the natural heat, of being possessed of secrets to prolong life till an advanced age, he just tells you the romance of physic. But when you come to the truth and experience, you find nothing of all this; and it is like those beautiful dreams, which on awaking leave you nothing but the regret of having believed them.

About a half century later, LeSage (1668- 1747), the French dramatist and novelist, in his "Gil Blas" has a physician, Dr. Sangrado, thus instruct his new apprentice, Gil Blas:

Bleeding and drinking water are the two grand principles; the true secret of curing all the distempers incident to humanity. Here you have the sum total of my philosophy. You are thoroughly bottomed in medicine [in three weeks] and may raise yourself to the summit of fame on the shoulders of my long experience. While I dose the nobility and clergy, you shall labor in your vocation among the lower orders.

The following is part of a conversation between Dr. Sangrado and one of his distinguished patients, the 70-year-old Canon of Valladolid Cathedral,

The question here is to remedy an obstructed perspiration. Ordinary practitioners in this case would follow the old routines of salines, diuretics, volatile salts, sulfur and mercury; but purges and sudorifics are deadly practice. Chemical preparations are edged tools in the hands of the ignorant. Your usual diet? 'I live pretty much on soups,' replied the canon, 'and eat my meat with a good deal of gravy.' 'Soups and gravy!' exclaimed the petrified doctor, 'Upon my word it is no wonder you are ill. High living is a poisoned barb, a trap set by sensuality to cut short the days of wretched man. We must have done with pampering our apetites: the more insipid, the more wholesome. The human blood is not a gravy!

Smollet translated LeSage. In his "Roderick Random" there are physician-surgeons who belong in the dreadful pictures of Hogarth. Bernard Shaw's "The Doctor's Dilemma" belongs in this group, even though when it was written in 1906 it was more than a century out of date. The criticism of doctors in this play is that of Molière in "Le Malade Imaginaire" in twentieth-century terms.

The foregoing quotations are probably unfair to the doctors of their time. Nevertheless, one is struck by their sameness. It must be that doctors' language and method of treatment changed very little from the Middle Ages through to the end of the eighteenth century. Every physician, good or bad, had a philosophical system by which he treated his patients, and he held to it, come what may, to the bitter end of his patients. The worst of these physicians were charlatans, the best were quacks, and the more sincere the quack, the more dangerous he was to the patient. Medicine, as a therapeutic art, was, in the main, premature until the end of the nineteenth century. But doctors might have done better by their patients, for all the paucity of their facts, and their misconceptions, if they had not been obsessed by their systems. Systems such as theirs were bad medicine because they were constructions into which the physicians forced their patients. Systems which claimed to explain everything did not encourage observation of new facts.

Surgery in the Early Centuries

Surgeons were more highly thought of as healers because they were more down to earth and more successful, even though their social status was lower. The physicians were differentiated from surgeons from very early times. Asklepios, whom Homer calls "the good leech," had two sons, Machaon, a surgeon, and Podalirius, evidently a physician. Homer called Machaon "Shepherd of the Host," and when Machaon was wounded before Troy (doctors fought then), Idomeneus, a famous, tough spearman, urges Nestor quickly to get Machaon to the ships.

> "For," he says, "a leech is worth many other men, to cut out arrows, and spread soothing medicaments."

All that one finds said of Podalirius is that he had the gift from his father of recognizing what was not visible to the eye and tending what could not be healed. There is no record of anyone saying that the physician son of Asklepios was "worth many other men." There is a puzzling passage in the Hippocratic oath:

> I will not use the knife, not even, verily on sufferers from stone, but I will give place to such as are craftsmen therein.

Nowhere else in the Hippocratic literature is a physician prohibited from use of the knife. Indeed there are references to physicians doing surgical operations. The Hippocratic books dealing with fractures and dislocations are, by modern standards, by far the best. From Hippocrates on, a physician was a learned man, he had book knowledge and philosophy, and the Greek, upper class disdain of manual labor; the Oath refers to surgeons as craftsmen. Scattered references and the long lineage of barber-surgeons suggest that surgeons were a lower class than physicians. Paré (1510-1590) began as a barber-surgeon, and after he became famous wrote his books in French, not Latin. He was opposed by the faculty of medicine even though he was held in the greatest esteem by several kings and the army. The same writers who jeered at physicians were respectful of surgeons. Thomas Dekker in 1625 dedicated one of his books "To the noble gentlemen, Mr. Thomas Gilham, Chirurgian. I honour your Name, your Art, your Practice, your profound Experience." Montaigne in full blast against medicine, wrote of surgery, "Whereby I judge the arte of Chirurgery much more certaine; for it seeth and handleth what it doth; and therein is less conjecture and divination."

For all the greater respect accorded the surgeon as a healer, he did not come up to the physician socially until the end of the eighteenth century. A surgeon said of John Hunter (1728-1793): "More than any other man he helped to make us gentlemen." Physicians had the classical learning, by this they were gentlemen, even if as healers they were considered inferior.

The Rise of Modern Medicine

It would take too long to even touch on the rise of modern clinical medicine beginning with Sydenham (1624-1689) and Morgagni (1682-1771). Fundmental changes in outlook did not start until the end of the eighteenth century, although the knowledge had been accumulating for nearly two centuries. Vesalius (1514-1564) and Fallopius (1523-1562) had built the foundations of our modern anatomy in the sixteenth century; even Harvey's discovery of the circulation of the blood in 1628 had little effect on medicine for a long time. Malpighi (1628-1694) from the 1660s onward saw the capillaries with his compound microscope, the histological structure of lung, kidney, and glands; he described the developing chick embryo. Leeuwenhoek (1632-1723) was less systematic, more of an amateur microscopist; but he saw and drew muscle fibers, blood corpuscles, spermatozoa, and bacteria. Yet medicine lagged behind physics and astronomy; because the leaders in medicine were still striving for complete systems in the classical manner; and dazzled by the grand generalizations of astronomy and physics, they wished to do likewise in medicine.

A title to this part of my lecture might have been "Our Forefathers: Guides, Mentors and Bad Examples." The fault was not only that they knew so little, but the philosophical posture kept them from learning. The classical philosophies were dogmas. Dogma is static. It is in the very nature of dogma that it claims more than it has a right to. No wonder independent spirits among the writers reviled physicians. In the Book of Genesis is stated:

> God made the beast of the earth after his kind, and cattle after their kind, and everything that creepeth upon the earth after his kind: ...
> And God said, Let us make man in our image, after our likeness: and let them have dominion over the fish of the sea, and over the fowl of the air, and over the cattle, and over all the earth, and over every creeping thing that creepeth upon the earth.

God in his infinite wisdom encompasses all creation; He comprehends all the wonderful, infinite diversity of the world; He understands all. But when man tries to understand, all he can do is to simplify by stripping off and casting aside all that makes for individual difference. In this simplification the phenomenon is belittled, it is cut down to the size of man's mind. For example, there is little structural difference between the steroid male and female hormones, testosterone and estrone. The whole difference between the two is transposition of hydroxyl and ketonic groups and two more double bonds in the first ring of the female hormone, estrone. It need not be stressed that there is more to the differences between man and woman.

Herein is the root of the canker that classical philosophy was for medicine. Plato taught, for example, that all tables had in them the essence of tableness. This essence is the truth, the differences in shape and materials are accidental and unimportant. As an example he took Hippocrates' teaching: "disease" is what is important, not "diseases;" disease, is, essentially, always the same, the differences are accidents of form like the shapes of tables. What does not fit into a classical system is left out, is not seen. It is at most an irritating irrelevance. A sick human being becomes a case.

It is illustrative that an early European writer such as Chaucer made fun of a doctor's show of learning, his vanity, his greed, but he respected the doctor's ancient authorities and believed in his medicines. Even a Rabelais lectured on Galen and Hippocrates. There is a different temper in the writers that came with and after the Reformation. The intellectual leaders of the Reformation, Erasmus, More, and Montaigne, revolted against the intellectual authoritarianism of the religious and philosophic systems of Rome; they did not abjure the hierarchy of the Church. And so, in the quotations above from Montaigne, Molière, and LeSage, the attack (and a savage one it is) is on the pretensions of medicine practised as one philosophical system or another. The Reformation was the revolt of the individual against the authority of system, whether in religion, politics, art, or literature. The sick writer wanted his own illness treated, and had no concern for the system, no matter how learned. He could have found authority for this too in Hippocrates.

> The art has three factors, wrote the author of "Ancient Medicine," the disease, the patient and the physician. The physician is the servant of the art. The patient must cooperate with the physician in combating the disease.

Of course Hippocrates did not know that each foot stood on a different road that led to two vastly different countries. Who can see so far? Two thousand years later even a Svdenham who strove to study disease without preconceptions, and without necessarily explaining the disease (in this he was more Cnidian than Hippocratic), said:

> Disease is an effort of nature to restore the health of the patient by the elimination of morbific matter.

Sydenham took Hippocrates as his model, the "natural history of disease," *Vis medicatrix naturae,* and all. A Sydenham could borrow all Hippocrates' words, but the forces that gave a doctrine of a bygone age its life could not be borrowed; they were spent. The fifth century B.C—the seventeenth century A.D.? No. An idea to come again must be born in a new incarnation.

But we cannot think, we cannot see much without an hypothesis, a theory, a system. If systems are bad, and yet we cannot get along without a system, what are we to do? The writers of the Reformation were aware of the difficulty. The answer in religion, Erasmus proposed, is that every man must make his peace with God by himself. Montaigne gave the general answer, which is a basis for all empirical philosophy. (He would have hooted at a statement about him such as I have just made.) When he was asked for advice on the education of a young kinsman, he wrote:

> The bees fly about here and there among the flowers, and from what they cull they make honey, which is all their own, neither thyme nor marjoram. So of pieces [of learning] borrowed of others, he may alter, transform and mix them, to shape out of them a piece of work all his own.

Montaigne is our philosopher. He noted:

> 'Amongst so many millions of men, you shall scarce meet with three or four that will daily observe and carefully keep a register of their experiments. Physics is grounded upon experience and examples.' He said with tongue in cheek, 'So is mine opinion. Is not this a manifest kind of experience and very advantageous.'

Montaigne's advice was to get the facts, all you can, but the facts, and then shape something out of them all your own. What could this mean in medicine? Make a theory, a general picture of a disease, and overall pattern. Superimpose on it and have stand out from it, the individual, both in contrast with the pattern and blending with it. To see the particular in the general is to catch life.

Of course this is what the good physician does all the time; it is what we mean by "judgment." It is to treat a sick person as an individual human being, and not as a case in a statistic.

The Patient in Modern Medicine

Our scientific medicine is a system too. Unlike our forefathers, we admit we do not know everything. But the establishment of the "Franz Groedel Memorial Lecture" testifies to the concern of the American College of Cardiology that in our scientific system, for reasons inherent in it and in our present society, there is danger that the result may be the same as in the former philosophical systems of medicine, in that the patient may be degraded from a human being to a case, to the detriment, humanity apart, of the good treatment of the patient. The problem has arisen out of the great scientific progress in medicine. Modern science, being what it is, entails specialization. Specialization is fragmentation. Instead of, as in systems of the past, making the mistake of seeing only the general, there is danger of seeing only separated aspects of the patient according to the specialty, of fragmentation of the patient. What are we to do?

Of course there is no turning back

"To see the particular in the general is to catch life. Of course this is what the good physician does all the time; it is what we mean by 'judgment.' It is to treat a sick person as an individual human being, and not as a case in a statistic."

from scientific medicine, from specialization. The famous first aphorism of Hippocrates holds for us:

> Life is short, the Art long, opportunity fleeting, experience treacherous, judgment difficult.

The development of psychology (another specialty) has led us to see that a person who is ill may undergo important changes in his outlook and personality, and that these changes need to be taken into account in treating him. The danger in the very success of psychology (and psychiatry) is that care of the patient as a human being will become a specialty. Are we to send every patient to a psychiatrist to have this aspect of his illness looked after, as we send him to a radiologist for x-ray diagnosis or treatment? The psychiatrist is trained in these matters, why should he not be used as other specialists are? This is the way to dehumanize medicine completely.

Yet, how is the patient to get the benefits of all that modern medicine has to give him? There are the many interrelated problems of patients not having enough money, of doctors not having enough time, of there not being enough doctors, of the possibility that doctors may not be getting the right education for our time. All the pressures of modern life are toward standardizing us: "It is cheaper and more efficient this way," they tell us. And yet we know that the best medicine is to treat the patient as an individual.

Medical Education and Specialization

You know these problems better than I do. Probably no one of these problems can be solved separately. I beg your indulgence to make a few comments on what might be done in the way of the education of the doctor. The doctor's task requires sympathy and scientific knowledge. By sympathy I do not mean feeling sorry for the patient or his family; that, surely, we may take for granted. The sympathy I mean is insight into how the patient feels and thinks, in short, to understand him as a person, before and during his illness and what he may be like afterward. This is the art of medicine. Our great engineering works are often also fine works of art. How beautiful are the great new bridges, the mountain roads, and the dams! It will be sad if medicine ever ceases to be an art and becomes only science, solely a matter of test, technic, and prescription by IBM machine. I believe that sympathy can be fostered, that it can be taught. I know it will be objected that the sympathy I mean is like the feeling for poetry or the state of grace, that it is a state of grace. Yet, throughout the ages the state of grace has been taught, a feeling for poetry is fostered: it is done by indirection, by the study of noble examples, and by the luck of having a good teacher. Surely it needs no pleading that it is good for the student to know critically as well as sympathetically, the ideas, feelings and actions of the great men of the past. The study of the humanities predisposes to sympathy.

We need sympathy also in a broader historical sense: to apprehend the different systems of values by which men lived. Let me give you a recent example of how scientific concepts were formed by society's needs. The steam engine dominated nineteenth-century Europe. In order to make better steam engines the science of Thermodynamics arose. Its name connotes steam engine, its terminology even today is of the steam engine. Incidentally, the first law of Thermodynamics was discovered by a physician, Mayer, and first given its mathematical exposition by another physician, Helmholtz. Thermodynamics dominated all nineteenth-century science. Physiologists, not thinking very much and overawed, probably, by their physicist colleagues, taught that the animal body was like a steam engine, with a stable structure that suffered only slight frictional wear and tear, which was replaced from a small part of the food, and that the bulk of the food was the fuel. Hence the terms "endogenous" and "exogenous" metabolism. This is an entirely unbiologic concept. It is now proved that there is no utility in distinguishing between fuel and structure. Some ostensibly stable structures are breaking down and rebuilding very fast. Half the liver protein in a healthy adult is new every week. Muscle, including cardiac muscle, is breaking down and rebuilding more slowly than liver, but, nevertheless, it too is in a dynamic state. A living thing is not like an engine, it is not like anything else, it is only like a living thing.

To return to my theme of the value of having students specializing in science also learn non-scientific subjects, I would draw your attention to the fact that in some of our leading engineering schools 25 per cent of the under-graduate curriculum is devoted to the humanities. This has been done for about a quarter of a century, and the consensus of opinion is that it is good. On the scientific side, it seems to me that what the modern medical student needs to be taught is how to be, as it were, an administrator of all the medical specialties. It is not good, I believe, to teach the subjects of undergraduate medicine as introductions to or pseudo preparations for research in these subjects. It may be that what I have in mind would be best in graduate medical instruction. I have in mind somebody like the administrator of a great department of government, more nearly as in the British government than ours. The head of the department need not be, often is not, a specialist. He was chosen in the first place on the basis of his record at college. He has the kind of mind that can use the knowledge and advice of specialists; he can put it all together, he has the judgment to shape it into a possible policy, which he then presents to his cabinet minister, who takes the responsibility for it. I believe it would be possible to train a doctor so that he could appraise critically the findings of all the medical specialties, including psychiatry, and base treatment upon that knowledge. My proposal entails a reversal of the medical hierarchy, with the general practitioner at the top and the specialists below him. I believe that it could be worked out so that even less than brilliant minds could be taught to practice medicine in this way. Such men would prevent the fragmentation of medicine by specialization, as the clinical pathologist, aided by the roentgenologist, has done in the past.

We in medicine are involved in the general problem of our time of keeping up with the very rapid progress of science, the problem of finding a way for the healthy assimilation of the flood of new and often strange scientific knowledge into the life of society. In medicine there is, I think, a better chance of our solving our part of the problem than in other branches of science. The drive to do so is felt more directly because the need impinges directly on the individual, on his freedom from pain and disability, on his chances of living or dying. And the doctor is, I think, more broadly trained within his discipline, relatively, than the engineer, the physicist or the chemist. There is an opportunity for medicine to give a lead, and there is a chance that the consequences may not be as bad as was the lead Hippocrates gave to Plato and Aristotle.

A few weeks ago I was at a symposium on the subject of sickle cell anemia. Among the participants were clinicians, pathologists, chemists, physicists, and geneticists. The findings of an anthropologist and of an epidemiologist were cited: malaria is involved in the persistence of sickle cell anemia. Some of us felt it was a pity that the anthropologist and epidemiologist were not personally invited. Anthropology, the *logos* of man, it would seem is a proper subject for the medical student; and geography too. We are returning here, in principle, to a teaching of Hippocrates.

In the argument over the hydrogen bomb are clinicians, radiologists, geneticists, physicists, the military, politicians, and those with the responsibility of government. Just now it is more an argument than a discussion in which men of different points of view try to understand each other and come together.

Obviously, it would be wrong to describe present day science, let alone present day medicine, as being altogether like the astronomers' picture of our expanding universe, with all its different disciplines moving farther and farther apart in chaos. They can be, they have been, here and there they are brought together, and out of them is shaped "a piece of work all [its] own." But this does not happen by itself. We have to will it, to go out and seek situations and means of doing it, to foster the purpose in our teaching. In medicine there is a choice in several senses as to whether to practice as an isolationist or as part of the entire world.

In the long bibliography of Franz Groedel there is a paper of 1929 entitled "Heart Disease and Modern Life—A Preachment to the Profession and the Public." The paper begins:

> It is not rational for the heart patient to lose hope—the most important cause [of heart disease] is modern life. A good method [of treatment] is to go away from home for some weeks or months—to go to a place which is especially adapted for the treatment of overworked people.

He recommended Bad Nauheim.

> It is not only the Nauheim cure which will help a patient; if the patient has a will to become healthy and if the physician understands to prescribe individually the treatment according to personal circumstances, nearly every heart case may be improved or cured.

I believe that Franz Groedel knew the following passage in Montaigne on cures at spas such as Bad Nauheim. "I have by occasion of my travels seene almost all the famous Bathes of Christendome and some years since have begun to use them: I have as yet found no extraordinary good or wondrous effect in them – Yet have I seene but few or none at all who these waters have made worse – and no man can without malice denie, but that they store up a man's appetite, make easie digestion . . . Whosoever goeth to them, and resolveth not to be merry, that so he may enjoy the pleasure of the good company resorts to them, and of the pleasant walks or exercises, which the beauty of those places where bathes are commonly seated doth affoord and delight men with all; he without doubt loseth the better part and most assured of their effect . . .."

Dr. Groedel's paper concludes with a quotation from Hippocrates, from "Airs, Waters and Places." His preachment in this paper is according to Hippocrates' precept for the good physician.

References

Groedel, F. M.: Heart diseases and modern life, a preachment to the profession and the public. *Medical Review of Reviews* 35: 63, 1929; Anniversay Volume: *Exper. Med. and Surg.* #2-4, May, Aug., Nov., 1951; Dedication, Bruno Kisch, p. 209; Bibliography of main publications up to 1951, p. 221.

Hippocrates. The Loeb Classical Library. Vol. I and II (trans. by W. H. S. Jones), 1923. Vol. III (trans. by E. T. Withington), 1928. Vol. IV (trans. by W. H. S. Jones), 1931, Harvard Univ. Press, Cambridge, Mass.

The Dialogues of Plato (trans. by B. Jowett), Macmillan, New York, 1892; Oxford University Press, 1920.

Jaeger, W.: *Paideia: The Ideals of Greek Culture* (trans. by G. Highet), Oxford University Press, 1945.

The Essayes of Montaigne (trans. by John Florio), Modern Library, New York, 1933.

The Canterbury Tales (trans. by N. Coghill), The Penguin Classics, Middlesex, England, 1951.

6

Casey Truett, Athur W. Douville, Bruce Fagel, Merle Cunningham, "The Medical Curriculum and Human Values," *The Journal of the American Medical Association* 209: 9 (1969), 1341-1345.

The following three articles are presented as a group, in the manner they originally appeared in the *Journal of the American Medical Association*, reflecting a panel discussion and commentaries presented before the 65th annual Congress on Medical Education sponsored by the American Medical Association council on medical education in 1969.

The first article in "The Medical Curriculum and Human Values" series, subtitled "Panel Discussion," presents views and arguments from four medical students attending different schools around the country. Each student was a member of the Commission on Medical Education within the Student American Medical Association (SAMA), an organization established through sponsorship of the American Medical Association (AMA) in 1950, but at the time of these presentations had become independent, with student representatives acting as liaisons between the two bodies on AMA committees. It was at a SAMA Medical Education Conference, preceding the AMA's Congress on Medical Education, that students first articulated the problems with the medical curriculum. Students then "confronted" deans at a meeting of the Association of American Medical Colleges (AAMC) to air their grievances. At first characterized as a "radical minority" of confrontational students, it was decided that their views on the limitations and imbalances of the curriculum needed further consideration. Dropping the explicit language of "radical minority," the students themselves helped define a role for "student activism" in placing human values central to the practice of medicine.

Three general areas are addressed by the students with regard to the "dehumanizing nature of the present curriculum." First, the structure and rigors of the curriculum content led to physical and spiritual isolation, resulting in a diminished ability for the student to relate to the concerns and interests of other people. The consequence of this was that students felt they were learning to identify and treat disease and not how to care for patients with disease. Second, the "dehumanizing process" works on both the physician and the patient. For the physician, it was considered a defensive mechanism to deal with the shock and sometimes helplessness of confronting disease and death. The patients, on the other hand, become the case or room number associated with the disease. While the perceived problem here with the dehumanization process involves the way physicians-in-training are told to diagnose and treat disease, a corollary problem emerged in how students (and patients) react to the process. This was, all too often, by becoming cynical and apathetic toward their profession. Thus, an important reason to find a place for humanities in the curriculum, besides being a useful route to contemplate human values, is to service the psycho-social needs of students in search of something more than what the curriculum offered. Third, the students identified a problem of representation and dialogue in shaping curricular content.

Two replies were published that are included with this triad of articles. The first, from a health education expert at the University of Connecticut Health Center, recognized that the larger challenge to curricular design was shifting focus away from personal development to fostering a social consciousness that embraced the activism and health movements characteristic of the social milieu. Whereas medical schools had provided research and clinical opportunities for each student to develop individualized skills on a one-to-one relationship with patients, it was time to invite broader perspectives on the role of the healthcare profession in addressing the healthcare needs of society. While brief, the author alludes to a number of ways in which medical school curricula will need to adapt to provide more diverse options for students wishing to address broad social problems as relate to healthcare, suggesting a more interdisciplinary approach to education.

The second reply comes from Edmund Pellegrino, who is introduced more fully in a later chapter of this volume (see Chapter 10). A physician and pioneer bioethicist, Pellegrino addresses the points about how faculty mentors have failed medical students by not fully demonstrating humane behavior toward students as well as to patients. For a physician who became so well known as a champion of curricular innovation and medical humanities – indeed, who here points to budding medical humanities programs at medical schools as examples of where things should go – his tone may be surprising. Rather than overwhelmingly proselytizing others on the need to develop a more interdisciplinary philosophy of medicine in the curriculum, Pellegrino checks the students' fundamental concerns against realistic demands on medical training and broader expectations for social responsibility. As Pellegrino puts it, "Much of the rhetoric generated about medical education and human values is an expression of deficits elsewhere in society or in individuals." He implores his readers to think carefully about the extent to which social problems are primary concerns of the medical school, and what problems are best left to other scholars and activists.

Together, these articles represent the articulations of deficits and possible curricular solutions to challenges of preparing students to deal with highly complex biological and social problems. A conclusion that resonates in each perspective is that medicine cannot be separated from human values, and that the practice is entrenched in social behavior. As such, there is agreement among students, physicians, and educators of a need for creative educational responses to a new social conscious-ness, which sets the stage for the propagation of ideas and programs to integrate the humanities in medical schools over the following decades.

The Medical Curriculum and Human Values
Panel Discussion

Casey Truett, Arthur W. Douville, Bruce Fagel, and Merle Cunningham

The student presentation before the Congress on Medical Education on "Medical Curriculum and Human Values" represented a radical change in student input. Originally, the student panel was designed to respond only to the faculty presentations. However, following the student confrontation before the Association of American Medical Colleges deans' meeting, it was appropriately decided that what the students had to say was more important.

To facilitate the presentation, the subject was divided into four major parts, with each student presenting one part. Casey Truett began with an analysis of human values in present curriculum. Art Douville then indicated how concern over loss of human values in medical school was being transformed into activism. Bruce Fagel followed with a survey of student activism and a review of the present status of student programs in curricular reform. Merle Cunningham then concluded with a look toward the future and an appeal for cooperation from the present medical profession.

The student presentation and the ensuing discussion period made four major points. First, that the AAMC confrontation was not an isolated event by a radical minority, but represented an honest sincere effort to raise issues which must be discussed in the open. Although some students feel that discussions with deans and faculty will not lead to the solution of their problems, they are committed in the belief that these issues must be openly exposed. And if the initial confrontation is followed by a meaningful discussion of issues, as occurred at the Student American Medical Association Medical Education Conference sessions, then the confrontation is a valuable mechanism for change. Second, the vast majority of students are concerned about many of these issues and are now beginning to discuss them. Today few medical students are apathetic or unconcerned. The goals of these students, although not often openly expressed, are generally the same as those of the "radical minority." Third, all medical schools are in need of vast curricular change to make medical education more relevant to the needs of all people in society.

It is the dehumanizing nature of the present curriculum that students are concerned about and reacting to. Fourth, the forces that have created the present curriculum are the same for the faculty as for students. Many active faculty members are faced by the same problems as the active students. Change in curriculum and solution to the problems of medical education will occur only through the combined efforts of concerned students and concerned faculty working in an atmosphere of mutual trust and understanding.

CASEY TRUETT: —Human values are perhaps the crux of the ferment in medical education today. The student today comes to a school of medicine with its highly structured atmosphere from a system infinitely more loose in its organization, and, if you will, more mature. He comes from the college campus where he had large amounts of free time, large numbers of opportunities for contact with people and for personal exploration, and where he had a more self-directed learning process.

He comes to the medical school where he is faced by very little free time, small numbers of opportunities for personal contact, and a learning process which is highly controlled by others.

The atmosphere is changing, but I think this is a fair characterization of the situation as it exists now.

The student becomes, in a sense, isolated, or at least markedly restricted in his contact with his previous world – the nonmedical world – to that point in time, his only world. He becomes occupied learning a vast amount of material about disease. His first two years in medical education are very limited in terms of contact with people—any people. His circle of friends has become restricted. His time is restricted by classes and by study. He has an earnest interest in mastering the material presented. He is motivated by his idealism to help people through learning this material. His faculty is dedicated to teaching him, and in a sense afraid that he will not acquire the information on disease which he needs to be a competent physician. In this process there is a tendency to neglect human values.

The monopoly of the student's time even impinges on his following the news of the day, much less his following what is happening to his wife, his children; and it gets no better in the last two years of medical school.

The student considers himself a mature individual, and yet he is often required to relate as a child. He sees examples of loss of concern for the human dignity of patients—a point much belabored; but he also sees a loss of concern for the human dignity of his fellow students, which may disturb him even more than the former. He may come to believe that he has lost his place in the world. He transverses an almost schizophrenic spectrum, from leader to neophyte, back to leader, many times.

The medical student is often heard to say, "When I get out of medical school . . . when I get out, it will be different"; but the fact is that the process of medical education stretches over four years of medical school, one year of internship, two years, as a very minimum, of residency. This is a seven-year minimum. He has, by that time, in all probability lost something.

The medical student of today sees this happen to those ahead of him in the medical education process, and he reacts by saying, "I cannot let this happen to me. I *must* not let this happen to me. There must be a salvation from this fate."

He often decides that he must maintain or return to his interest in human beings, in people, not in himself, and in his immediate selfish goal of learning. He must return to a primary concern for others. Humanism – compassion – consideration of others – these are often passed over in the rush of learning medicine, of teaching medicine, and of treating disease, instead of *caring* – caring for patients with disease.

Arthur W. Douville: —My thesis this morning will be that there are forces operating with in any system of medical education which tend to cause the medical student to feel "dehumanized," to feel that the process which leads to the MD degree and the opportunity to practice medicine leads as well to a kind of spiritual isolation from his nonmedical peers and degrades his sensitivity and compassion. His discovery of these processes often leads to an alienation from the medical education which he may regard as being responsible for these changes within himself and in his relations with others outside the world of medicine.

Perhaps I could best initiate my argument by pointing to the incongruity of the title of our discussion this morning, "Health and Human Values in Medical Education," with the reality of medical education in this country. First of all, medical education is not concerned with health, it is dedicated to the study of disease. It becomes clear to the student that he is being inured to the kind of reductionist analysis which sees the patient as a system of matter in motion, and the categories of the understanding which he is encouraged to develop stress not an individual human being with a disease, but rather a disease to which is attached an often vexing and more or less irrelevant personality. One is taught not an ideal of health, whatever that might be, toward which he is to impel his patient with his understanding of the natural history of disease process and therapeutics, but rather a compendium of disease states and the deranged laboratory values which go with them. Thus, the patient is "dehumanized," as it were, from a particular individual human being with individual capabilities and aspirations to "the irritable colon in room 309," or, "the myocardial infarction in the intensive care unit." Briefly stated our medical education is disease-oriented rather than patient-oriented or even health-oriented. We are taught to eliminate disease rather than to preserve health, to alleviate symptoms and restore laboratory values to the normal range rather than to help each individual whose care is given to us to acquire and maintain his own maximum potential to lead a happy and productive life.

Another facet of the dehumanizing process in medical education is its tendency to isolate the student from his nonmedical peers. This isolation is enforced on the medical student by not only the enormous demands made by his education on his time and energy but also the attitudes which develop in his nonmedical friends. The demands on his time and energy make it difficult to share experiences with those outside the medical community; and since the sharing of experience involves a sharing and evolving of feeling and attitude, it is difficult for the student to avoid becoming separated from his nonmedical peers. He has less time to read what they read, to go where they go, to do what they do—his world is the world of the hospital, the very smell of which is alien and a little upsetting to his old bierstube college friends. The political and philosophical rhetoric of the "bull sessions" which entertained him and his friends a few years before is useless in the frightening crises surrounding diabetic ketoacidosis or a "code blue," and somehow the subscriptions to *The Saturday Review* and the *Atlantic Monthly* become piles of magazines stacked neatly and unread in the corner. *The New England Journal of Medicine* and THE JOURNAL are much more helpful on morning rounds.

The isolation is reinforced by the obvious recognition on the part of his nonmedical peers that he is somehow different from them. Their recognition ranges from cynical comments about how much "loot" he will be "raking in" as a successful practitioner to a more subtle but no less significant deference to the mystery which still surrounds the physicians' trade. The knowledge of life's workings in terms of physiology and biochemistry and the little skill which the physician possesses to stay its passing for a time, to relieve suffering in the crises of men's lives—this, too, separates the physician from other men, who are more or less helpless in the grip of disease. The medical student shares this aura of mystery to a great extent.

Finally, there is another quality to the experience of medical education which tends to make the student feel that he is being "dehumanized." The uniqueness of this factor lies in the fact that the student comes to regard himself as the principal agent by which it is enforced, and thus accrues to himself a certain feeling of guilt. Let me elucidate this assertion by calling to mind, as a point of meditation, your first experience with the cadaver. "What a piece of work is man," says Shakespeare's Hamlet,

> how noble in reason, how infinite in faculties, in form and moving how express and admirable, in action how like an angel, in apprehension how like a god; the beauty of the world, the paragon of animals!

Pah! A rotten bit of carrion stewing languorously in its pot of phenol and formaldehyde solution. Perhaps I need not point to the fact that should we have done what we did to our cadaver outside the walls of the medical school we should have been arrested and tried as the vilest sort of criminal who would take such fascination in so brutal a mutilation of the human body. Most of us handle the shock with jokes and a casual familiarity with this desiccated horror, which commonly is invested with a kind of personality by its dissectors, who soon are taking care not to slobber crumbs from their lunchtime sandwiches into the day's dissection.

This first shock is followed quickly by others—the confrontation with death itself, then the heartbreaking variations of its theme: the degradation and dependency of illness, the deaths of children, the helplessness of the physician and his student colleagues in the face of metastatic disease in a young person. All of these realities are productive of psychic shocks with which all of us must deal. And in the process of this acclimatization to these hard realities, the student begins to realize that he is no longer as sensitive to sights and sounds which earlier would have shocked and disgusted him. He begins to ask himself, "Am I really human? Am I still feeling and thinking the things I should be feeling and thinking as a human being?" Initially, the student looks to the individuals in the faculty to help him react appropriately to these situations. The staff man is supposedly less vulnerable and has come to terms with the frightening psychological forces surrounding debility and death in the hospital setting.

But in reality the student must himself come to terms with these "dehumanizing" elements in his education—the reduction of human beings to their component parts and a series of abnormal lab values, his isolation from the nonmedical community, and the psychological shocks of dealing with the sick and dying. He resists this dehumanization process in several ways. He may, for example, develop and maintain a certain cynicism. He becomes cynical about his teachers, most of whom seem to lack sensitivity to his needs in the area.

The student may reject those teachers who seem to deal coldly and distantly with the patients, who the student sees to be crying out so desperately for help. The student will do so with distant contempt or, if he is a little bolder, vociferous protest. Alternatively, he may adopt these attitudes of coldness and indifference for himself, often a useful defense against the emotional demands of a situation with which he is not prepared to cope with equanimous warmth and understanding. He may become cynical about patients. They are, after all, often difficult and discouraging. Often a patient seems querulously over-dependent, manipulative, unappreciative, or just stupid. "Psychoceramics" becomes a topic of discussion in the students' room, and debate concerning the acceptable levels of serum porcelain is common. Yet the student may feel guilty about this very cynicism, not feeling the compassion and warmth which he regards as necessarily part of the physician's emotional armamentarium.

Another way of resisting the dehumanization process is one of rebellion, of refusing to fit into the "scientific mold," of insisting on the importance of feelings and being sensitive. This rebellion of feeling, aside from the genuine social issues involved, partly expresses itself in the form of what many have termed "student activism," which I once attempted to define as,

> resistance to models of behavior which include coldness and indifference to patients, inadequate or outdated scientific skills, and irresponsible principles of self-interest in dealing with the legitimate demands of the community for a reasonable level of care.

In terms of the discussion of health and human values in medical education, the task of the activist is to define for himself and meet high standards of scientific excellence and human understanding, to acquire a demeanor of equanimity, devotion, and human warmth. The activist finds the episodic treatment of disease unsatisfying in many ways, accepting as he does the importance of the continuous maintenance of health, which has social, as well as strictly biological determinants. Many students of medicine find that their search for the human values in medicine is part of a larger enterprise, that of discovering a new set of values to lead them toward the good life in a just society, a new life style, if you please. They seek in medicine a new balance of scientific excellence and the ability to think and to feel in areas of experience beyond the merely scientific and analytic. Finding the human values in medicine is finding, really, a balance of scientific excellence and human understanding.

BRUCE FAGEL: —Much of what is going on in American medical schools today is focused toward change. The concept of student activism, and how students are using this process toward bringing about meaningful change, has to be examined in detail.

The aspect of activism of medical students is not a new thing at all. There have always been interested, involved students who have seen something that is wrong in their education and have desired to change and improve it.

But the activism of today is very much a consequence of the social milieu in which we all live. We cannot help but be affected by what is going on around us, although our insights as medical students are often confined to the four walls around us. But the growing interest among medical students is a social phenomenon and should be considered as such, and not be discounted as a passing fad occurring in the medical school, but rather as an important process occurring throughout all education and in an important way in our entire society.

Medical students who call themselves "activists" have one goal in mind, and that is the improvement of American medicine toward meeting the needs of society; and in this context medical education, as a process of changing American medicine, is paramount. This is the context in which student activism is working in the medical schools—changing the curriculum to meet the needs of society. When we consider the problem of human ethics and medical curriculum, and other problems involved in American medicine, we must analyze the processes which are being used to initiate changes. These processes are centered in American medical education. Medical students after much deliberation, are taking several approaches. There has been no single approach. Very often, however, we see confrontation as being the only approach used and ignore as being meaningless and irresponsible the other approaches that do not seem to have been considered as carefully as we would have liked. It is important to realize, however, that there is no one single approach to solving such problems. There are many approaches, all of which have some value; all of which have some problems; and all of which are being attempted.

It is important to realize, however, that there is no one single approach to solving such problems. There are many approaches, all of which have some value; all of which have some problems; and all of which are being attempted.

Beyond initial confrontations, the process most readily evident is the involvement of medical students in long-term analysis, an approach which even the most conservative would consider as being "responsible."

The Student Health Organization Community Projects, begun a couple of years ago, was one which involved changing medical education while being involved in it.

The Conference on Medical Education, which was recently concluded, represented the first attempt by medical students from around the country to gather in one place and discuss the complex problems of medical education. Those who were present at the final session showed that once the initial confrontation focus concluded, people were able to talk; and the evening sessions resulted in dialogue and discussion on the same issues as the confrontation.

We are trying now to bring forth more mechanisms for people to engage in this dialogue. The Student American Medical Association has created a student commission on medical education to provide meaningful, cooperative, coordinated input on a long-term basis, to supplement the activities of our 100-member Student Committee on Medical Education.

The most important aspect of mechanism for change, however, is occurring in every single medical school across the country. The 300 students who gathered here a few days ago represented a very significant part of that mechanism, but they are not all.

There are people in medical schools all across the country who are involving themselves in the educational process through specific meetings and committees and in a larger context they are involving themselves in their own education now and in the future, and I think it is extremely important to understand this.

In short, the dialogue has started, and the success of this dialogue – and I think it is important to understand the complexities of this dialogue, and how it will function – the success will depend both on the responsiveness of the medical community, in and out of the medical school, and the interpretation of the intent of such dialogue.

Far too often we focus on what we call irresponsible action and miss the real point of what people are saying. The sincerity of medical students is there. Our intent is to create mechanisms for dynamic interaction which can be responsive to the changing needs in a rational and purposeful manner.

MERLE CUNNINGHAM: —After consideration of the present state of affairs of student activities on our medical school campuses throughout the country, we must necessarily and obviously look toward the future. Student forces have already begun to make their contribution toward changing the established system of medical education.

In order to put this activity into perspective, let us consider the philosophical intention of these students. The overriding goal is to create a peaceful, prosperous, and just society by working to improve the physical, emotional, social, and economic wellbeing of our fellowmen. In the words of the late activist, Senator Robert Kennedy: "Some men see things as they are and say 'why'? We dream things that never were and say, 'Why not'?"

You who are supposed to be our models have traditionally and historically been reluctant to recognize the responsibility and accountability of organized medicine to the people of our country. You have been slow to acknowledge the importance of student and community involvement as a key to the realization of our dream of a "healthy society."

We fully realize the manifest complexities that unfortunately bog down the good intentions that emanate from so many ivory-tower pedestals. We stand prepared, however, as a viable and potent force to translate these intentions into action.

Our immediate goal is to help you to humanize the environment of our training, and to make it more relevant to the preparation that we need to meet the health care problems of our people, so that we will become physicians whose ideals remain oriented toward the improvement of society, physicians who will be responsible to the changing needs of our country, physicians who will be the educators and leaders in creating and enacting the necessary programs to meet those changing needs, and physicians who will be, besides excellent technicians, fully human beings with a compassion for our fellow men. In terms of specific ways of implementing these goals we do not have all the answers, but there are increasing numbers of us around the country who are trying to find partial resolutions and who are not afraid of trying radical new approaches.

In terms of specific ways of implementing these goals we do not have all the answers, but there are increasing numbers of us around the country who are trying to find partial resolutions and who are not afraid of trying radical new approaches.

As Mr. Fagel mentioned, we now have a nationwide communications network which includes most of the nuclei of student activism at almost every medical school in our country. Through this network we are providing positive, constructive mechanisms that have been successfully used in various schools to increase student and community involvement in decision making, and to make the curricula more relevant to our needs.

Our greatest potential lies at two levels: One, in educating our fellow-classmates about the exciting and dynamic new programs that are starting around the country; and two, in organizing and mobilizing the student dissatisfaction in order to bring about meaningful change.

All medical schools are in a state of flux. We feel it is our responsibility to ourselves and to our countrymen to work toward guiding the direction of meaningful change and toward speeding it up. Our sincerity and commitment in relating ideas into action speak for themselves, but we need your help.

Only with your cooperation can we effectively treat the sickness of our society and transform it to the just society of tomorrow of which we all dream.

There is no time to wait. We must work together to be a unified, viable, potent, and successful force. We must work together to attain the goals we mutually seek. We must work together to insure a humane society. Will you join us in stepping forward to address the unmet needs of our people? Will you be a part of our effort?

We stand ready in anticipation of your answer.

7

Edwin F. Rosinski, "Human Values and Curriculum Design: A View for the Future," *The Journal of the American Medical Association* 209: 9 (1969), 1346-1348.

Editorial note - This article is the second of a triad of articles published as part of a panel discussion on human values and the medical curriculum hosted by the American Medical Association. For more information, see the introduction at the beginning of chapter 6.

Human Values and Curriculum Design
A View for the Future

Edwin F. Rosinski, Ed.D.

I would like to do three things—make some observations as to what has been said; reflect on what is our present status; and, as the charge has been given us, see if it is possible to chart a course for the future. To those not directly involved in medical education or the practice of medicine, it might seem unusual, if not somewhat disarming, that the profession is devoting time and attention to the subject, "human values." Unusual and disarming, for traditionally human values have been considered synonymous with medicine. To the layman it is inconceivable that anyone could practice medicine without a deep commitment to human values, for from his initiation to the profession to the time of his death, the physician is instilled with a profound respect for human values.

The initiation takes place in medical schools which pride themselves on their educational objectives. These usually begin with a phrase, such as "to develop in students a respect for the dignity, self-esteem, and value of man." These educational goals clearly inform the student that he must direct his professional activities toward the personal wellbeing of man, well-being that influences his physical, psychological, social, and spiritual makeup.

With such noble goals being imbued in the student, it is no wonder that the physician is stereotyped as "healer." The image has emerged because the role of the physician as healer has been extended beyond producing tangible physiological results. It appears that to medicine has been ascribed a dualism that is perhaps (and I say this with profound respect) analogous to the Trinity. Where we attribute three persons in one to the Trinity, two persons in one are attributed to the physician—the healer in the physical sense and the healer in the spiritual sense, both inseparable and directed toward the patient as an individual.

If these attributes are inherent in medicine then why devote time to discussions on human values? Why the emergence of a group of interested individuals such as the Committee on Human Values in Medicine? Why the appointment of theologians to medical school faculties? One could legitimately ask whether medicine has lost sight of its noble goals because "human values," as a distinct topic, is receiving so much attention recently.

The response to that question must be a definite *no*. What is happening is that medicine is entering, better still, *must* enter a new era, an era in which human values are not only redefined but more broadly applied.

Medicine has earned its status in the eyes of the public because it has always adhered to its humanistic goals. The goals, however, have been achieved within the limitations of the one-to-one relationship between the physician and his patient. It is relatively easy to define the bounds of human values when a one-to-one relationship exists, but when the physician is asked to define his, and his profession's responsibility to human values that encompass society collectively, the task is much more difficult. As a matter of fact, the usual response is that the physician's responsibilities do not legitimately extend beyond that of what is expected in the physician-patient relationship. The very source of the profession's strength – respect for individual human values – has also become a source of its weakness; human values are applied to individuals, but not to society at large.

The reason, then, that human values are now receiving, and must continue to receive, renewed and constant attention is that a number of profound questions are being raised as to the limits of the profession's humanistic responsibilities. It is not just a matter of obtaining answers to questions and problems relating to such currently publicized issues as organ transplants. Transplantation is, and probably always will remain, an issue that involves a physician-patient relationship and it is an issue that physicians generally are equipped to handle. (If physicians, however, wish to ignore this issue, a host of self-ordained experts are ready to offer answers.) But when the question is raised as to where the profession's responsibility in meeting the health needs of all segments of society lies, easy answers are not forthcoming, and the answers proposed are not universally agreed on.

The human values dilemma in which medicine finds itself is manifested in the current controversy going on within its ranks as to the responsibilities of the profession and its individual members for providing medical services to the indigent; correcting the problems of the urban ghetto and rural poor; and, guaranteeing quality care to all who need it regardless of their ability to pay. Inseparable from these issues are matters of hunger, infant mortality, family planning, poor sanitation, and housing. There is no consensus as to what the profession's response to these issues involving human values should be because many physicians believe they should not be of concern to the profession.

A number of individual physicians, however, are addressing themselves to these issues with vigor. They are concerned, not because of what was instilled in them in medical schools, but because they, as individuals, are sensitive to the needs of society. These are individuals who can be best described as possessing a social consciousness or social awareness—a consciousness and awareness of societal human values, values exceeding those prescribed in the Hippocratic oath.

If most physicians lack a sense of social consciousness, or concern for social human values, on whom can the blame be placed? It would be comforting to be able to identify a simple cause or reason, but it just does not work out that way. The reasons and causes are interwoven, interrelated, and complicated. As complicated as the reasons are, however, it is obvious that medical schools, which have done such an excellent job in developing a respect for individual human values in the physician-patient relationship, have fallen down in developing in students a social awareness, a respect for societal human values.

Just why medical schools failed in this area suggests a number of tentative diagnoses. The most convincing is that because the way medical school curricula are presently organized, students have little opportunity to come to grips with social humanistic issues. Educational experiences now offered in most medical schools militate against this occurring. The educational system provides for research and bedside-care experiences—all fostering the development of human values on a one-to-one relationship. The educational reward system is such that faculty members pursue activities that unfortunately exclude the profession's responsibility to society.

If medical schools have failed, then what must be their future course? While a number of significant steps have already been taken, far more needs to be done. It must be done in the context of the curriculum, curriculum defined as the total educational environment of a medical student.

First of all schools must learn to live with two sets of educational goals. Educational goals based on biomedical science must continue – for a great deal of medicine's strength lies in science – but more socially based goals must be developed and have equal prominence.

As important as the goals are, the actual educational experiences provided to meet those goals are what will truly make the difference. Only if students have an opportunity within the educational environment to deal with broad social issues revolving around the health needs of society will they confront problems involving societal human values. Just as many educational situations now require students to make ethical decisions about individual patients at the bedside, so must future experiences require students to make ethical decisions involving sections of society.

Yet even before socially based educational objectives can be developed, and appropriate educational activities provided, medical schools will have to foster, extending respect and encouragement to, faculty who shape their careers to help meet the health needs of society. The time must come when faculty who have an interest in developing ways to provide quality health care to all segments of society are extended the status and rewards accorded those doing laboratory or clinical research. There must come a time when developing new models of patient care is considered as legitimate a scientific activity as finding a cure to some esoteric disease. There must come a time when faculty who explore and develop ways to reduce infant mortality in an urban ghetto, or eradicate hunger among tenants on a marginal rural farm, will be accorded academic rewards despite the fact that their results are not published in "refereed" journals.

When an interested faculty has an opportunity to develop educational experiences to meet socially based educational goals students will have an opportunity to grapple with humanistic issues. It is essential that medical schools become interested in all of the health matters of the community for only as students have an opportunity to deal with broad problems will they be able to pose questions and raise issues of societal human values in the same way as they now consider individual human values within the one-to-one physician-patient relationship.

What it boils down to in simple terms is that social values cannot be developed if there is no opportunity in medical school for related questions to be posted or raised during educational activities. If we sincerely want physicians to develop greater social awareness and social consciousness, ie, concern with societal human values, then medical schools will have to create the educational environment where these objectives can be developed.

While it was pointed out earlier that medical schools have failed in this regard, there is little evidence that a "ground swell" is developing among medical educators to correct this shortcoming. Much of the problem seems to lie with our faculties who do not see that medical education needs renewal. As John Gardner said it so aptly.

> One reason the individual can rarely think clearly about the renewal of society or of an institution to which he belongs is that it never occurs to him that he may be part of the problem, that he may be part of what needs renewing.[1]

Some new medical schools are deliberately making an effort to remedy this situation by planning unique educational programs in which students must face up to the humanistic issues created by the health needs of society. The University of Connecticut is a good example of an attempt to move in this direction.

For the new schools to move into this area will be relatively easy for they are not bound by the traditions and interests that permeate existing medical schools. The hope for existing schools is that the new breed of entering medical students – students with commitment – will force the change. It is my hope that they will shock faculties out of their lethargy and force the issue to the surface. The students could demand that medical schools address themselves to the health needs of society, thereby developing in all students and future physicians a concern for societal human value.

As medical education moves into this arena, administrators faculty, and students will have to turn to resources currently not available in most medical schools. Curricula will have to be designed so that the biomedical and social components are in balance. Curricula will have to be designed to provide a wide range of educational experiences through which biomedical and social goals are attained. Curricula will have to be designed to permit students to choose a purely biomedical professional goal, a purely social medical professional goal, or a blend of the two. Expert help in curricula design will be needed.

As schools attack the health problems of the ghetto or rural poor so that these become part of the educational experiences of students, they will have to deal with problems of economics, ethnic and social values, community attitudes, health mores, religious attitudes and beliefs, incidence and patterns of disease, transportation, housing laws, governmental restrictions, and the community's suspicion of the medical schools' interest and concern in these issues. Expert help from medical economists, sociologists, cultural anthropologists, social psychologists, demographers, lawyers, and clergymen, to mention just a few, will be needed. Other resources toward which medical school faculty can turn must be available.

As schools examine ways to measure the outcome of medical care, researching the delivery of health care, looking for more efficient ways to deliver care, using existing and new levels of health personnel, students and faculty will have to become involved.

As medical education embarks on this new course, as it develops more responsive curricula, demands will be made of it that will dwarf those made after the Flexner Report. Medical education will have to deal with profound questions and issues deeply rooted in societal human values. This is the course medical education and medicine must take if it wishes to maintain its image and continue its trust embodied in the educational goal "to develop . . . respect for the dignity, self-esteem, and value of man."

References

1   Gardner, J.W.: *Self Renewal*, New York: Harper & Row, Publishers, Inc., 1965, p. 130.

8

Edmund D. Pellegrino, "Human Values and the Medical Curriculum:
An Educator's Response," *The Journal of the American Medical
Association* 209: 9 (1969), 1349-1353.

Editorial note - This article is the third of a triad of articles published as
part of a panel discussion on human values and the medical curriculum
hosted by the American Medical Association. For more information, see
the editorial introduction at the beginning of chapter 6.

Human Values and the Medical Curriculum
An Educator's Response

Edmund D. Pellegrino, MD

What youth thinks of us is very important, for youth is the beginning of
our posterity.
    Aphorisms—Juan Ramón Jiménez[1]

Our students this morning have cogently and feelingly detailed a damaging
case against contemporary medical education and practice. They have
also literally pleaded for us, their older colleagues, to listen to this case. Their
sincerity and their urgency demand not only that we listen, but that we *hear* and
that we *respond* responsibly and with a concern at least equal to theirs.

It is my delicate task to attempt such a response. I speak as one member of
the educational establishment who shares their interest in change, relevance,
and the primacy of human values in medicine. I must, however, underline the

personal nature of this response. I disclaim any role as an official representative, but I hope some of my thoughts are representative of those entertained by other concerned educators and practitioners.

The students have used commendable clarity and brevity to detail the deficiencies in human values which now characterize medical education. The crisis they aver is a crisis in human values. The present system induces, they say, a feeling of dehumanization, a blunting of sensitivities for people, and an obtundation of social awareness. They see their teachers emphasizing disease rather than the care of patients and science at the expense of a concern for social ills. They describe the scene as a "wasteland." They fear, I presume, that they are being turned into "hollow men"—if I may add one of T. S. Eliot's more pungent phrases to theirs.

Finally, and most tellingly, they assert that we, their elders, who should be their models and their guides, have failed them. In our practice we are characterized as inconsiderate, unresponsive to community and social needs, indifferent to the poor and the outcast, too concerned with money, prestige, and comfort. And this, it is concluded, is the consequence of an education which has exalted all the wrong values—authoritarianism, rigidity, excessive respect for the intellectual, and underrecognition of the creative, the human, and the intuitive.

Despite these indictments, they turn to us for help. They plead that we awaken to our responsibility to help them to humanize medicine and to work toward a more just society.

How shall we respond? The temptation is to polarize our reactions into denial and righteous indignation on the one hand or penitential acquiescence on the other. Both positions are morally feeble. The former will terminate the dialogue but submerge the questions only to have them reappear later in more violent form or action. The latter is irresponsible for it does not confront the issue; it does not gain the student's respect and it admits too much. After all, a concern for human values is hardly new in medicine. It is its actualization in terms of today's problems that we must all seek.

Any morally sensitive person must first of all admit the many deficiencies of contemporary medical education as a humanizing experience. Such deficiencies cannot be tolerated in a profession so inextricably bound with the human condition and so necessary to improving it. Indeed, those of you who regularly attend these congresses have heard equally critical comments for the past decade and a half from concerned educators and practitioners. Their language might have been more reserved, less emotionally charged, and less given to hyperbole. Yet, the litany of errors recited by concerned educators almost parallels the one recited by today's students. This is so true that the response of medical educators to current student criticisms is frequently one of hurt surprise. How can this happen? Haven't we been undergoing ferment, crisis, and even revolution in medical curricula and with the same aims in mind?

What is the "hang up?" It is worth analyzing the discontinuities separating the student viewpoint from that of the enlightened leaders of the establishment who also want to close the credibility gap between themselves, their patients, and their students.

Some Student-Faculty Discontinuities

The first, and perhaps the most serious discontinuity is in behavior. This is more pertinent than the "credibility" or "generation" gaps.

Since the 1940's, educators have questioned the human and social values of medical education and have expounded reforms. They have effectively raised student and public expectations that changes would indeed occur. But sadly, little has actually happened in either medical education or patient care to make these reforms really operative. Our proclamations which are essentially valid, therefore, have not had behavioral authenticity. Nothing is more demoralizing to the young, and nothing more quickly discerned, than the appearance of hypocrisy induced by failure to meet expectations.

Let us admit it—we still tolerate several standards of care in teaching hospitals. The very terms "private" and "teaching" service proclaim the differences. We have not yet learned how to meet a community on its own terms, to engage that community in the determination of its own needs. We have yet to learn how to meet those needs unselfishly.

We do preach and teach care of the person, in a comprehensive and humane and respectful way. Yet, in our institutions there are still too many tolerated violations of the human dignity of the patients we serve.

The essential point is that we of the faculty and administration have not consciously undergone the necessary transformations of behavior in all our medical transactions. We have freely asserted that we are, and the student should also be, humane without providing consistent examples of this humaneness in all our own attitudes and actions. The big gap then is an existential and behavioral one which curricular design alone cannot possibly close.

A second source of frustration is uncertainty about the mechanisms through which the physician's concern for human values can be adequately taught. We hear a recurrent plea from the students—"please teach us to take care of people," "teach us how to be considerate and responsive," and "teach us to understand the roles of other health workers."

The classical roles of clinical clerk and housestaff catapult the student immediately into positions of authority. They leave little room for comprehension of the frightening experience of illness, the importance and the tediousness of meeting the personal needs of a sick person for comfort, feeding, and care of his bodily functions. These are things often done without comprehension and easily delegated to others. Even community medical experiences, while becoming common features of the new curricula, are usually designed as "teaching" sessions. They should also be "helping" and "serving" experiences which derive their teaching value from their authenticity and concern for patient needs.

Students have shown imagination in devising experiences which they feel will teach them to care for people. The roles of patient advocacy, family care in neighborhood clinics, and work as orderlies and as nursing and psychiatric aids bring them into literal touch with the odors, the pains, the anguish, and the helplessness of illness. Medical faculties should show more respect for the student desire for nonauthoritarian, helping roles in clinical medicine.

What needs to be assessed is how far such experiences can be used to advance competency as well as compassion, how effective they really are in inculcating attitudes of concern for patients and whether their benefits are lasting. Faculty members must realize that they cannot teach effectively in these service-oriented settings unless they are personally comfortable in them, ie, they must believe in them and be sincerely interested in sharing the student experience. Faculty who cannot honestly see the "values" of such experiences ought not to undertake them.

One almost indispensable way to demonstrate concern for human values is to establish a model of patient care under faculty auspices. Here, teachers and students can openly state their own hypothesis on how best to deliver care which is technically competent and humanely delivered. Students and faculty can "lay it on the line" so to speak as they cope with the vexing human problems of illness and try specifically to humanize the whole process. It is not perfection that the student wants to see, but rather a demonstration by his teacher of genuine commitment to confront the issues in a concrete situation outside the restricted setting of the university hospital. The student himself will learn in such a model that sheer good will and a romantic devotion to change are not enough. They must be coupled with patient and competent wrestling with frustrating and often petty obstacles, otherwise the result can only be greater confusion and more hypocrisy.

Perhaps the point at which the sharpest divergence occurs between the designers of new curricula and the student activist is in the matter of technical competence. This, too, is an issue of human values. The physician "professes" a certain knowledge and skill not possessed by his fellows in society. If he is not to be a fraud or a hypocrite, he must be competent in what he professes to know. There are few abnegations of the humane more blameworthy than incompetence under the guise of compassion. Not only is truth violated, but the patient is deceived in the personal contract he implicitly enters with the physician—the expectation that he will be helped. We all want to be treated courteously when we ride an airplane, but we first assume the pilot is competent. The alternative is a pleasant and short trip to eternity. An incompetent physician has a lifetime to spend at this macabre enterprise.

I am worried about the paucity of discussion about competence and proficiency in current student demands. This very important professional value is also an important human value without which the physicians whole being is compromised. We must guard as carefully against the romanticism of service without knowledge as against proficiency without compassion.

Compassion, too, is not enough as we are learning in our ghetto experiences today. We must *understand* our patient's responses, as well as *feel* for them, or else we will not know how to make our well-intentioned efforts effective for a culturally different group of humans.

Another major area that may divide the educator interested in reform from students and public expectation is the need to recognize a certain "economy of pretensions" as the philosopher Ortega y Gasset put it in speaking of universities.[2] The goals set for medical education are becoming global. Granting medicine's profound influence, we can hardly expect medical schools to solve every social, political, and economic ill of the ghettos, the rural areas of suburbia, and the developing countries. Racism, poverty, environmental contamination, housing, welfare, the rights of workers, the wholeness of family life—all of this can obviously affect health and induce disease.

We must be much clearer, however, of the extent to which these should become the primary concerns of medical schools. The physician sensitive to human beings as persons must, of course, concern himself with these matters. But, to the extent that they become his overwhelming concern, as student or practitioner, he becomes more a sociologist, economist, or political scientist— and an untrained one at that! Our curricula must discriminate between those things which enhance our primary functions and those which constitute the primary function itself. Much of the rhetoric generated about medical education and human values is an expression of deficits elsewhere in society or in individuals. Medicine, because of its involvement with the human condition, tends to become a lightning rod for all of the student's dissatisfactions with the world as it now exists.

Another point is the proper placement of the responsibility and control of medical education. I accept the view that medicine is an instrument of society, operating under a social mandate and ultimately responsible for the relevance of what it does. I accept, too, the concept of a community establishing the framework and even the ends to be served by medicine. Community participation in defining policies is justifiable and essential. But, to state that a community should *control* the medical school is to assign a task which demands competence to those who lack that competence. The community should have a real and direct voice in the operation of the university hospital and clinics, for example. Likewise, students as the persons most seriously at risk in medical education must have a powerful influence on the goals and means of their education. But, here too, emotional charges notwithstanding, the faculty does possess the knowledge the students wants and needs. A balance of faculty and student power must be struck which drastically alters the present authoritarian academic structure without relieving the faculty of its responsibility to determine academic questions.

A final and particularly significant source of divergence between students and faculty members lies in their disparate expectations of the medical school. Each group sees the school as an instrument designed primarily to meet its own needs. The student expects it to concentrate on his learning and personal development. He assumes the faculty is also ordained almost exclusively for this purpose. The faculty member, for his part, sees the school as a source of his own satisfactions. Teaching is only one of these satisfactions. The opportunity to engage in research, to care for a specific group of patients, or to share intellectual experiences with colleagues of like interest are often of more importance to him. Protection by students or faculty of medical schools as the sources of their own satisfactions is at the root of many confrontations. It is essential to recognize and to admit the existence of these divergencies in expectations before they can be dealt with effectively. A rapprochement is impossible without the early recognition that some accommodation of the needs of each group, and not total capitulation, is the only reasonable goal.

This vexing question is further complicated if we also interject the expectations of the community which are different from those of both the students and faculty. For the community, the medical school is an instrument designed to provide services and personnel to meet public needs as defined by the public and not by the physician.

Much more conscious definition of these divergencies in expectation is needed if something positive is to come out of the current academic confrontation syndrome.

I have just outlined some major points at which there should be a more effective intersection of the hopes and desires of educators, students, and laymen for medical curricula with more sensitivity to human values. Much valuable time will certainly be lost in confrontations and maneuvers if the nature of the discontinuities separating students and faculties are recognized. A more humane process of medical education is needed now. The teaching of human values should not be delayed while students and administrators indulge in the new academic gamesmanship of crisis and confrontation.

Features of a Curriculum Sensitive to Values

With these considerations in mind, we can outline the essential configuration of a curriculum which will be effectively attuned to human values.

First, the curriculum must have behavioral authenticity—the student must see the faculty in every medical transaction acting out its preaching about compassion and consideration. Every student experience, every teacher, and every patient-care activity should be scrutinized for behavioral credibility. The patient-care model is an invaluable way to demonstrate this creditability for student and faculty.

Second, a human-value oriented curriculum must provide a variety of experiences which first introduce the student to the patient on a personal, nonprofessional level. In this way, he can see illness as a personal assault on the patient and understand the many nonprofessional levels of care which are often of prime importance to the patient.

Third, humane behavior and attention to humane values must be manifest in our behavior toward the student as well as the patient. Students must be admitted to medicine on a wider variety of criteria, not just the intellectual. Where disparities in the educational, racial, ethnic, or social profile of a student body exist, they should be redressed. Once admitted, the course of study should be variable and individualized to meet the student's level of preparation and sophistication. Medicine can be entered at a variety of points—directly from high schools in some cases or after one, two, three, or four years of college. A variety of pathways to the MD degree must be developed to recognize the differences in interest, personality, and preparation of students and the ultimate roles they will choose in medicine.

Thus, no two students need have the same curriculum. For some roles in medicine the current standard regimen of the basic sciences may be of only cultural interest. For others, it is vital. For many important new roles in medicine an entirely different set of basic sciences will be more relevant than those now taught.

Professional competence must be assured. This is another human value and this means evaluation of the student's ability to use knowledge in a skillful and considerate way. The evaluation of competence must not be limited to the intellectual, but should also include the ability to function as a human being. The real test is not the ability of all students to pass the same kind of examination. Rather, each student should be evaluated in the pathway he has selected, ie, the one he "professes" and intends to proclaim in society.

The student must share responsibility in curricular design and evaluation. The community must participate in defining the purpose to which the curriculum is put, but neither group should usurp the faculty's responsibility to develop a curriculum relevant to those needs.

Finally, there must be concrete evidence of commitment on the part of faculty and administration to the importance of human values in the medical curriculum. Without this, much of our talk about "human values" will seem to be idle prating which can only exacerbate the tensions between students and faculties by adding the suggestion of hypocrisy to an ever expanding catalogue of errors.

In this regard, wider attention and application should be given to the pioneering effort of Dean George Harrell and Professor E. A. Vastyan of the new school under Pennsylvania State auspices at Hershey.[3] They have established a Department of Humanities in Medicine dedicated specifically to injecting a concern for humanistic values in all phases of education, patient care, research, and even architectural design. Commitment of personnel and funds is the kind of evidence both faculty and students need to convince them of the authenticity of a school's interest in human values in the medical setting.

The Need for a Medical Axiology

The deep concern expressed by our students for a closer attention to human values in medical education is commendable, but it will suffer the attenuation characteristic of all intuitive movements if it is not given rational underpinnings. The activist student specializes in intuitive assertions about values and emphasizes the sampling of human experiences to teach them. Experience is assuredly an excellent teacher of what human beings feel. We need, in addition, a critical and cogitative analysis of those experiences. The study of human values on a more formal basis in all aspects of medicine – a medical axiology – should be established as a legitimate discipline. It would deal with the tensions in human values created by the progress of medicine itself; it would define how medicine might contribute to restructuring and resynthesizing a value system for contemporary man. And, it would define those values which should determine the social and personal behavior of every physician.

The laboratory for medical axiology is at hand and waiting to be used. I refer to the clinical contacts and experiences of students at every level of their education. Conflicts in human values are experienced by students as they progress from nonprofessional helping and serving experiences to more professional roles as clerks and housestaff members. Interdisciplinary analyses of these concrete experiences in a clinical context can introduce students to the study of values on a formal basis much more effectively than courses or lectures in sociology or the humanities. The cooperative involvement of clinicians, sociologists, philosophers, ministers, and others in these analyses will greatly enhance the medical student's liberal education. Moreover, questions of values must be examined rationally and critically if plans for future improvement of the health care system and the behavior of health professionals within that system are to be developed.

Medicine and the Search for Values

Every crisis in human affairs is indeed a crisis of values—those compass points by which a society orients itself and sets forth the thing it cherishes.

To challenge these values is to induce anxiety in those who proclaim them and expectations for relief in those excluded by them from full participation in the life around them—the young, the disenfranchised, and the poor. The resultant mixture of anger and anxiety is an exceedingly unstable one easily detonated in demonstrations, confrontations, and rebellion.

Today's rebellion, as Camus so trenchantly put it, is a "metaphysical rebellion." Contemporary man having actualized the Promethean myth is forced to fabricate a new set of values—his own values which will proclaim what human being means in a technological society. Medicine cannot possibly detach itself from this search for values. Rather, it must seek direct and deep involvement.

Medicine is in convulsion today because society is in convulsion. It offers hope for the amelioration of some of the vexations of our modern day Prometheus. It has a responsibility it cannot shun to reduce some of the explosive potentials which can bring our society to the edge of oblivion. Our students this morning have pointed to the loci of many of those explosive potentials. It is for educators to respond creatively and to work with them to rehumanize our curricula and our system of care. In this way, a medical education will become simultaneously an instrument for development of technical competence and the inculcation of a sensitivity for human values.

References

1   Florit, E. (ed.): *Selected Writings of Juan Ramon Jimenez* H. R. Hays (trans.), New York: Grove Press, 1957.

2   Ortega y Gasset, J.: *Mission of the University*, New York: W. W. Norton & Co., Inc., Publishers, 1966.

3   Vastyan, E.A.: Humanities in a Medical Curriculum, *Penn Med* 71:78-81 (May) 1968.

9

Institute on Human Values in Medicine, "Reflections, Refractions, and Prospectives," in *Institute on Human Values in Medicine: Proceedings of the First Session, 1971* (Philadelphia, PA: Society for Health and Human Values, 1972), 100-115.

Following the panel presentations at the Association of American Medical Colleges (AAMC) meeting, reproduced here in the preceding triad of articles, the AAMC, along with the National Endowment for the Humanities, sponsored a study to survey medical school faculty and administrators about the desire to establish humanities programs within their curricula. It goes without saying that reforming a national curriculum that corresponds to the requirements of a medical licensing examination, and which is already bursting with content, is no easy feat. Indeed, as the medical educationalist Edwin Rosinski indicated at the conclusion of his remarks about curricular reform (see chapter 7), "demands will be made of [a more responsive curricula] that will dwarf those made after the Flexner Report" of 1910 – the last major overhaul of medical education that set the standard for scientific and clinical instruction. The study concluded that there was a wish to find some immediate forum for humanists and medical educators to exchange ideas about a future course for medical humanities programs within medical schools.

Answering this call and in possession of a grant from the National Endowment for the Humanities on behalf of the Society for Health and Human Values, the Institute on Human Values in Medicine was established to coordiante small conferences aimed to foster such dialogue. Chaired by Edmund Pellegrino, MD, of State University of New York, Stony Brook, the first meeting was held at Arden House Conference Center in New York in April 1971. The hope for this Institute was that it would foster communication between practitioners of medicine and others in disciplines outside of medicine who have interest in the "human problems that arise in medicine" for the patient and the physician. Contemplating what curricular interpolations humanities might make in medicine, Pellegrino asked the group to consider, "What are our goals, and are the methods we are now using to achieve them satisfactory? Can we improve on these methods? Is there interest among humanists in working with us in the health professions toward some future defined goal?"

Reproduced here are the concluding remarks, lead by Edmund Pellegrino, that summarise the thoughts and directions of the interdisciplinary discourse. Among the many useful insights that are here articulated are practical problems of defining terms in a common vocabulary and dealing with insecurities among people asked to move beyond their disciplinary comfort zone.

Reflections, Refractions, and Prospectives

Institute on Human Values in Medicine

The task of the conference summarist is always unenviable. His options are limited: He can remain faithful to every insight and *bon mot* and turn in a compendious report—complete, precise, and lifeless. Or he can more boldly select those facets which best fit the topography of the issues as they appear to his own mind. The latter course will displease some, disappoint others, and inevitably reveal the summarist's own biases.

With full apologies for its inherent defects, I shall undertake the latter course. If the physiognomy of the discussion as I shall comment upon it seems unfamiliar, you may attribute it to the high refractive index of my own mind and not the erratic nature of the discourse. Happily, the tapes and the prepared speeches will be available to redress any serious aberrations produced by the faulty lenses of my intellect.

Clearly, we have experienced in the past several days the first stages of an intercultural exchange in which differences in language, values, and lifestyles were exhibited. Our participants share in common a university education, it is true. The physicians have had some exposure to humanist studies, even imbibing them to some degree. The humanists have devoted their lives to these studies and to their explication. But we still have much to learn of the differences in meaning of the terms "humanities" and "medicine" to each of us. Indeed, our discussion prefigures what must occur on the larger scene between humanist-physicians if fuller advantage is to be taken of the insights into man developed by each of us. Our hopes for the humanist education of physicians and for a more humane management of individual and social ills rests on the continuation of this intercultural dialogue on our campuses and elsewhere.

In addition to the manifest difficulties in definition of common terms essential for the discourse, there was considerable wariness of too deep an operational interpenetration of the humanities with medicine. As a consequence, the mutual benefits of closer associations were developed only sketchily. I propose to summarize the state of these problems at the interface, and then suggest what may be done concretely to over-come them at the operational level.

1. Problems of Definition and Language

Recurrent difficulty was experienced in defining precisely what it is we were talking about. Among both the humanists and the physicians, there was almost a polymorphic use of the terms "humanism," "humanitarianism," and "humanities." Despite a number of attempts at careful definition, no unanimity was achieved in any of the discussion groups. While this is not an unexpected problem, it complicates even the first steps at fruitful exchanges between humanists and medical people.

Some of the varied usages and interpretations of the term "humanism" as applied in medicine are worth examining.

For some, humanism is a rather vague symbol useful for referring to the sum total of defects, dissatisfactions, and discontent with medical education experienced by educated people in other disciplines. It expresses a certain antipathy to the presumed technical and vocational education which, in the opinion of educated people outside of medicine, so many physicians seem to possess.

For others, the term "humanism in medicine" has become the symbol for new sources of inspiration and inducing changes that will give fresh meaning to medicine and to life. Humanism in this sense somehow refers to bringing medicine and other intellectual disciplines into closer conformity with the concrete and existential experiences of modern-day man. It is a symbol also of concern for the person who is endangered by modern society, technology, and medicine, which tend to overshadow man.

Still another view equates humanism with a sort of utopian aspiration for a new society that will, in ways not defined, be more humane, more attuned to man and his intuitive aspirations for the good life. This utopian view symbolizes on a grand scale a disaffection with human society and existence, and questions its quality and its very purposes.

> *"Clearly, one of the first issues to be addressed in any fruitful dialogue between humanists and medical people is finding a suitable operational definition of the term 'humanism'."*

Humanism is used by still others to be equivalent to the medieval *Trivia* in modern dress. Grammar, rhetoric, and logic are translated as Communication, Continuity, and Criticism. These three attitudes of mind and human skills are considered essential for the genuine physician who wishes to be humanely educated. This is not far from the view Scott Buchanan put forth so cogently in his *Doctrine of Signatures*.[1]

An additional recurrent theme was the concept of humanism as equivalent to an education based in the ancient languages and classical studies, but modernized by the addition of social, political, and scientific elements. This is not too different from the post-Renaissance view making humanism a mode or a system of education.

Underlying each of the definitions and often intermingled with them was the frequent equating of humanism with a compassionate, considerate, understanding, or sympathetic approach to other human beings and particularly, of course, to patients. Indeed, at times it would appear that humanism was confused with humanitarianism. There was the repetitive notion – or perhaps it was a hope – that a deeper study and appreciation of the humanities by medical students and physicians would make them more responsive to the personal and psycho-social dimensions of their patients' problems.

Clearly, one of the first issues to be addressed in any fruitful dialogue between humanists and medical people is finding a suitable operational definition of the term "humanism." It is unlikely, without pretension and the certainty of failure, that an educational program could attempt to inculcate all the attitudes or satisfy all the deficiencies implied in the spectrum of definitions used in this conference. Underlying these variant definitions there appears to be a common thread which might constitute an operational definition of humanism for the contemporary physician, a definition quite different from the one suitable for his Renaissance or Victorian counterpart.

The distinguishing feature for a modern-day humanism appropriate to medicine might well be its focus on human values: understanding and appreciating the values of individual persons and of human society, learning to respect the values of the patient in every medical transaction, and directing the technical and organizational panoply of modern medicine to human and humane purposes. For modern man – and the modern physician – the orientation is more pertinent than a humanism based in a familiarity with the ancient languages and classics or in literary and rhetorical skills or a knowledge of languages and literature. These latter are not to be demeaned, and the physician who combines them with a sensitivity to human values is unique indeed. But it is the primary emphasis on human value which is essential if medicine is to avoid being swallowed by its own technology or dehumanized by its complex organization.

Manifestly, a physician who understands the human dimensions of his practice will have a higher probability of consciously respecting the person of his patient. This may not be the same as compassionate care and humanitarianism, but it can move the physician further along this road. True compassion is more a matter of character and emotional development than of education. All may not possess this degree of sensitivity to another's suffering, but an education that encompasses a concern for human values should forestall the more obvious violations of human dignity which too frequently mar medical practice today.

2. Some Cross-Cultural Impediments

The problem of definition was more than surpassed by the exhibition of a set of attitudinal barriers that must be circumvented before humanists and medical educators can work cooperatively, each contributing to the intellectual growth of the other.

To begin with, most humanists and physicians really do not know much about each other, and have very little opportunity for formal contacts in the course of their professional or social lives. Sharp differences in experiences and life styles were experienced in a certain mutual wariness arising out of a series of unexamined assumptions—a veritable academic xenophobia.

The physician was too easily prone to take one or two rather extreme positions with respect to the humanities. At one extreme he had an excessive regard for the humanist's capacity to solve the value questions in medicine and to make educated men of physicians by mere exposure to the humanities. On the other extreme the physician could not at all see what the humanities could contribute to the daily practice of medicine. This vacillation between extremes of overgenerous adulation and over critical patronization has frustrated the early stages of the discussion.

Humanists, on their part, were wary of too close an approach to medicine, and experienced insecurity when dealing with physicians, especially in the clinical setting. Those who participated in medical school education confessed to being over-awed by the urgent demands for prompt decision-making on important issues. The undeniable primacy of the physician in emergency situations tended to be translated to the more ordinary teaching encounters. This understandably induced some reluctance on the part of humanists to penetrate too deeply into clinical territory. Some of the humanists, on their part, exhibited an over-acceptance of medical formulations, even in areas where they could afford, as educated and intelligent people, to be critical and to ask fundamental questions. A desire to be useful and to be wanted, coupled with the humanist's insecurity in the clinical context, seems to have compromised his true usefulness in the medical setting.

Differences in educational experiences contribute further to the difficulties in intellectual exchange. Very few humanists have had any genuine contact with laboratory or experimental science. Physicians have of necessity had considerable training and exposure to these fields. Physicians tended to overemphasize the values of experimental science, even though they might use very few of these elements in their own daily work. The "two cultures" dichotomy generated an even greater degree of xenophobia.

Disconcerting also was the variation in the urgency of the daily issues dealt with by both groups. The rapidly evolving state of medicine and its emergence as the major instrument of the new biology, force it to make value decisions well before they have received full cogitation.

The humanist can approach these questions in a more leisurely, abstract, and theoretical way. He is without the uncomfortable requirement of making daily decisions without all the needed data or the requisite theoretical substrata.

There are additional problems in being a humanist in a medical school. One is to acquire the stigma of the applied disciplines by too close association with what many university faculties regard as vocational or technical disciplines. To teach in a professional school – even if it is one's own subject – is to be relegated to a service role or even to become a Greek slave.

Then, there is the isolation from one's colleagues in the parent discipline and the real temptation to lose one's identity in that discipline—a true man without a country, unaccepted by either medicine or one's old friends. The possibility even exists that the humanist's research may be directed to experimental problems and questions somehow regarded as less rigorous and less pure than the humanist's usual fare.

All of these dangers require hardy and secure, well-established souls willing to run the risk of slowing or stopping the advance up the academic ladder. These are somewhat facetiously described matters, but they are also of the greatest importance in obstructing the free exchange between humane and medical disciplines so earnestly sought by so many today.

These impediments need not invalidate the attempt at dialogue, but they must be clearly recognized and specifically dealt with. Some "protection" should be afforded the humanist who ventures into the medical setting. He should be assured of an appointment in his primary discipline; he should not be alone, but be a member of a group of humanists sufficient in size to constitute a critical "mass" and allow for intellectual stimulation within itself. The physician can assist in breaking down these barriers by more deliberate efforts to reduce the anxieties of non-physicians in a clinical setting. He

"A desire to be useful and to be wanted, coupled with the humanist's insecurity in the clinical context, seems to have compromised his true usefulness in the medical setting. ... Physicians tended to overemphasize the values of experimental science, even though they might use very few of these elements in their own daily work."

can encourage criticism, comment, and participation; he can more frequently explain the technical bases for his decisions.

If there is to be a greater participation on the part of the humanities in medical education, cross-cultural barriers must be understood and circumvented. Too many humanists and physicians give up at the first encounter, and become discouraged by the differences in language, style, and behavior. Persistence and patience in the dialogue will carry it through to new levels of understanding. This, in fact, began to occur as the conference progressed.

3. Mutual Benefits to be Gained: Medicine and the Humanities

The initial stage of the discussion tended to focus around the issue of what the humanities can contribute to medical education. Medical educators asked the question in a somewhat challenging way: "Show me what you can do," they seemed to say. They were genuine in their seeking for help, but skeptical of what the humanities could do. Some humanists responded by trying to emphasize the utility of their disciplines to the physician. Later in the conference, the mutual benefits of the association were emphasized, and the pressure on the humanists to "prove themselves" was sensibly lessened. It became clear that *both* medicine and the humanities stood to gain from closer association.

Some of the advantages for medicine would appear to be as follows: In any dialogue with the humanities, medicine accrues the advantage of becoming a more fully examined profession. Opportunities are provided for critical inquiry into the uses of medicine for the individual and for society. In addition, the discipline of medicine itself, its philosophical assumptions, mode of reasoning, and epistemic basis, as well as its historical and intellectual development, can be clarified by the tools the humanists bring to such a study. As a consequence, medicine can acquire a deeper perception of its own nature. Its students, teachers, and practitioners will gain deeper insight into their own values and purposes as professionals. In addition, student and faculty in contact with the humanities can imbibe some of the attitudes of mind and modes of thinking of these disciplines. For the past fifty years the physician has had a modestly good scientific education, the principles of which he uses, at least to some degree, in his practice. He has been, however, innocent of any formal use of his education in humanities. The physician needs to develop a sense of human values as they pertain to his ordinary and professional life. He needs to understand something of the intellectual techniques, the modes of reasoning, and the rules of evidence used by philosophers and historians. These modes share some things in common with the sciences, but they are also different. It is these differences that need to be better understood.

Hopefully, as a consequence of this exposure, some physicians will be impelled to undertake an in-depth study of one of the humanities and devote their professional and research activities to the exploration of questions at the interface between medicine and philosophy. A very fine precedent can be found in the significant number of clinicians who have taken advanced study and researching the basic laboratory sciences and have brought these to the bedside. Similar immersion by medical people in the social sciences and humanities would open up areas of investigation in what might be called the "clinical context" of philosophy and the humanities.

For the majority of medical students and physicians, a closer contact with the humanities and the social sciences should help to make them more understanding of the value systems of their patients, of the importance of cultural and historical factors in the response to illness and in the acceptance or rejection of therapy. A study of the humanities cannot be expected to make a physician humane and compassionate. But it can do something to counter the overwhelming thrust toward the dehumanization in our medical care systems and the consequent alienation of patients from that system.

Some of the major problems now facing medicine and society are in the realm of what may be termed social ethics. Traditional medical ethics has been individual- and person-oriented. Its classic expression in the Hippocratic Corpus consists almost entirely in the responsibilities of individual physicians to individual patients. In the last half-century, it has become obvious that many of the more important medical issues transcend individual transactions, and that no physician can ignore the social consequences of his individual medical acts. We need today to develop an expanded and refurbished ethics of medicine equal to the new questions raised by recent medical progress. The development of such a new and expanded ethics is greatly enhanced by a deeper contact with colleagues in the humanities and social sciences. This may turn out to be the major benefit to be obtained by the exchange.

Last, acceleration of the medical curricula makes it almost mandatory that much of the liberal and general education of the physician take place in the course of his professional education. Many fertile possibilities for teaching humanities and human values exist in the concrete, specific, and clinical matters of a medical education. Properly utilized, a medical education can become a humanizing experience for the student and the faculty.

Teaching the humanities in the context of a medical education will provide a more lasting impression for the medical student than the present practice permits. Teaching art, literature, and philosophy, for example, as isolated phenomena or (as, unfortunately, they are too often seen) necessary obstacles to entry into medical school puts the humanities at an unnecessary disadvantage with this group of students. The relevance question can hardly arise if the humanities are concretized by permitting their discussion to arise out of the human situations which are the basis of a medical education.

There is little question that the personal growth of the physician as student is tied to his capacity to expand his own range of satisfaction – the antidote to the boredom of routine even when he is an able craftsman – is greatly enhanced by a serious pursuit of one of the humane studies throughout the life of the physician. This is far more securely based if the humanities are warp and woof of a medical education and not mere prolegomena, hastily to be put aside for the real matter of a medical education. The physician's capacity to satisfy the multiple needs of his patients is surely related to the degree that he is himself a more complete human being.

There are equal, but perhaps less well-recognized, advantages to the humanities by a closer concourse with the medical disciplines and the clinical setting.

To begin with, the humanities can gain by the exposure of their assumptions and theses to the concrete-minded attitudes one finds in the clinical setting. Thus, the humanities, like medicine, can become an "examined" discipline benefitting from the fresh points of view and, indeed, the challenges they will encounter in dialogue with medical faculty and students. An increasing number of humanists are aware of the need to make their studies relevant to the concrete and pressing problems of contemporary existence. Deeper involvement with medicine and the other health professions provides a rich phenomenological base for the humanist's cogitations and formulations. Indeed, there are in this contact real possibilities for a close approximation of theory and practice, as yet rare in the history of western culture. A very distinct and yet-to-be-utilized advantage.

A very distinct and yet-to-be-utilized advantage of a closer association with medicine lies in the use of the health sciences center as a research resource for humanists and social scientists. The university hospital, its clinics, neighborhood extensions, and ambulant facilities provide settings for the study of phenomena of interest to the social scientist and the humanist. For the theologian, there are the existential and theological problems of illness, incurable disease, and the dying patient. Here, the lawyer and philosopher can study at first hand the process of evaluation and surveillance of human experimentation, value systems of students, faculty, patients, and the community. These immediate and concrete opportunities are nowhere explicitly provided. In short, the health sciences centers provide entry into a phenomenological cornucopia of concrete, immediate, real, personal, changing human experiences. These phenomena will help the humanist to ground his cogitations in the "real life" situations he is so often accused of forgetting.

Perhaps equally helpful is the exposure of humanists to the mode of teaching employed by clinical academicians. This mode is rooted in the concrete case—a case "worked up" by the student himself. The development of ideas is from this concrete "case" and detailed to the abstract and general. There is little question of "relevance," since the student is "involved" with his own case and the discussion starts with his case. Students nowadays often complain of the abstractness of liberal studies. Because of the preference these days for images rather than ideas, they miss the utility and the "relevance" of the humanities. By learning more about the case method, the humanist can adapt it to his own needs and capitalize on a mode of teaching and hearing which has a long tradition behind it.

Finally, there is growing interest in the idea that medicine can be taught as a liberal study in the undergraduate years. The newer knowledge of medicine and its growing perceptions of the totality of human biology in health and illness has not yet been exploited this way in universities. If the proper study of man is man, then should we not give serious thought to the design of an undergraduate educational program built on an expanded conception of human biology? This conception includes the physical and anatomical constitution of man, as well as his social and emotional behavior and intellectual modes of existence. This may well be the basis for contemporary liberal education for today's bewildering world, in which the nature and purposes of human existence are so much a puzzle to old and young alike.

In such a study, medicine, the humanities, and the social sciences could all learn as they enable the student to see the folly of a fragmented conception of man's totality. This program could not succeed without the further extension of the intimate and continuing exchange between medicine and the humanities envisioned in this conference. An exchange would then continue without interruption through the course of professional and continuing education.

The conference discussion repeatedly fortified the view that the humanities, as well as the medical sciences, have much to gain by closer dialogue. What is puzzling is why this dialogue is not further along than it has been and why such wariness as does exist has not been dismissed. Sometimes, the best way to deal with a new or threatening situation is to engage it directly. We are probably at that precise point so far as the relationships of humanities and medicine are concerned. What concrete steps can be taken even now to open up the dialogue more fully, to integrate humanities into the fabric of medical education, and to open up mutual opportunities for joint study in depth of each other's phenomena as a source of mutual inspiration?

4. Next Steps

The purposes of this conference have been in considerable measure achieved: issues have been defined, needs identified, obstacles delineated, and mutual benefits enumerated. The next conference will have a somewhat different composition: i.e., a predominance of medical educators and a smaller number of humanists—some drawn from the participants of this conference for the sake of continuity, and some from those who have not participated. The second conference will concentrate on specific measures that can be used to introduce the teaching of the humanities into the fabric of medical education. But even in this first conference there was recognition of several basic requirements which would probably characterize any effective program. These conditions or requirements were derived from the experiences of those who had actually participated in teaching humanities in medical settings. There were on these points rather general agreement:

(a) First, there must be a "critical mass" of humanists in any endeavor to teach humanities in the health sciences. This derives from a need to retain identity with the parent discipline; from a need for the discourse with others in one's own field so essential to "keeping up" and to generating new ideas; and, finally, from a need to protect the humanities against being overshadowed by the medical subculture and the urgent requirements of the clinical setting. Joint appointments in departments of humanities whenever possible might supply and satisfy some of these needs, but not entirely. It would assure academic advancement in the parent discipline—a matter of personal significance to those who teach in the medical setting.

(b) The necessity for teaching in the actual clinical setting, with concrete and individual situations encountered by students, was affirmed. All participants agreed that standard lectures in "principles" of humanities or social sciences had been quite ineffective. But philosophy, theology, ethics, history, etc. could be taught readily in clinical situations. Such teaching is probably best conducted in seminar fashion built around specific topics illustrated by the case in question. Readings also should be designed around the exigencies of the cases and the subject to be explored, rather than the standard texts used in humanities courses.

(c) Several levels of study were recognized. The first level would be for all students, directed to introducing them to the ways of thinking and intellectual tools and values of the humanities. Some elements of logic and rhetoric could, for example, be included in the analysis of the student's presentation of the case, its history and analysis. A second level – for those who wish more depth in specific fields – could be offered as electives and consist of seminars, readings, and research in particular subjects of special interest to medical students, in which the approaches of the humanist would be vital. Last, those students who wished to study the medical humanities in greater depth could spend a full year or two, or go on to graduate work for an advanced degree in one of the humanities, with thesis work directed to some problem in the expanding zone of concern between medicine and one of the humanistic disciplines. Out of this latter group, we might eventually expect to see a new group of faculty members emerge who would themselves teach the medical humanities in health sciences centers at all levels.

(d) There was about equal emphasis placed by the participants on the importance of teaching the content of the humanities on the one hand, and their methodology and intellectual processes on the other. No one favored content or method exclusively, but there was considerable variation in the importance attributed to each.

These matters of how best to introduce the humanities operationally in medical education will come under further scrutiny in the second conference. That conference is designed to take the issues defined in this first conference and carry them further into program design, feasibility, and methodology. The work of the last several days will provide the basis for this further discussion, and will be made available to the participants in the second conference well before the meeting date.

I hope these selective comments will not have skewed the actual discussion that took place, or imposed a conceptual structure that was not present. This is the way the conference looked to your summarist, and how it squared against the matrix of his own thoughts.

I would like to leave you with the thought with which the poet St.-John Perse closed his Nobel lecture:

> In these days of nuclear energy, can the earthenware lamp of the poet still suffice? Yes, if its clay remind us of our own. And it is enough for the poet to be the guilty conscience of his time.[2]

Is it too much to expect that we must each be the guilty conscience of the other so that our respective disciplines can be made to serve humane ends and not their own? This is justification for this institute and for its continuation into the next.

References

1   Scott Buchanan, *The Doctrine of Signatures*. London: Kegan, Paul, 1938.
2   St.-John Perse, *Collected Poems*. Princeton: Bollingen Series, LXXXVII, 1971.

10

Edmund Pellegrino, "Educating the Humanist Physician: An Ancient Ideal Reconsidered," *The Journal of the American Medical Association* 227: 11 (1974), 1288-1294.

Edmund D. Pellegrino, MD, passed away in 2013. He was Professor Emeritus of Medicine and Medical Ethics at the Kennedy Institute of Ethics and the founding director of the Center for Clinical Bioethics, which was renamed the Edmund D. Pellegrino Center for Clinical Bioethics in his honor in 2013, at Georgetown University Medical Center. From 2005-2009 he served as Chairman of the President's Council on Bioethics in Washington, DC., and earlier in his career was president of Catholic University of America.

Dr. Pellegrino was immensely prolific, authoring over 600 publications in medicine, philosophy, ethics, and humanities. He had particular interest in researching the history and philosophy of medicine, moral philosophy and the virtue tradition, professional ethics, and the physician-patient relationship.

His contributions to the field of bioethics are well documented, but here I wish to mention a few aspects of his career that impacted most directly the development of medical humanities in medical education. We saw in previous chapters his participation in the AAMC discussions on Human Values and the Medical Curriculum (see chapter 6) and he spent many years thereafter developing a philosophy of education and medical practice where science and the humanities remain closely interdependent. As he wrote,

> Medicine has great, and almost unique, cultural force precisely because it is a discipline in need of both...the sciences and the humanities.... Medicine is a human science since it must examine man as person and object simultaneously. On the one hand, to understand Man the object, it uses the objective, factual, experimental language and method of the

sciences, necessarily "expurgating" itself of myth; on the other hand, to understand Man the person, it must examine man in all his subjective, imaginative, purposive, self-conscious, and mythopoeic activity."[1]

While later advocating bioethical positions that adhered closely to Christian principles, his early concerns about ways the humanities can help shape humane medical practice were more pragmatic and programmatic, arguing for the benefit of using resources from the National Endowment for the Humanities to enhance medical education. As he explained to the readers of the *New England Journal of Medicine* in 1974, the same year as the *JAMA* article reproduced here, an engagement with the "humanistic disciplines" to engage human problems "may constitute the only preventive we possess against man's being overwhelmed by his own technology, institutions, or bureaucracies."

> Few things are more crucial for medicine in its present state of technologic development than a continuing and deepening discourse with the disciplines that can critically examine the personal and social values governing the uses of medical knowledge. The authenticity of medicine as a humane science and the most scientific of the humanities rests on the viability of just such an exchange at every possible level.[2]

Historical perspective, critical self-reflection, philosophical insights, and literary expressions were all part of Pellegrino's repertoire of making medical students and practitioners more sensitive to the complex needs of their patients and social dilemmas faced in medical practice.

The following article, written just as Pellegrino assumed his position as Chancellor of the University of Tennessee Medical Units and Vice-president of Health Affairs for the University of Tennessee System, addresses critics of modern medical practice by pointing out challenges and remedies in inculcating compassion and care through liberal education.

1.   H.T. Engelhardt, Jr., and F. Jotterand, eds, *The Philosophy of Medicine Reborn: A Pellegrino Reader* (Notre Dame, IN: University of Notre Dame Press, 2008), p.328.
2.   Edmund Pellegrino, "Medical Practice and the Humanities," *New England Journal of Medicine* 290:19 (1974), 1083-1084.

Educating the Humanist Physician
An Ancient Ideal Reconsidered

Edmund D. Pellegrino, MD

> We must understand what man is, for he is the subject matter of the science
> of medicine for whom it is promulgated. To understand him is to under-
> stand the world, for he is similar to the world in his construction. He is the
> microcosm, the macrocosm in miniature.
>
> *The Caraka Samhita*[1]

In the growing litany of criticism to which our profession is increasingly
exposed, there is one that in many ways is more painful than all the rest. It
is the assertion that physicians are no longer humanists and that medicine is
no longer a learned profession. Our technical proficiency is extolled, but in
its application we are said to be insensitive to human values. We are, in short,
presumed to be wanting as educated men and as responsive human beings.

The assertion is painful because there is some truth in it. Moreover, it
comes from those who experience our behavior—our students and our
patients. And, in truth, our art is indeed in danger of being engulfed by its
technological apparatus. But most painful of all, the assertion strikes at the
reality that alone gives authenticity to our profession—our unique charge to
answer the appeal of a sick and anxious person for help that is both competent
and considerate.

The criticism is especially poignant for medical educators, at whose door
much of the responsibility is laid. We are told that we neglect the teaching of
human values and the art of medicine; that in our zeal for science we ignore
liberal studies; and, most telling of all, that the patient care we provide in our
teaching hospitals and clinics is itself dehumanizing.

Even our friendlier critics are alarmed by the recent trend to shorten medical education. They fear that our haste will further erode the liberal education
of future physicians and thus accentuate the dehumanization of the student

and the depersonalization of the patient. These anxieties reach crucial dimensions when viewed against the context of the erosion of personal elements inherent in medicine's increasing institutionalization and specialization.

The terms *humanism, compassion,* and *liberal education* are all shibboleths easily employed to advance one's own political, social, or educational ideologies. Without some clear display of the anatomy of these concepts, physicians will only respond with defensive denial, while their critics will yield to enraptured denunciations. As always, the patient will be victimized by an exchange of diatribes, rebuttals, and contumely. Worst of all, we will miss the opportunity to reexamine these terms and redefine them in their contemporary setting.

There is indeed a genuine and urgent dilemma. Society has the right to require that physicians be competent, that they practice with consideration for the integrity of the person, and that some of them also be educated men who can place medicine in its proper relationship to culture and society.

Medicine enjoys a unique position among disciplines—as a humane science whose technology must ever be person-oriented. Its practitioners are, therefore, under an extraordinary mandate to live and work within a humanistic frame. What does it mean to educate a humanist physician in contemporary society?

To answer this, we must first examine more closely what we mean today by this ancient ideal. The term *humanist* is too often appended to the term *physician* in an intuitive and altogether imprecise fashion. I suggest that the ideal encompasses two essential but distinct sets of components: one affective and one cognitive. These differ markedly in content; the one does not guarantee the other. In the best examples they are complementary, but they may also be in conflict. Each requires a different mode of learning and teaching.

The failure to make these distinctions leads to pretension, on the one hand, or unfilled expectations, on the other. In either case, the concept loses credibility, and this must be prevented in these times when medicine faces unprecedented demands on all its humane components.

The Physician as Humanist—a Bimodal Concept

So much feeling surrounds the idea of the physician as a humanist that it is somewhat precarious to attempt a clarification, for clarification requires a dissection of the major components of the idea of humanism. Thus, we run a risk of generating an antinomy where ideally none should exist. Nonetheless, much confusion will arise if we fail to comprehend fully the differences in the two concepts that are inextricably associated with any discussion of humanism—medical or otherwise.

Two concepts of the idea of humanism were recognized by Aulus Gellius, the second-century grammarian, when he spoke of the meaning of the word *humanitas,* from which "humanism" was later derived. He distinguished *humanitas* – education and training in the "good" arts – from a "good" feeling toward all men. *Humanitas* is more properly subsumed under the Greek term *paideia* – an educational and cognitive ideal; and the "good" feeling – what we would call compassion – is more akin to the Greek concept of *philanthropia.*[2]

Following Aulus Gellius, we can discern the same two ideals when embodied in the term *humanism in medicine.* One, the cognitive, deals with the physician as a man, a cultural being possessing ideas, values, and modes of expression in word and art. The other, the affective, concerns the feeling of the physician for the person-as-patient experiencing the existential trials of illness. Together, these ideals enable the physician to understand his science and also to identify with the humanity of those he serves.

These two ideals must further be built on a firm basis of technical competence. Without clinical craftsmanship, the physician-humanist is without authenticity. Incompetence is inhumane because it betrays the trust the patient places in the physician's capacity to help and not to harm. Throughout this essay, I shall assume that education in clinical competence always proceeds, *pari passu,* with the affective and cognitive elements of humanism, our major concern. The Compleat Physician is one who is capable in all three dimensions: he is a competent practitioner; he is compassionate; and he is an educated man. To use the classical terminology, he combines *techné* with *philanthropia* and *paideia.* Few men can perform with perfection, or even adequately, at all three levels. We must repress the tendency to apotheosize our profession by expecting all physicians to excel in all three. No educational formula, ancient or modern, can make of everyone who studies medicine the renaissance men or polymaths some vainly hope for.[3] A more realistic educational goal is to open the possibility for all students and practitioners to live in some measure at each of these three levels. Competence and compassion are clearly requisites for each physician if he is to meet his social responsibilities adequately. The extent to which he must also be an educated man is more variable and less intimately related to his social utility.

The Affective Components

Compassion: Its Meaning and Erosion. —Of the two components of humanism, the affective is more frequently mentioned by today's critics of medicine. They decry the lack of compassion they perceive in the care of patients. Compassion is most often equated with humaneness and even with humanism. What do we mean by compassion as an affective attribute of the humanist physician?

Com-passion means co-suffering, the capacity and the willingness of the physician somehow to share in the pain and anguish of those who seek help from him. It connotes some understanding of what sickness means to another person, together with a readiness to help and to see the situation as the patient does. Compassion demands that the physician be so disposed that his every action and word will be rooted in respect for the person he is serving. Compassion is reflected in a disposition to "feel" along with the patient. When it is genuine, compassion is unmistakably sensed by the patient and it cannot be feigned. It is not to be confused with pity, condescension, or paternalism. Clearly, compassion is an affective and behavioral characteristic that bears little relationship to a cognitive appreciation of any of the humanities. Nor is it altogether synonymous with the political or activist bias of many students and young physicians, however well-motivated they may be, to help the socially and economically disenfranchised members of our society.

Potent influences in modern medicine and society now conspire to erode and even extinguish compassion. Among the most influential are our fascination with technology, gadgets, and instruments; the inherent depersonalizing influences of our highly institutionalized social structures; the replacement of care by individuals with care by the "team"; the thrust of a scientific medical education that focuses on man-the-object-of-study; and, finally, a medical education that itself is fraught with rigidities and does little to help the student develop his own humanity.

Can the affective components of humanism – the *philanthropia* of Gellius – be assured in the education of physicians? Formal education would appear to be of limited value, since humaneness and compassion are not disciplines to be learned in classrooms. Indeed, whenever we study man, even his affective and behavioral components, we must in some sense make him an object and distort him. This is true even of those disciplines, like the social sciences and the humanities, that look at the conscious and imaginative dimensions of man's existence. They may help us to understand humanity abstractly, but not to behave compassionately. We must remember with Jung that "the patient is there to be treated and not to verify a theory."[4]

Compassion in the Student-Teacher Relationship. —Before the student can begin to feel the plight of his patient as that of a person seeking help, he must develop a fuller insight into his own developing humanity. The affective education of the student starts with the means most significant for him—the humanization of his medical experience. By dealing in a personalized and compassionate way with the special circumstances into which a medical education places young people, the teacher may forestall that subtle erosion of sensitivities that is a genuine danger of too much immersion in the study of man as an object of science.

The student-teacher relationship has many similarities to the patient-physician relationship. In both circumstances, one person is seeking help from another who is presumably wiser and has power over the petitioner. Both student and patient must face personal challenges in emotionally trying situations. When the teacher helps the student in a compassionate and understanding way, he illustrates how the student can in turn give the same understanding to the patient, who is dependent on his humaneness as the student is dependent on the teacher's.

The rigidity of current curricula and testing methods, as well as the trial-by-ordeal proclivities of some faculty members, are perceived by many students as "dehumanizing." This experience erodes their own capacities for humane relationships with patients. Granting a certain inevitable hyperbole in such assertions, the only effective way to inculcate compassion is to practice it. In each of their contacts with students, patients, and even with experimental animals, the faculty must exhibit genuine care. The clinician-teacher has truly awesome responsibilities here. One careless action at the bedside will undo hours of lecturing about the dignity of patients. Conversely, one act of kindness and consideration will make compassion a reality and an authentic experience. Student disaffection is often a masked appeal for models they can sincerely imitate.

There are some obvious critical incidents in the life of a medical student that can have a profound effect on his emotional maturation as a person. The way the faculty handles his responses to these experiences may determine whether or not the student later approaches his own patients humanely. Some of the nodal points at which a student may need help in dealing with his own feelings are the first encounter with the cadaver or with the hopelessly ill or dying patient, the death of his "own" first patient, identifying with young patients who are seriously ill or disabled, and trying to help patients seeking assistance in the vast, impersonalized, hurried, and often physically depressing circumstances prevalent in too many large teaching hospitals.

Opportunities must be provided for students to express their feelings of conflict and anxiety with many of these potentially shattering experiences.

Some personal adaptation must be effected that avoids rejection of self or profession, on the one hand, or too ready acceptance of the inevitability of an impersonal attitude, on the other. A judicious and interested faculty can encourage students to persist in gaining competence while simultaneously working to make the care of patients more humane. Even the well-intentioned student may be tempted to subvert the effort required to attain competence by self-righteous attacks on the "system" and the human failings of the clinical faculty.

Compassion and the Patient. —Humaneness and compassion in dealing with patients, the focal point of our concern, is not easily measurable. Yet, there are some rather simple behavioral criteria that can be monitored specifically as a beginning effort in any attempt to see whether at least the rudiments of humaneness and consideration are being exhibited. Clinical faculty and students might repeatedly ask themselves a series of very simple questions that arise in every patient-physician encounter.

First, do we teach students to satisfy the fundamental questions every person who is ill and anxious brings to the physician? The patient wants to know: What's wrong? How did he get that way? Is it serious? Can you cure it? What will it cost in money and loss of dignity? What are you going to do? Will it hurt? These are simple questions, but to an alarming degree, patients may see many doctors, have many tests, pay many bills, and not receive answers to these simple questions.

The issuance of a diagnosis and a standardized explanation may be convenient for the physician or all that his time will permit. Yet, this can be the first step in making the patient an object and not a person. Each patient wants answers to all these questions put into the context of *his* life. This is more than individual treatment, which merely means treatment as a unit. Personal treatment, instead, gets at the uniqueness of the person behind the unit. Or, as Thomas Merton said so sagely, "The person must be rescued from the individual."[5] Physicians who have neither the time nor inclination for this degree of personalization are bound by the first rule of humaneness to see that other members of the health care team are permitted to answer the personal questions that lie at the root of the patient's plea for help.

Second, can we accept the patient for what he is and not what we think he should be? The German novelist Hermann Hesse puts it well: "No man has ever been entirely and completely himself. Yet each one strives to become that—one in an awkward, the other in an intelligent way."[6] To be compassionate, we must accept each person's striving—the ignorant and the intelligent, the successes, the failures, the poor, the wise, the weak, the strong, and even the evil ones. All must receive our expression of willingness to help. This is impossible unless we continue to grow as persons ourselves. "If the doctor wants to help a human being, he must be able to accept him as he is. And he can do this in reality only when he has already seen and accepted himself as he is."[7] We can never feel with another person when we pass superior judgment, only when we see our own frailties as well as his.

Third, do we handle our authority in a humane way that respects the life values of the patient? The health professional is always in danger of extending his authority in technical matters over the patient's system of beliefs and values. Dag Hammarskjöld articulated the unique responsibility of those in authority thus: "Your position never gives you the right to command. It only imposes on you the duty of so living your life that others can receive your orders without being humiliated."[8] This is sound advice, to which we must attend whether we deal with patients, students, or our own professional colleagues. It has an important corollary: We must not "put down" the patient when he detects our uncertainties and even our errors. To be humane, we must ever be ready, as Galileo said, "to pronounce that wise, ingenious, and modest statement—"I do not know.""

Compassion, practiced in these terms in each individual patient transaction, is the irreducible base for mitigating the inherent dehumanizing tendencies of today's highly institutionalized and technologically oriented patterns of patient care. The student's distress with deficiencies in our present system is meaningless unless he realizes he can remedy them by humanizing his own relationships with the patients he is privileged to examine and help.

Compassion and "Humanistic" Psychology. —Recently, a variety of means derived from "humanistic" psychology have been introduced to improve the experiential-affective elements of learning. Carl Rogers has called for the use of the encounter group involving faculty and students in an attempt to forge a better unity between cognitive and affective learning. He has urged a reappraisal of all education from this point of view and has already initiated a series of encounter sessions for medical educators for this purpose.[9] Other measures, like psychodrama and psychosynthesis, are sure to be explored in an effort to remedy the defects in affective learning among medical faculty, students, and practitioners.

The success of such measures will be difficult to evaluate. For some, they will no doubt leave a lasting impression; others will reject them. For many, a transient experience of limited value will probably occur. We must avoid the conclusion that the only way to learn the affective components of humane medicine lies in any particular psychological mode. There is as much danger of psychologic overkill in medical education as there is of scientific overkill. We cannot ignore the capacity of at least some students to become empathetic, humane, and sensitive practitioners without necessarily dissecting their emotional lives to this fine degree.

Little of a lasting nature will be achieved until the affective components in the student's learning become the conscious concern of the majority of clinical teachers. To limit this concern, and the teaching that goes with it, to those whose specialties are in psychology or the behavioral sciences is to create a pedagogic ghetto that many students and faculty will eschew.

Before they can be evaluated properly, the newer psychologic techniques must be continuing experiences for teachers and students in their own institutions. One possible achievement, as judged by my conversations with those who have attended the Rogers sessions, is a reduction in the emotional overtones that seriously impede discussions of even the cognitive elements in medical education. If encounter sessions encourage a more reasonable dialogue in the cognitive domain, they will be well worth the effort.

Affective experiences and behavioral enhancements of humane attitudes by newer psychological techniques are promising, but the affective elements in the patient-physician transaction must also be studies in an intellectually rigorous fashion. The Spanish medical philosopher Pedro Lain Entralgo has undertaken a comprehensive analysis of this subject.[10] His work is an excellent starting point for those who wish to approach the subject cognitively. Ideally, the affective training of both student and teacher should be united with the cognitive examination of the affective components in the personal relationships of patient and physician, student and teacher, and student and patient.

The Cognitive Components

The Domain of Liberal Studies. —Medical students today are, commendably, most concerned with the affective components. They exalt them, perhaps too readily, over the cognitive in their zeal to remedy some of the more obvious depersonalizing tendencies in medical education and practice. In the past, we have run the danger of suppressing the human values in medicine by an overadulation of its rational and scientific elements. We will not serve mankind any the better if we now yield to the dominance of romanticism, intuition, and introspection propounded by some under the heading of medical humanism.

As a cognitive entity, humanism has a complex history, which Kristeller and others have attempted to clarify.[11] It originated in the 19th century with Niethammer as *humanismus*, an ideal of the classical and liberal forms of education to be set against the vocational and scientific then gaining ground in education. *Humanism* itself derives from the word *umanista* used in the Italian universities of the Renaissance to designate the teachers of the humanities—those studies included in the *studia humanitatis*, the language and literature of Rome and, to a lesser extent, of Greece.

In this older sense, humanism is a literary and educational ideal, one that has lost much ground in today's universities. But almost from the outset, the term became identified with a certain set of values that set man as the central focus of concern—belief in the dignity and worth of the person, the democratic process, and human rationality. These values, as Edel has emphasized, are not a philosophical system *sui generis*, but rather what he terms a "philosophical strain" or "a corrective process, the guardian of a human balance against seeing man as more than a man or less than a man."[12] This "strain" is expressed in an extreme form in the religion of man proposed by Auguste Comte. More commonly, it is a bias found in many philosophical systems. Thus, we can speak of Christian, marxist, atheistic, or scientific humanisms. The humanist strain deals with values, and it is thus quite different in cognitive content from the more classical form of literary humanism.

Classical and Literary Humanism. —Let us first examine the cognitive elements in traditional or literary humanism. This ideal was best exemplified in the lives of such physician-scholars as Linacre, Caius, and their modern counterpart, Sir William Osler. Gilbert Murray said of Osler, in nominating him for the presidency of the Classical Association, that

> he stands for a type of culture which the Classical Association does not wish to see die out of this world—the culture of a man who, while devoting himself to his special science, keeps nevertheless a broad basis of interest in letters of all kinds.[13]

Osler is essentially the physician as educated man, combining superb clinical talents, scientific perspective, and human concern with the capacity to excel in those skills that traditionally have been identified with a liberal education—the ability to think, write, and speak with clarity, taste, persuasiveness, and moral sensitivity. As Else has pointed out, language was the principal means through which these goals were attained.[14] These were the skills which freed man, "liberated" him, and made him human.

The cognitive skills thus subsumed in this sense of humanism were those that uniquely belong to man—the capacity to speak, write, reason, invent, create the beautiful, and judge it. Traditionally, they were taught by formal study of the disciplines of languages, literature, history, philosophy, and especially as exemplified in the writings of the Roman and Greek classics.

"Not many students today perceive the value of a rigorous education in the cognitive elements of traditional humanism. Some will perceive them later in life, when medicine itself becomes so routinized as to verge on boredom."

Education of this type is no longer a common denominator for professional people. Indeed, it is regarded by some as elitist and even antithetical to the major social responsibilities of physicians. It is, moreover, an education increasingly difficult to obtain by reason of today's crisis in the humanities. This crisis is the culmination of several factors: a decline in the teaching of the classical languages in which literary humanism is based; transformation of the humanities into technical specialties; and a decided shift in cultural ambience toward the nonliterary and more intuitive modes of communication and expression.

Genuine literary humanism has always been a rare accomplishment for physicians as for other men. Some medical educators and practitioners still persist in the hope that some formula can be found enabling us to produce physicians who are educated men in this sense, and this is essential if medicine is to be humanized. The cognitive elements of classical humanism are undeniably important for physicians as professionals; even more so if physicians are to transcend the confines of even so broad a discipline as medicine. It is as Berenson said of the Italian painters of the Renaissance, "Painting therefore offers but a partial and not always the most adequate manifestation of their personality, and we feel the artist as greater than his work, and the man as soaring above the artist."[15] The cognitive elements in literary humanism can enable the physician to "soar above" his profession.

Not many students today perceive the value of a rigorous education in the cognitive elements of traditional humanism. Some will perceive them later in life, when medicine itself becomes so routinized as to verge on boredom. Others, perhaps the majority, will never perceive the life-enhancing qualities of traditional humanistic study. What, then, is a realistic future for the cognitive skills and knowledge supposedly imparted by liberal studies in the education of physicians?

Humanities in Medicine: Approach for Today. —We cannot permit the possibility of contact with traditional humanism to decay completely. Too much of man's capacity for a life of satisfaction is contained within it. We owe every student at least the opportunity for contact with liberal studies at some point in his education. But today we are required to offer this opportunity in a variety of ways not limited to the premedical years.

Some students will continue to follow the pattern of a professional education built on a prior base in the liberal arts. For the majority, the most effective teaching of humanistic studies will occur within the context of medical education itself. Here, the student's motivation and goal directedness will help to focus the cognitive features of the humanities. The medical context is rich in possibilities for explicating the essential cognitive skills unique to humane and liberal studies. The pedagogic aim in the predegree years is to uncover the student's interest in these skills and, in the years of continuing education, to reinforce them in his own experiences as a person dealing with other persons in the medical transaction.

This mode of teaching the cognitive components of humanism will require special adaptations of *what* is to be taught, *how* it is taught, and *who* teaches it. At this time, a variety of approaches is being tried in a dozen or so medical institutions attempting to infuse humanistic elements into the corpus of medical education. Two recent institutes on this subject, under the auspices of the Society for Health and Human Values, summarize these current experiments.[16] While these reports indicate a wide range of approaches, some conclusions seem quite clear.

First, what is to be learned? There is no one discipline or combination of disciplines that will assure acquisition of the requisite intellectual skills. Instead, what we must seek is to inculcate that knowledge an educated man must have to distinguish him from his colleagues who are merely competent. Professor Wayne Booth succinctly summarizes these skills as learning how to think critically for ourselves, how to experience beauty for ourselves, and to make our own choices among possible actions.[17] These are the skills that make a man free—the "liberal arts." If he possesses them, he is no longer subservient to the thoughts, actions, or esthetics of those who can examine these matters critically. Neither the sciences nor the humanities can encompass these skills entirely. Each can contribute to their development. The traditional emphasis on the literary content of the humanities must be expanded to include some of what the scientist now contributes to our cultural milieu.

Second, how shall these skills be taught? To be most effective with the goal-oriented medical student, the cognitive skills should be taught within the framework of a medical education—indeed, as an integral part of that education. Medicine is admirably suited to this purpose. It abounds in experiential data about the human condition and illustrates easily the concrete importance of the cognitive skills of humanism in clinical decision-making, the lack of which, in my opinion, is one of the major defects of clinical medicine today. Medicine is also the focal point for much of our most recent and important knowledge of man and his behavior.

Teaching in such a context necessarily proceeds from the concrete, personal, and immediate to the abstract, general, and more ultimate concerns of mankind. It demands use of the case method and seminar rather than the lecture and reading assignment. It centers on personal involvement by the student with the specific concerns of his patient and thus gains a relevance scarcely equaled in other types of teaching.

These teaching modes are quite unfamiliar to the usual teacher of the humanities, and this brings us to our last question: Who shall teach? Certain special characteristics are demanded of the teacher who essays to teach the cognitive skills of humanism in the medical setting. He must be an able and secure scholar in his own discipline; he must be committed to communicating that discipline to medical students and physicians; and he must be willing to enter serious and continuing dialogue with the medical culture, while bringing his special viewpoint to bear on the phenomena of the medical experience.

Not many bona fide humanists are prepared for this sort of teaching. Hopefully, more of them will see challenges and benefits for their own studies in an intimate exchange with medicine. If current interest among medical educators grows, we will need to educate some humanists specifically for the engagement with medicine. There is some danger at present, as with any new field as yet unproven intellectually, that the field may fall to the willing and eager rather than to the most competent teachers.

Clearly, the cognitive components of traditional humanism embracing its literary elements and its intellectual attitudes are important in the education of the physician-humanist. To be effective and useful in today's university and with today's student requires a mode of teaching and a faculty with characteristics different from those that prevail in the universities' departments of humanities at present.[18, 19]

The Domain of Values. —There is another domain of cognitive knowledge that is contained in the concept of the humanist-physician, and that is the domain of values as objects of serious study in medical education. We cannot provide medical care within a humanist frame without a knowledge of the intersections in values that occur at every stage of the medical transaction. The meanings of these intersections for the patient, the physician, and society bear directly on the outcome of medical management. Medical teaching now requires the infusion of a perception of the value questions as a correlative device, much in the spirit of the humanistic strain alluded to by Edel.[12]

At every step in the medical encounter, human values are set against each other: those of the patient with those of the physician, those of society with those of the individual, and those of the physician as scientist and teacher with those of the physician as healer. Each person and each community is identified by commitment to a certain configuration of beliefs, choices, and priorities about the things believed to be important. These values have meanings quite specific for each person and each community, and these meanings must be understood by anyone who presumes to treat either the person or the community.

We now live in an era in which the ancient and long-standing image of the physician as a benign authoritarian is intolerable to most educated people. Patients have the right to make choices among alternative modes of management in keeping with the values they conceive to be most important to them. The physician must understand the basis of the patient's value choices, respect them, and work within their confines much more sensitively than ever before. In a matter so personal as health, the imposition of one person's values over another's – even of the physician's over the patient's – is a moral injustice.

Practitioners, students, and faculty members, therefore, need a formal knowledge of the meaning of values and the varieties of systems within which values are expressed. They need especially to understand the genesis of their own value systems and to recognize the gap that inevitably develops between the values of the professional and those of the society within which a profession may function.

Physicians do not reflect very often on the values peculiar to the process of professionalization through which they pass. Nor are they and their teachers sufficiently conscious of the imprint made by the prevailing mode of medical education and its traditional orientation on their own value systems. These values very soon become the prelogical foundations for the physician's behavior, for his normative ethics, and for his apodictive statements on what is good for the patient and society.

The significance of an orientation to values as objects of more serious study and experience in medical education is very much heightened by the new problems of individual and social ethics which derive from the enhanced capabilities of modern biomedical science.[20] The physician's stance with reference to abortion, euthanasia, human experimentation, genetic manipulation, behavioral control, and a variety of other urgent and dramatic new issues in medical practice is based in a set of values the foundations of which he rarely examines critically.

It is impossible to confront these and other new questions in the ethics of health care without a reconceptualization of the foundations of medical ethics. Such a restructuring of traditional normative and deontological ethics is dependent on a reconceptualization of the values on which traditional and contemporary ethics systems are based. Value questions underlie the legal, political, and social mechanisms for decision-making in the public as well as the most private matters of medical and health care.

Medical axiology is an underdeveloped – indeed, almost nonexistent – discipline at this time. It can be taught at several levels—at the fundamental level of value theory, then at the applied level of clinical decision-making, and finally at the community level of public policy-making. Integration of knowledge from a variety of disciplines is requisite if a true medical axiology is to emerge. Law, ethics, political science, philosophy, and social and cultural anthropology are intermingled in any critical inquiry into the value questions in health care.

"Medical" axiology, like "medical" philosophy, "medical" history, or "medical" sociology, demands an interdigitation of principles from the humanities and the social sciences with the concrete experiential data derived from specific clinical situations in which value questions influence the outcome for human beings seeking help. A whole new set of questions of very great human concern is emanating from the emerging dialogue between medicine and biology, on the one hand, and various of the humanities and social sciences, on the other.

These questions at the interzone between medicine and the other university disciplines have not been explored in depth. Yet, even at this early stage, they must be taught and exemplified in medical education. The content and the methods requisite to teaching at the junctions of medicine, the humanities, and the social sciences are just beginning to receive explicit attention.[16] No success-assured formula is available for wide application. The impatient student who hopes to humanize medicine overnight through some curricular thaumaturgy is sure to be disappointed.

In the immediate future, we face a tense period in our attempts to develop a more humanistic frame for medical education. On the one hand, our knowledge of human values is rudimentary and needs deepening. On the other, we face the urgency and the high expectations of all who hope for elimination of the deficiencies in our present modes of learning. Faculties in medicine and in the traditional disciplines must undergo significant attitudinal adjustments before these nascent studies can flourish. Concomitantly, they must also develop the intellectual rigor without which they cannot survive in the medical curriculum.

Nevertheless, the formal teaching of human values, at all levels of medical education, offers a sound mechanism for liberalizing and humanizing the student's technical and professional learning. The study of values may well provide a more realistic and a more widely applicable avenue for liberal education for today's medical students than the cognitive elements of traditional or literary humanism. Without deprecating the latter, it seems more likely that the study of human values will open a more attractive road toward attainment of those attitudes of mind formerly associated with the best in traditional humanistic studies.

"'Medical' axiology, like 'medical' philosophy, 'medical' history, or 'medical' sociology, demands an interdigitation of principles from the humanities and the social sciences with the concrete experiential data derived from specific clinical situations in which value questions influence the outcome for human beings seeking help."

It goes without saying that learning the cognitive domain of human values will be totally ineffectual if it is not accompanied by affective learning and by explicit example in the behavior of the faculty, especially its clinical members. In the realm of values, the humanistic strain is attainable only where the patient is in fact treated with full dignity as a man, enabled to participate democratically in decisions that affect his being, and approached with tolerance for his fallibility and that of his physician.

The Ideal Resynthesized

For the purposes of clarification of the goals of his education, we have intentionally disassembled the ideal of the humanist-physician. This disassembly enables us to understand the full spectrum of meanings within the ideal and to denote educational goals specifically designed to explicate each of the integral components of humanism. By so doing, we can avoid diffusing our educational goals over a vague territory more emotionally than rationally defined. More important, our dissection may perhaps permit a resynthesis of the ideal in terms more consistent with the motivations of today's students and the contemporary responsibilities of the profession.

The ideal humanist-physician would fuse all elements – the affective and the cognitive domains we have described – the whole built on a base of technical competence. Professional education, then, has as its goal the making of a competent clinical craftsman; affective learning has the goal of making a humane and compassionate practitioner; and the cognitive elements of humanism, modified in the two ways I have suggested, should make for an educated practitioner. These three levels in the life of the physician should interpenetrate and reinforce each other. Very few persons will ever experience excellence in all dimensions, but recognition of the full expression of the ideal establishes a benchmark against which the degree of an individual's humanistic education can be assessed.

Medicine enjoys a special position among the disciplines. It centers on man in all his dimensions and shares some part of his reality with the humanities, the social sciences, and the experimental sciences. Pursued to its fullest expression, medicine can be truly humanizing, for its object of study and concern is man.

John Ciardi's recent exposition of the concept of esthetic wisdom is apposite: "the sum total of all the great artist becomes in his life's exposure to his medium. The artist's environment," he adds, "is not the world but the world as his medium reveals it."[21]

I submit that medicine, like the arts, also provides a kind of human experience that makes it a special medium for revealing the world. It, too, can yield an esthetic wisdom of its own special object, man. Medicine taught in a humanistic frame prepares the student for its humane practice. Practice in a humanistic frame reveals even more about the microcosm, as Caraka perceived in the quotation that opened this essay.

References

1. *The Caraka Samhita.* S. Gulabkunverba (trans), Jamnagar, India, Ayurvedic Society, 1949, vol 1, p 469.
2. Aulus Gellius, cited by Crane RS: *The Idea of the Humanities and Other Essays Critical and Historical.* Chicago, University of Chicago Press, 1968, p 23.
3. Pellegrino ED: The non-Renaissance man. *Pharos of Alpha Omega Alpha* 32 (No.1):16-17, 1969.
4. Jung C: *Psychological Reflections.* J. Jacobi (ed), Princeton, NJ, Bollingen Series XXI, 1970, p 84.
5. Merton T: *New Seeds of Contemplation.* New York, New Directions, 1961, p 38.
6. Hesse H: *Demian.* New York, Bantam Books Inc, 1970, prologue.
7. Jung C: Psychological Reflections. (op. cit.) (Ref. 4), p 90.
8. Hammarskjöld D: *Markings.* New York, Alfred A. Knopf Inc, 1965, p 105.
9. Rogers C: Bringing together ideas and feeling in learning. *Learning Today* 5 (No.2):32-43, 1972.
10. Entralgo PL: *La Relacion Medico-Enfermo Historia y Teoria.* Madrid, Revista de Occidente, 1964.
11. Kristeller PO: *Renaissance Thought: The Classic and Scholastic and Humanist Strains.* New York, Harper Torchbooks 1961, pp 8-23.
12. Edel A: Where is the crisis in humanism? *Rev Int Philosophie,* fasc 3-4, 1968, pp 284-295.
13. Murray G, quoted by Cushing H: Introduction to Sir William Osler: *The Old Humanities and the New Science.* Boston, Houghton Mifflin Co, 1920, p x.
14. Else G: The old and the new humanities. *Daedalus* 98:803-804, 1969.
15. Berenson B: *Italian Painters of the Renaissance: Florentine and Central Italian Schools.* New York, Phaidon, 1968, vol 2, p 1.
16. *Proceedings of the Institute on Human Values in Medicine.* Philadelphia, Society for Health and Human Values, 1972, vol 2, p 83.
17. Booth W: Is there any knowledge that a man must have? in WC Booth (ed): *The Knowledge Most Worth Having.* Chicago, University of Chicago Press, 1967, pp i-28.
18. Pellegrino ED: The most humane science: Some notes on liberal education in medicine and the university, the sixth Sanger lecture. *Bull Med Col Va* 2:11-39, 1970.
19. Pellegrino ED: Reflections, refractions, and prospectives, in *Proceedings of the Institute on Human Values in Medicine.* Philadelphia, Society for Health and Human Values, 1972, vol 1, pp 99-115.
20. Pellegrino ED: Physicians, patients, and society: Some new tensions in medical ethics, in Mendelsohn E, Swazey JP, Taviss I (eds): *Human Aspects of Biomedical Innovation.* Cambridge, Mass, Harvard University Press, 1971, pp 77-97, 219-220.
21. Ciardi J: Esthetic wisdom. *Saturday Review,* April 8, 1972, p 22.

11

Suzanne Poirier, "Teaching in Literature and Medicine: An Overview and Commentary," in Delese Wear, Martin Kohn, Susan Stocker, eds., *Literature and Medicine: A Claim for a Discipline* (McLean, VA: Society for Health and Human Values, 1987), 43-50.

Editor's note: As with other more recently published articles in this volume, I asked authors if they would be willing to reflect on their piece and add introductory comments that would help frame it, or enable them to address issues raised since its original publication. The following remarks are from the author Suzanne Poirier.

When I wrote "Teaching in Literature and Medicine," not only was the field of literature and medicine still relatively new in academic terms, but so was I. In fact, I was probably preparing my promotion and tenure about the same time, so I was particularly interested in making a case for literature and medicine. That said, as I reread this article, I'm surprised that much of it remains relevant a quarter-century later.

However amateur the methodology of my survey, I drew from its contents two, as I then called them, tensions, one within literature and medicine, and the other more generally within academic literature. The latter had to do with the challenges to the definition of literature itself, the hegemony of "the canon," and the rise of a raft of new theoretical tools for plumbing literature and other cultural documents. This broadening movement in traditional humanities departments proved synchronous with literature-and-medicine teachers' realization that new theories, texts, and contexts were needed for their work. Missing from my awareness then, was narrative, a concept that was to be embraced early and enthusiastically by many people in literature and medicine—and a concept, again, that has likewise transformed many traditional humanities fields.

The conversation (more accurate today than tension) about the goals and methods that should characterize our work, still exists today, but, its participants are more assured than defensive. In the past thirty years, the courses, conferences, journals, and degree programs have proliferated, and with the growth of our field has come a body of discourse and a breadth of scholarship—and scholars!—that has fostered both rigor and creativity. Faculty in literature and medicine are no longer tentative about the critical, intellectual, and expressive tools that literature brings to the study of the work of medicine and its practitioners. I am delighted to have been a part of that adventure.

Teaching in Literature and Medicine –
An Overview and Commentary

Suzanne Poirier

"Back to the basics" and "general education" are phrases frequently heard in current discussions of higher education. Expressing a belief in the need to develop intellectual rigor in students through the establishment of a firm training in the humanities is a goal that few humanists would criticize. Going on, however, to suggest that such a goal can be achieved primarily by returning our attention to traditional curricula and texts seems to assume that studying current concerns or specialized issues cannot foster clear, disciplined thinking. If the goal is to educate creatively sound thinkers, then *how* one teaches should be of equal importance to *what* one teaches. The challenge to higher education today might be more accurately described as a need to create a contemporary curriculum which is based upon recognized standards of intellectual excellence.

Literature has always been in a unique position to develop and proclaim the relationship between academe and modern society. Its existence as both a popular medium and an intellectual discipline make of literature a dynamic, eclectic field. Literature has always been political. Writing about Virginia Woolf, Louise DeSalvo says, "Literature teaches us ... about the way we are supposed to behave and about the consequences of certain types of behavior. Woolf reminds us of how profoundly influential literary texts can be in the formation of character and in the formation of a nation's character."[1]

"Literature and medicine"* addresses both apolitical and theoretical nature of literature as well as the broader issues of current educational debate. A survey of the kinds of literature courses being taught to practicing or future health professionals reveals the challenging relationship between the perceived need of a diverse student body for a worthwhile education and the intellectual

---

* I do not limit the term "literature and medicine" to teaching only about medicine, but refer to courses for all health professionals.

requirements for an academic teaching discipline to remain substantial and vital. Most of the information in the following discussion is based on a document entitled "Teaching and Research in Literature and Health Care," a collection of course descriptions reported voluntarily and compiled for a session of the 1984 national meeting of the Society for Health and Human Values. Not all courses have been reported, though the 37 reports represent probably 85% of the courses of this nature taught in health sciences centers. (A few undergraduate courses were reported but are not a clear representation of the number and nature of such courses.) The original questionnaire did not ask all the questions to which this paper is seeking answers, but the information provided leads to some conclusions and raises questions that have perhaps not always been drawn or asked in the enthusiastic and often spontaneous growth of this field.

Sounding throughout the reports is a tension between tradition and innovation at all stages of course design, instruction, and evaluation. Most of the questions deal, at root, with the purpose not only of the course but of literature itself. In this sense, a study of the evolution of teaching in literature and medicine may present not a unique dilemma but rather a debate in microcosm of the role of literature in higher education in general.

One general theme ties together all of the teaching in literature and medicine: "to complement ... scientific and clinical study" (Joanne Banks).[2] Professors of literature and medicine almost unanimously express reservations about the highly technological, information-oriented curricula of the health professions. In presenting the objectives of their courses, instructors refer repeatedly to the needs to see illness and health from perspectives other than the scientific one, to introduce questions of ethics and values, to consider historical and cultural context of medical care, and to present the human dimensions of the healer. Such objectives lend themselves most readily to thematically organized courses which consider what it means to be a physician in terms of the physician's humanity, the dynamics of the physician-patient relationship, and the dynamics of the physician-illness relationship. These themes continue to underlie other courses about death, metaphors of illness or illness as a metaphor, developmental issues, ethics, the body, and women (listed in descending order of frequency taught).

The emphasis on the physician is understandable, perhaps, but also limiting. Phil Davis from Southern Illinois University states: "I have limited the *content* of the course to literature which directly addresses the role of the physician in health care. While I gain in the immediacy of relevance, I lose in limiting the potential exposure that students could have." At a time when we are generally complimenting ourselves for widening our students' horizons, the absence in many of our courses of a broader consideration of the "health care team" (although the subject may arise in the course of the class discussions) may be a notable omission. That most of our teaching is geared only to medical students may be partly to blame. Four of the reported courses are designed for students in nursing and pharmacy, but how they present these professions within the broader context of health care is clearly defined as a component of only one course ("Humanities for Nurses: The Professional's Perspective" by Alvin Seltzer at Pennsylvania State University).

A look at topics selected further reveals a predominantly medical orientation toward health care, an orientation which emphasizes disease and medical intervention. In sharp contrast are the few courses which study literature about patients and families at various stages in their life cycles, an approach used almost exclusively in the courses taught to nursing students or in departments of family practice. Although courses in literature and medicine in general brought in students' awarenesses of their personal and professional limitations, perhaps we could go even further in challenging the traditional orientation of medical practice and philosophy itself.

One underrepresented area in the course offerings is ethnic or multicultural concerns, with reports on only two courses: "Cross-cultural Images of Pain" (Northeastern Ohio Universities College of Medicine) and "Afro-American Literary Perspectives on Health, Illness, Aging, Death, and Dying" (Howard University College of Medicine). Non-white writers are also underrepresented in the syllabi of most of the courses. Women writers and women's health issues, on the other hand, appear in relatively large numbers on reading lists, perhaps because of an awareness fostered by the women's health movement which has led us to define "women's health" and sources of women's disease more broadly. Approaching the writings of other minority groups with the same alertness to social and cultural influences on physical and mental health could contribute a much broader bibliography than is currently being taught. (A proposed anthology from Howard University may help correct this deficiency.)

Central to nearly everyone's planning a new course in literature and medicine is the bibliography, *Literature and Medicine*, edited by Banks and Pollard, now in a second, revised edition from the University of Pittsburg Press (1982). Nevertheless, each course presents a variety of unique titles and authors, which attests to the pervasiveness of health issues in practically all literature and the diversity of interests and backgrounds of the instructors. Instructors frequently bemoan the paucity of anthologies for their use, but a perusal of their reading lists suggests that each instructor would create a distinctively different reader. A few writers are mentioned with greater frequency than others. They include, in alphabetical order: Albert Camus, Anton Chokhov, Norman Cousins, Charlotte Perkins Gilman, Ernest Hemingway, Henrik Ibsen, Franz Kafka, Sinclair Lewis, Thomas Mann, Flannery O'Connor, Katherine Anne Porter, Richard Selzer, Anne Sexton, George Bernard Shaw, Susan Sontag, and William Carlos Williams.

Of special note in these courses is their eclectic reading lists, striking even for a thematically organized course. Course titles and syllabi seldom focus on one period or genre as are traditionally taught in English departments. Of the few genre courses reported, drama, autobiography, and the novel occur most frequently (and in the order named). The thematic organization of the courses and the diverse syllabi generated reflect several challenges to the definition of literature as well as to traditional methods of teaching.

The first challenge concerns the definition of *literature* itself. The debate often appears in such questions as, "Do we have an obligation to introduce students to 'the best that is thought and said,' or do we teach, for example, *The House of God?*" The increasing presence of film, autobiography, and popular fiction in these courses and growing references to case histories or pathographies suggest at least a consciousness of *literature* in a broader sense then it is approached in traditional English departments. This situation is not a new one: English department courses in "popular culture" address these issues also. In this sense, courses in literature and medicine are not unique in their concerns about their syllabi, but they are in a particularly appropriate position to study and contribute to the debate.

Questions raised about the purposes and evaluation of literature should at least be clearly thought through in the instructor's own mind as reading lists for courses in literature and medicine are being designed.

Another challenge, this one unique to teachers of literature and medicine, is to understand the consequences of the setting of their teaching. Although over half of the courses reported are taught pre-clinically or even (in only a few cases here) on an undergraduate level, a growing number of them take place during the clinical years, and a few courses are open to or even directed exclusively toward residents and faculty. Some humanities electives at the Northeastern Ohio Universities College of Medicine, for example, can be taken simultaneously by undergraduate students to fulfill a humanities requirement and by practicing physicians for continuing education credit.

Thoughtfully designing a course to complement a student's professional knowledge and experience can create of the same syllabus completely different courses, depending on when in a student's education the course is taught. Teaching different levels of health professionals simultaneously requires special kinds of planning to include and stimulate all students. Variables and potential problems also exist more when students represent different professions. Laurel Brodsley (UCLA) reports that while her audience of English, pre-law, and pre-med majors in "Images of Health Care in Contemporary Literature" "enjoyed the diverse point of view and developed a personal sense of the underlying 'gestalt' of the humanities/consumer/physician/scientist through seminar debates [s]ome of the 'pure' material (e.g. descriptions of coronary artery surgery or Frye on myth) lost some of them, so they found it challenging." The need to choose a teaching style and goals commensurate with the needs and abilities of the students exists as much in the teaching of freshman composition as it does in literature and medicine, but the untraditional nature and setting of the latter courses bring these concerns into high relief.

Nearly all the courses are taught in a seminar fashion. The role of the instructor, however, varies widely. Linda Garcia Shelton reports a literature seminar at the University of Texas Medical Branch in which "leaders serve mostly as conveners, not instructors, although the literature professor was particularly helpful with the most structurally complex work." Sometimes literature comprises only one component of a broader course, such as "Illness and Meaning" at University of Rochester School of Medicine and Dentistry. The disparity of professional interests within the summer teaching teams as well as between literature professor and health sciences student is reported as both advantageous and disadvantageous. While Peter Reinke (Medical College of Pennsylvania) reports that the "differences between the instructor's 'humanities' (literature) background and the class's 'scientific' background prove to be stimulating rather than problematical," David Smith (Temple University School of Medicine) observes that humanities faculty occasionally exhibit "an inadequate sensitivity to the clinical milieu and a perception by students that non- physicians have little to offer." In team-taught courses, Lou Borgenicht (University of Utah) reports on and undergraduate team-taught course, "The Language of Healing," which "stimulates new thoughts on the part of the faculty, new connections." Albert Keller (Medical University of South Carolina) writes of a clinically-based course, "Death in Human Experience," which combines literature seminars with a family medicine preceptorship in a way that the "degree of integration achieved in discussion between academic reading and clinical experience has invariably proved fulfilling of our expectations."

Not reported in this survey are the countless special programs, guest speakers, and workshops in which literature is featured. Although special programs are also part of all English departments, they do not always occur with such frequency, are not usually a regular part of one instructor's job description, and are not usually aimed at campus-wide audiences. In these ways, faculty who teach literature and medicine are learning to define "teaching" (or, perhaps, "learning") in a much broader sense. How to teach the qualities we value in literature to a diverse, busy, often skeptical audience may call for methods unfamiliar to our own experience as students as well as teachers.

"How to teach the qualities we value in literature to a diverse, busy, often skeptical audience may call for methods unfamiliar to our own experience as students as well as teachers."

All of these variations on traditional teaching settings, constituencies, and formats emphasize the value of creating appropriate goals for literature and medicine courses. As already mentioned, the most frequently cited objectives for courses in literature and medicine deal with course content and design. Less clearly spelled out are the goals of these courses as they relate to the teaching of literature itself. Although these more pedagogical goals may have been considered when designing the courses, the lack in printed reports of clearly stated goals for the use of literature raises several questions.

Stated more generally, Why teach literature? That it presents ethical situations more concretely than do philosophical hypotheticals is an answer that addresses the *content* of literature. Literature in this sense can be used to *illustrate* ideas. This argument is presented by Joanne Trautmann Banks in her article "The Wonders of Literature in Medical Education."[3] She then goes on to talk about the ability of literature to *illuminate* a subject, to present the details of a situation in all their "subtle and ambiguous and rich relation" to each other. Ambiguity, the touchstone of nearly all literature, pervades the practice of medicine. A practitioner must develop an awareness and tolerance of ambiguity. Thus, "to teach a student to read in the fullest sense," Banks concludes, "is to help train him or her medically."

Such statements address the *craft* of writing as much as the content. The "illustrative" and "illuminative" dimensions of literature require two quite different teaching approaches. The approaches *can* overlap, especially if you choose to read *The Magic Mountain* rather than *Moby Dick*, but time still needs to be spent teaching a more technical vocabulary and understanding of literature—and then making clear the connection of those skills to the skills of a health professional. To what extent or how successfully we have been able to teach the "illuminative" qualities of literature has not been clearly reported, but the comments on strengths and weaknesses of the courses may begin to give us some answers.

One reported problem with courses in literature and medicine lies in the nature of the reading assignments. Many instructors expressed disappointment or discomfort with the amount of reading students can (or will) do for their courses. "Lack of time" and "a lot of reading for very busy practitioners" are representative of the comments offered. Some solutions are proposed. Paul Royce, a physician from the University of Minnesota-Duluth School of Medicine, conducts a seminar in "Medicine Viewed by Poet and Physician" for which no outside reading is required. Doris Vidaver and Maynard Cohen, a humanist-physician team from Rush University, solve the problem of conflicting demands by urging students "to attend class even if heavy demands in their technical studies prevent them from completing their reading assignment. This faculty preference, announced at the first class meeting, has resulted in excellent attendance and the eventual covering of the material."

This statement is particularly interesting, as Vidaver and Cohen have stated at other times their commitment to teaching only literature of a recognized high-quality. Although attending class discussions and eventually "covering ... the material" can give the students exposure to what is of value in the nature of writing itself, such a stance serves more to keep students up-to-date on the ideas being presented by the literature. This is not to say that such an approach necessarily favors "illustration" over "illumination," but it does underscore the problems created by the press of time when there are two quite different teaching goals to be met. The tendency on the part of many instructors to use short stories or poems is probably as much an unspoken reflection of a hope to gain time in the classroom to discuss both style and content as it is to assure that students will read the assignments. Courses designed to explore metaphor or only one genre also lend themselves more easily to a consideration of the craft of writing.[4]

While it is not always clear how much of teaching in literature and medicine directly addresses analytical reading skills, it is significant to note that instructors seldom report this accomplishment as part of their students' appreciation of the courses. The most frequently mentioned value of literature courses to students is their uniqueness. Phrases such as "change of pace," "stand-back time," and "different points of perspective" echo throughout the reports. These values concur with the findings of Martin Kohn in his study of students' responses to the humanities courses at Northeastern Ohio Universities College of Medicine.[5] Although such results have merit, they refer more clearly to the content of the course rather than to lessons uniquely literary.

This is not to say that learning critical reading skills can't occur even if the subject isn't directly discussed. What is needed, however, is a careful self-examination of the goals of courses in literature and medicine, an honest appraisal of exactly what we intend to achieve in each course and a deliberate effort to realize those goals. As professors of an intellectual discipline, we need to ask whether we are fully presenting that discipline to students or primarily applying its content to situations of interest to them. And, if we really are primarily doing the latter, is that enough? Is that "literature"?

Two correlative observations emerge here. First, a review of the reported courses reveals only one course which takes a specifically theoretical approach to literature: Claire Kahane's "Literature and Psychoanalysis," an English graduate seminar at SUNY-Buffalo. Most of the courses reported teach literary analysis on a rather loosely-defined base of "New Criticism," though frequent references to real-life parallels of the readings often modify a purely textual analysis. Current literary theory may inform some instructors' teaching, but that theory itself is seldom a part of the instruction. In this sense, courses in literature and medicine probably most clearly resemble undergraduate, non-major English education, although the sophistication of the students' analyses will probably surpass those of most college sophomores or juniors. Questions of intellectual and pedagogical theory arise that are not encountered by either literature or medical professors in traditional academic departments.

Second, if methods of literary analysis are being taught in some sort of deliberate way, we must then ask who can/should teach such courses. The subject is a sensitive one; some physicians can undoubtedly teach skills in literary analysis as well as do many Ph.D.'s in literature. Simply stated in terms of teaching goals: if a person not formally trained in literature can teach and articulate an understanding of these skills of literary analysis, then a course in *literature* and medicine is being taught. If any instructor cannot or chooses not to do this, then the course is a topical course in which literature illustrates the topic, and the goals and description of the course should be accurately represented.

A review of the teaching currently being done in literature and medicine reveals two processes in flux. The definition of literature itself is being broadened to include genres not traditionally a part of English courses. Perhaps our uncertainty with how to treat these forms as "literature" influences the second area of instability—the balance between content and craft in defining the use of literature in these courses. In these issues, the tensions inherent in designing and teaching courses in literature and medicine are no different from the tensions present in liberal arts institutions today, which express concern over a proliferation of "specialized" (read "nontraditional") courses lacking the "intellectual rigor" of days gone by. Most courses of literature and medicine, while vulnerable to the same attacks against topicality, have one major advantage–they cannot be made to "go back" into a traditional department or curriculum because none exist. By this same token, however, literature and medicine is susceptible to becoming an anachronism while still in its infancy if it allows itself to lose its identity as a "literature" course in the fullest intellectual sense of that term.

Perhaps we will want to make that sacrifice. The greater challenge, I believe, is one which gives us, both health and literature professionals, in our continued efforts to define literature and medicine intellectually and pedagogically, the opportunity to redefine the definitions and methodologies of teaching literature in general. As we explore ways to teach the qualities inherent in literature that made it a vital discipline, we will make the value of those qualities recognizable to students of literature in whatever setting. In fashioning a workable union between tradition and current relevance, we may discover ways in which to make the "basics" something which can be brought into the present rather than gone "back" to.

References

1   Louise DeSalvo, "A Portrait of the Puttana as a Middle-aged Woolf Scholar," *Between Women: Biographers, Novelists, Critics, Teachers, and Artists Write about Their Work on Women*, ed. Carol Ascher, Louise DeSalvo, Sara Ruddick (Boston: Beacon Press, 1984), 52. (inclusive pages of essay 35-53)

2   Reference to comments or information from the report for the Society for Health and Human Values meeting will not be cited but will be informally credited within the text.

3   Joanne Trautmann (Banks), "The Wonders of Literature in Medical Education," *Mobius* 2 (July 1982). Subsequent quotations are from pp. 25 and 26.

4   I thank Joanne Banks for the conversation that led us to this observation.

5   Martin Kohn, *An Ethnographic Account of an Intensive Humanities Learning Experience for Medical Students*. Doctoral Dissertation. The University of Akron, 1984.

12

Lester D. Friedman, "See Me, Hear Me: Using Film in Health-Care Classes,"
The Journal of Medical Humanities 16:4 (1995), 223-228.

Editor's note: As with other more recently published articles in this volume, I asked authors if they would be willing to reflect on their piece and add introductory comments that would help frame it, or enable them to address issues raised since its original publication. The following remarks are from the author Lester Friedman.

I first started teaching within a Medical Humanities Program (initially labeled a "General Studies Program") that originated in the College of Health Professions and the College of Nursing at SUNY Upstate Medical Center (Syracuse), a program that eventually migrated to the College of Medicine and became part of the Center for Bioethics and Humanities. I was fresh out of my graduate school English program (emphasis on British Romantic Literature) and found the medical environment a confusing mélange of foreign terms, macabre discussions, disdainful colleagues, and troubling encounters. Frankly, I hated it. I grandly pictured myself among the cadre of cultural warriors who stoutheartedly defend the barricades against the invading hordes of barbarians, and these white-coated figures nicely filled that role in my self-aggrandizing scenario. After about a year of feeling emotionally battered and intellectually bruised, however, I started to listen, really listen carefully, to the myriad conversations swirling around me. Much to my amazement, I came to understand that the medical culture I initially found so oppressive was actually, undeniably, dominated by something I loved and had been studying for years: a broad spectrum of narratives. I wish I could declare that this insight struck me like the proverbial lightning bolt, but in truth it occurred in dribs and drabs, until the accretion of stories finally led me to the now commonly accepted role of narrative. It was a pretty short leap from this realization to seeing how my literary background could allow me to carve out a significant space within this world of bravado and broken bodies.

At the same time as I was struggling to adjust to the medical world, I was simultaneously teaching cinema studies within the College of Visual and Performing Arts at Syracuse University. My screening room, located just across the street from my classroom in the Medical School, seemed light years away from anything to do with health care. It was far more familiar terrain, a landscape of classes permeated with the traditional values of a liberal arts education, despite its embrace of emerging technologies. Unlike the connections I now saw between medicine and literature, I could not build a bridge that would link my world of visual pleasures to my world of cadavers and operating rooms. What did Peckinpah have to do with Pediatrics, Ford with Family Practice, or Spielberg with Surgery? The answer, of course, was an offshoot of what I was already doing with literature within the health care curriculum: putting a human face on abstract issues, encouraging a deeper and broader understanding of medical culture, and exploring complex ethical dilemmas within the structure of dramatic narratives. Fortunately, I had colleagues across the country who also recognized the power of the visual image and encouraged me to write about how to incorporate it effectively into the training of health care professionals.

This article was my first foray into finding a balanced interplay between my two worlds. I was not a film teacher dabbling in medicine or a medical humanist without training in cinema studies and firmly believed that skills garnered from one realm could engage (and perhaps even enlighten) students in the other. That said, I knew that I could not teach film at Upstate the same way that I taught it at the University. But, then, I never taught literature to medical students in the same manner as I taught English majors because the classroom goals in each setting were decidedly different. For me, the medical and the film cultures can enhance and harmonize with each other, like different sections compliment each other within a symphony orchestra. The essay, fueled by the excitement of discovery, was meant to be shared with my colleagues and to offer practical strategies for using documentary and fiction films in the medical humanities classroom. Rereading it some 20 years after it was first published, the examples seem dated, but the basic philosophy of using visual texts within the medical humanities classroom seems even more relevant, given the flood of new technologies that have and will continue to dramatically alter the topography of health care education and delivery. I am honored that the editors of *Humanitas: Readings in the Development of Medical Humanities* have chosen to include this essay within this volume. It represents an important period of my own development as a teacher and a scholar; hopefully, it will also prove to be of value to new generations of students and teachers who choose to enter the world of the health care humanities.

See Me, Hear Me: Using Film in Health-Care Classes

Lester D. Friedman, Ph.D.

Abstract. This essay argues that film deserves a place within the medical humanities curriculum and demonstrates effective strategies for employing it within medical ethics and humanities classrooms. Part One of the article emphasizes how and why medical ethics teachers can utilize documentary and fictional films, such as *Thomas Szasz and the Myth of Mental Illness*, *The Deadly Deception*, *Whose Life Is It Anyway?* and *Voices From the Front* in their courses. Such films encourage students to move beyond abstract debates and confront the human pain inherent in all ethical dilemmas. Part Two focuses on documentary and fiction film in the medical humanities classroom. In this section, the author details how to incorporate films, such as *The Doctor*, *The Waterdance* and *Hospital*, into the humanities classroom, juxtaposing them with various literary works, such as *Other Women's Children*, *Borrowed Time*, and *Ceremony*. Part Three of the essay presents a detailed discussion of *The Elephant Man* and *Frankenstein*, illustrating how visual and literary texts compliment each other within the humanities classroom. Overall, the author demonstrates how films function as engaging and complex visual texts providing unique insights in the particularities of American health care and, as such, can become valuable components within medical ethics and humanities classrooms.

Part One: Non-Fiction and Fiction Films in the Ethics Classroom

As a professor of English/Humanities at the SUNY, Health Science Center (Syracuse, New York), I teach a variety of classes that either incorporate or highlight the relationships between the arts (particularly literature and film) and medicine. Some of my courses, such as health-care ethics, include movies which illustrate dramatic moral dilemmas faced by doctors, nurses, and allied health professionals. Many of these are various types of documentaries. For example, *Dax's Story*, the portrait of a man who would rather die than face a long and painful recovery from severe burns, functions as one approach to explore passive and active euthanasia; such a direct encounter with individualized suffering forces students to see, and ultimately to feel, beyond the abstract debates that swirl around the right to die controversy. Other non-fiction films used at various times in this class include: *Code Gray* (about nursing ethics); *Voices From the Front* (about AIDS activists); *Thomas Szasz and the Myth of Mental Illness* (about the medicalization of moral issues); *The Deadly Deception* (about the Tuskegee Experiment). All function in a similar manner: they force students to confront the human pain inherent in all ethical dilemmas.

Though the bulk of this essay centers primarily upon fiction films in a humanities rather than an ethics classroom, I feel compelled to comment upon the inherent advantages and disadvantages of using documentaries to explore moral issues. Teachers often include such works to hook the imaginations and stir the emotions of their students; that done, they quickly move on to the specifics of an ethical dilemma. Their ultimate focus remains firmly on the ethics and not the art work. In such settings, the most effective films present elements beyond textbook or lecture possibilities in an engaging visual manner. For example, *The Deadly Deception* mixes historical perspectives with vivid depictions of the Tuskegee Experiment, including actual statements by government officials, images and music of rural Alabama, newsreels from that time period, interviews with the participants (both subjects and physicians), and contextual comments by ethics and history experts. Similarly, *Thomas Szasz and the Myth of Mental Illness* first traces the biography and then examines the philosophy of this controversial psychiatrist, integrating this information with comments/questions by experts, a dramatized case history and a debate with one of Szasz's staunchest opponents. No teacher could possibly duplicate the time, effort, money, technical expertise, historical research, and dramatic flair that characterize these types of documentaries.

While the advantages of employing documentaries appears obvious, some problems do inevitably arise. Teachers who utilize so-called "talking heads," those productions that consist mainly of an expert basically lecturing into the camera or even a panel of scholars energetically arguing about some issue, rarely add anything dynamic to the health-care ethics classroom, no matter what the topic under discussion. At most, such films function as a "teacher's manual" of sorts, one that imparts valuable information instructors can incorporate into their own lectures. My general rule remains that if I can adequately summarize the major points in the documentary, and if the material fails to engage the viewer visually, then I need to find another film, one using filmic elements not easily duplicated in the classroom. Good documentaries, therefore, can add a valuable and unique dimension to ethics classes; they impart a bristling feel of bedside reality that often remains frozen beneath esoteric tracts of abstract disputations. To do so, however, such documentaries must move far beyond the realm of taped lecture.

A second, more philosophical problem when using non-fiction films is how (or even if) to confront the issue of documentary "truth" in the medical ethics classroom. On some intellectual level, students usually recognize that fiction films are artistic constructs, the best ones skillfully luring us into a "willing suspension of disbelief." Even such sophisticated viewers, however, seldom apply the same critical perspective to documentaries, naively assuming that a filmmaker's camera accurately and artlessly captured the unfolding events. The very name "non-fiction" confers an aura of authenticity upon the images presented, so most viewers rarely question the reliability of a documentary. Yet, Italian director Federico Fellini's remark accurately characterizes documentaries as well as feature films: "people think of cinema as a camera loaded with film and a reality out there all ready to be photographed. Instead, one inserts himself between the object and the camera" (Friedman 30). Put another way, every artistic decision made by a documentary filmmaker is, simultaneously, a value judgment meant to make us see events through his/her eyes. So, the documentarist's choice of a particular shot, a specific angle or some special lighting all coalesce – along with various camera movements, editing techniques, sound effects, and structural principles – to make the non-fiction film as purposefully manufactured, as carefully assembled, as the more obviously simulated Hollywood production.

"How much technical film knowledge must students possess to analyze cinema productions as unique art forms and not simply transcriptions of literary conventions?"

Though most ethics professors have neither the time nor the knowledge necessary to analyze non-fiction films extensively from a technical perspective, it remains important for them to reveal the truth embedded in documentarist John Grierson famous definition of his craft: "documentary filmmaking is the creative treatment of actuality." First, of course, such disclosures contribute to the student's cineliteracy, his/her ability to interpret visual information from a more sophisticated point of view. This deeper understanding of how filmmakers manipulate seemingly neutral materials make students more wary of unacknowledged bias in the guise of dispassionate impartiality: paid commercials camouflaging themselves as informational programs, philosophical preconceptions masquerading as universal truths, evening news shows feigning objectivity, O.J. Simpson's picture four shades darker on *Time*'s cover than on *Newsweek*'s. More importantly, the unmasking of a documentary's subjective nature further accentuates the multiple value judgments characterizing all ethical dilemmas. Good documentaries force students to probe beyond verbal statements for crucial beliefs, often communicated visually (as they are in life). Film scholar Bill Nichols aptly sums up the partisan component of documentaries when he argues that we should not view them as "a special use of the film medium that affords a 'privileged' view of reality but as a genre ... The comfortably accepted realism of one generation seems like artifice to the next. New strategies must constantly be fabricated to re-present 'things as they are' and still others to contest this very representation" (Nichols 259).

In addition to these documentaries, I sometimes use fiction films to explore ethical problems. A film like *Whose Life Is It Anyway?*, about a quadriplegic who uses legal measures to battle a physician who will not allow him to die, dramatically raises questions about the rationality of suicide, as does *'night, Mother*, where an unhappy daughter tells her distraught mother that she plans to kill herself that evening. *Promises in the Dark* examines the ethical principle of fidelity, as a doctor must choose between her promise to a young cancer patient and the wishes of the girl's parents, as well as the controversy over physician assisted suicide. *Coma* raises concerns about the allocation of scare resources and the morality of paying for and selling organs for transplantation. In essence, these films function as extended case histories that encourage students to see various sides of an ethical dilemma. They contribute to classroom activities by providing an accessible point of reference that personalizes the often arcane philosophical commentaries that characterize health-care ethics debates. By introducing such provocative narrative experiences into the educational setting, the ethics teacher stimulates students to integrate abstract principles with concrete situations, a methodology which encourages students to combine theory and practice into an organic whole.

Part Two: Non-Fiction and Fiction Films in the Humanities Classroom

While these fiction films play an important role in my ethics classes, they, like the documentaries, function mainly to motivate students to examine their feelings about a particular issue. The artistry of such works – the narrative, visual, aural and dramatic elements that coalesce to make them such effective pedagogical tools – rarely enters our discussions, since the films remain a pathway to moral dilemmas rather than the focus of critical analysis: the medium is certainly not the message. Conversely, in my "Medicine in Literature and Film" course, a more traditional humanities offering, I juxtapose films to literary works and explore a series of interactions within the health-care environment. My class during the Spring 1993 semester, for example, consisted of the following units: "The Responsibility of Medical Research" (*Frankenstein* and *The Elephant Man*); "The Physician as Writer" (*Other Women's Children, The Doctor, The House of God, Hospital*); "The Experience of AIDS" (*Inventing AIDS, Voices from the Front, Borrowed Time, The Destiny of Me, Longtime Companion*), "The Patient's Perspective of Illness" (*The Alchemy of Illness, The Waterdance, Ceremony*). But before delving into why I teach certain books in conjunction with particular films, I want to discuss some preliminary concerns about fashioning a course that includes both visual and verbal texts.

To design a medical humanities class that includes film, particularly in conjunction with literature (fiction and non-fiction), teachers first need to delineate the broad, general characteristics that distinguish cinema productions from literary works. "All these differences," observes George Bluestone in his classic text on the subject, *Novels Into Film,* "derive from the contrast between the novel as a conceptual and discursive form, the film as a perceptual and presentational form" (Bluestone ix). Put as another and even more general oversimplification, good literary works seem better suited to probe internal realities while films appear more adept at depicting external situations. Such sweeping statements spring from the diverse language systems employed by writers of literature and makers of film; the essential methods by which each communicates to a spectator/reader are fundamentally different: one is primarily verbal, with its highly connotative component, and the other visual, with its direct presentation of sensory images. Yet, approaching a film as simply pictorial prose, and analyzing it only via the elements common to literature (narrative structure, theme, characterization, point of view, setting, etc.), remains the most common mistake committed by teachers trained in literature who use film in their classrooms. Though common elements certainly exist, a basic grasp of film's visual language remains a crucial component for analyzing its meaning. Here, unlike in the ethics class previously described, Marshall McLuhan's dictum proves vital, "the medium is the message."

My fundamental belief that how a director tells a story visually is part of the story itself creates the most perplexing pedagogical question I face in creating a "Medicine in Literature and Film" syllabus: how much technical film knowledge must students possess to analyze cinema productions as unique art forms and not simply transcriptions of literary conventions? During the early years of my class, I simply ignored this question. I arrogantly assumed that health-care students, because of their scientific bent of mind and educational priorities, were ill-equipped and essentially uninterested in learning about camera angles, compositional patterns, editing techniques, sound effects, and narrative structures. Yet, I brooded over my failure to educate them about visual techniques, feeling I had totally ignored a crucial segment of cineliteraey. About five years ago, I finally began including these technical components and, much to my surprise, the health-care students responded (at first fearfully and then quite enthusiastically) to this particular aspect of the class. I now assign Louis Giannetti's *Understanding Movies* (an alternative would be Bordwell/Thompson's *Film Art*) as a required textbook. This clearly written and lavishly illustrated introduction to the art of filmmaking, complete with an extremely useful glossary of terms, contains chapters which isolate the various language systems and spectrum of techniques used by filmmakers in conveying meaning. Students concentrate on the book's first nine chapters: photography, mise-en-scene, movement, sound, acting, drama, story, and literature.

In the past, I would test the students' understanding of the terms and concepts in *Understanding Movies* via a traditional examination. Yet, this format provided little feedback about how well students could employ the ideas in Giannetti's book to "read" visual texts. So, during the last few semesters, I abandoned conventional testing formats; instead, I require each student to analyze one or two television commercials in front of the class, paying specific attention to the elements covered in Giannetti's first nine chapters. Typically in this exercise, students show one or two commercials completely, then break down their constituent components and analyze each one in detail, and finally play the commercials in their entirety once again. I determine each student's grade by how well he/she demonstrates a comprehension and application of basic filmic techniques. While such a "test" definitely takes more time (15-30 mins. for each student) than a written examination, I find it a far better gauge of a student's ability to know and apply the basic concepts of film art. In addition, students generally love this assignment. A new and exciting world of visual language and media communication captures their interest: commercials that once washed unconsciously over them now suddenly become complex and quite fascinating sites of visual meaning. Such a practical exercise also provides a firm foundation for the continued analysis of feature films throughout the rest of the semester.

13

Kathryn Montgomery Hunter, "Narrative, Literature, and the Clinical Exercise of Practical Reason," *The Journal of Medicine and Philosophy* 21 (1996), 303-320.

Editor's note: As with other more recently published articles in this volume, I asked authors if they would be willing to reflect on their piece and add introductory comments that would help frame it, or enable them to address issues raised since its original publication. The following remarks are from the author Kathryn Montgomery Hunter.

I think of this essay as part of the "handmaiden" controversy, the now obscure debate in the 1990s between philosophers and literary scholars. The medical humanities had been accelerating in numbers and sophistication, and literature in particular enjoyed (as Howard Brody once put it) a bull market. The controversy was prompted by the view of some philosophers that bioethics was the exclusive province of their discipline. Historians might supply background; literature scholars provided usefully illustrative stories, but bioethics was theirs. The word "handmaiden," used more than once to describe literature's relation to philosophy, was especially incendiary since at the time the two fields were dominated by different genders: men in philosophy, women in literature. Given the politics of the time – including divergent views about the best disciplinary mix in an institution's scholarly group as well as age and the question of who had tenure and who did not – the "handmaiden" label quickly seemed to spill over to the literature scholars themselves. We were not happy.

C. Danner Clouser, one of the founders of bioethics and an editorial board member of *Journal of Medicine and Philosophy*, was a stalwart proponent of the philosophers' view. He invited Anne Hunsaker Hawkins, recently hired by his department at Penn State-Hershey Medical Center, to co-edit an issue of *Journal of Medicine and Philosophy* (21:2[1996]) that would examine the relationship between the two fields. Anne solicited the submissions, and they each contributed an essay to conclude the volume. Dan gallantly gave her essay the last word, but then – as first editor, her departmental senior, and a member of the editorial board of JMP – did the final edit of their joint introduction.

Their essay titles are suggestive. Dan's is "Philosophy, Literature, and Ethics: Let the Engagement Begin" (21:321-40); Anne's is "Literature, Philosophy, and Medical Ethics: Let the Dialogue Go On" (21: 341-53). As its length suggests, Dan's piece engaged with each article in the issue. He maintained that, of course, anyone may "do" bioethics but only if they adhere to philosophical theory and method. Anne counters that other disciplines have valuable contributions to make and scholars in those disciplines have their own theories and methods to use.

My piece doesn't address the controversy directly but was meant to demonstrate what literature has to say about some important philosophical matters. Dan commented that there was nothing new in it. He had rejected the first essay Tod Chambers submitted; "From the Ethicist's Point of View: The Literary Nature of Ethical Inquiry" (which subsequently appeared in the Hastings Center Report 26 [1996] 25-32), but solicited Tod's landmark "Dax Redacted: The Economies of Truth in Bioethics." Both are collected in Tod's *The Fiction of Bioethics* (Routledge 1999); my piece was the germ of *How Doctors Think: Clinical Judgment and the Practice of Medicine* (Oxford 2006). Anne Hawkins was tenured— and went on to publish four books and a second edition of her first.

Literature and medicine as a field has moved on: it is far larger than the original "matriarchy" and has become gloriously diverse. But the controversy was undoubtedly valuable. It nudged us well beyond New-Critical or formalist assumptions about textual representation and clarified our thinking about the role of literature (including narrative) in bioethics and in the epistemology of medicine.

Narrative, Literature, and the Clinical Exercise of Practical Reason

Kathryn Montgomery Hunter

Abstract. Although science supplies medicine's "gold standard," knowledge exercised in the care of patients is, like moral knowing, a matter of narrative, practical reason. Physicians draw on case narrative to store experience and to apply and qualify the general rules of medical science. Literature aids in this activity by stimulating moral imagination and by requiring its readers to engage in the retrospective construction of a situated, subjective account of events. Narrative truths are provisional, uncertain, derived from narrators whose standpoints are always situated, particular, and uncertain, but open to comparison and reinterpretation. Reading is thus a model for knowing in both morality and clinical medicine. While principles remain essential to bioethics and science must always inform good clinical practice, the tendency to collapse morality into principles and medicine into science impoverishes both practices. Moral knowing is not separable from clinical judgment. While ethics must be open to discussion and interpretation by patients, families, and society, it is nevertheless substantively and epistemologically an inextricable part of a physician's clinical practice.

Matters concerned with conduct and questions of what is good for us have no fixity, any more than matters of health. The general account [of practical knowledge] being of this nature, the account of particular cases is yet more lacking in exactness; for they do not fall under any art or precept, but the agents themselves must in each case consider what is appropriate to the occasion, as happens also in the art of medicine and navigation.
     -Aristotle, *Nicomachean Ethics* II 2, 1104a 4-9
     (trans.). Ross

The twentieth-century philosophical debate about the status of knowledge and the possibility of representing reality has had little effect on the declared epistemology of clinical medicine. Although well educated in the biological sciences and keenly aware of the ineradicable uncertainty of their practice, physicians more often than not describe medicine as a science—and without a shred of epistemological doubt. Its short-comings as a science are regarded as local or temporary: the individual physician may lack knowledge, especially early in his or her career, and there are discoveries yet to be made; but everything is potentially knowable, predictable, quantifiable. Where doubt enters (often on the heels of artificial intelligence proposals to computerize the "rules" of expert clinical practice), physicians are likely either to appeal to the probability calculations of epidemiology as a surrogate, approximate certainty (Feinstein, 1987) or to take a prospective historical view, dismissing non-scientific subjectivity as irrational and temporary and looking forward to the day when biology will have exhausted its last mystery.[1] Meanwhile, as Aristotle implies in his frequent use of medicine as an analogue for moral reason, physicians employ another sort of reasoning, one that necessarily differs from science because it concerns judgments about actions for better or worse in an uncertain field of knowledge (E.N. II 2, 1104a7). Although science remains medicine's "gold standard," clinical knowing as exemplified in the care of patients and medical education is, like moral knowing, a narrative, interpretive, practical reason.

Midway through the *Nicomachean Ethics*, Aristotle distinguishes practical reasoning or *phronesis* from scientific knowing or *episteme* (VI 3, 1139b18-7, 1141b25). The distinction is essential to his account of ethics as a rational endeavor and especially to its difference from science: the knowledge of stable physical phenomena that can be generalized as necessary and invariant laws. *Phronesis*, by contrast, is a means of operating in the world, a matter of understanding how best to act in particular circumstances that are not (and cannot be) thoroughly expressed in general rules. Scientific reason has as its goals precision and replicability, while practical reason enables the reasoner to distinguish better from worse in a given situation. There is, as Aristotle declares, no science of individuals (*Metaphysics*, VII 15, 1039b27-1040c7). Thus, in realms where knowledge is necessarily particular and rules arise from individual instances of practice (rather than being deduced from a general law) – that is, in such fields as medicine, navigation, common law, meteorology, engineering, and moral conduct – a different kind of knowing is called for. It is not that abstractions – scientific truths, legislation, moral or religious principles – are irrelevant to practical reason, but that they cannot go the whole way alone. They must be applied, put into action, in varied, changing, or incompletely specified circumstances; these abstractions sometimes fit well and sometimes poorly, but never in detail. Indeed, to decide that a principle or a law is applicable to the here-and-now, the reasoner begins by recognizing the situation as one to which it may apply. Is this a case of physician-assisted suicide? Or is it rather a withdrawal of treatment at the patient's request? The circular, hermeneutic procedure that ensues is equally familiar to lawyers, physicians, and moral reasoners, all of whom are required to fit the overarching laws of their disciplinary world view to the particular circumstances—called in each instance a "case" (Jansen *et al.*, 1988).[2] Neither induction nor deduction, this nevertheless quite rational procedure is what the pragmatist C.S. Peirce termed "abduction" or "retroduction" (Eco *et al.*, 1983). Despite medicine's appeal to the canons of physical science as the model for its rationality, physicians practice abductively. No one denies that a few physicians spend time in laboratories where they engage in scientific research and that even more undertake the rational investigation of clinical practice; all physicians are well educated in science. But with regard to clinical knowing – whether diagnosis, treatment, or the choices that have in the past twenty-five years come to be known as bioethics[3] – physicians do not reason as they and their textbooks are inclined to describe it: top down, deductively, "scientifically." Instead, both the care of patients and the education of future practitioners have been organized so as to encourage and improve the exercise of a circular and hermeneutic, narrative, practical reason.

Narrative and Practical Reason

Narrative is essential to practical reason. It is the source and agent of both the knowledge of others and a sense of a moral or professional community, a community of practice. We take this knowing for granted, for we are narrative beings. Human life is pervaded by narrative: we read and tell and listen to stories, we watch them unfold in art, ritual, and social life; we perform them ourselves; they give form and meaning to our daily existence. The past is stored in large part as narrative, and visions of the future, if they are to have persuasive power, are narrative as well. We know ourselves (Macintyre, 1981; Rosaldo, 1984; Bruner, 1990) as selves and as members and heirs of families, communities, nations through the stories that exist – recorded, recited, sometimes whispered – about us and those collectivities. These narratives are the givens through and against which our lives and histories are played out.

In using the word "narrative" somewhat interchangeably with "story" I mean to designate a more or less coherent written, spoken, or (by extension) enacted account of occurrences, whether historical or fictional.[4] The two terms can be distinguished, however: "story" is used more often, especially informally, to denote spoken and fictional accounts, where there is a strong sense of the storyteller, while "narrative" emphasizes the inclusion of non-fiction or indicates a contrast with visual or numerical data, as in historiography or book production.

Foremost among the valuable things about narrative as a means of knowing are its unabashedly situated subjectivity and its entanglement with time. As it orders events – subjectively, chronologically – narrative asserts or connotes some causal relation among those events and imputes character and motive to their actors (Forster, 1972). Yet despite this linearity, narrative conclusions are never forgone. As narrative depicts events embedded in the lives and concerns of its protagonists, circumstances unfold through time in all their contingency and complexity (Ricoeur, 1984-1988). Endings may often seem inevitable—but only after the fact. Whether it is an individual's life story which is essential to moral understanding or the political history of a nation, narrative explores the way cause and effect are entangled with the variables of human character and motivation, and with luck and happenstance (Burrell and Hauerwas, 1977; Macintyre, 1981; Nussbaum, 1986). These details are left behind as inessential whenever moral principles or political generalizations are abstracted from events, even though for those involved such particulars may represent what is most valued in a life or a history. Narrative, unlike the abstractions of principles or laws, remains mired in the details of human experience, and, although from a scientific point of view this is a weakness, it is also the source of narrative's strength and value. From the designation of certain details as relevant "facts" and certain occurrences as "events" to the use of rhetorical strategies in the representation and description of those facts and events, story-telling is concerned with the construction and interpretation of meaning. Whether a fiction or history or that interesting amalgam, the individual's life story, narrative captures experience and offers it vicariously to readers and listeners, who learn not only from its explicit content but also through the interpretive process of making sense of what they read and hear.

Because narrative represents events as embedded in the lives and on-going concerns of human beings, it has been described by Stanley Hauerwas (Burrell and Hauerwas, 1977) and Alasdair Macintyre (1981) as essential to moral knowing. It is the means by which the meaning of lives and deeds is made known both to the actors themselves and to their community. In this light, moral choice must be seen not simply as a matter of logic or preference exercised in the moment but as a longer process intertwined with history, identity, culture, and life-meaning. Like reading itself, the exercise of practical reason is an act of interpretation. Practical reasoners draw upon experience, memory, and desire and assess the present situation in their light. In describing moral judgment, Aristotle held that experience was essential to practical reason and thus denied it to the young (E.N. VI 8, 1142a12-16). As Sherlock Holmes, expert in practical reason applied to moral puzzles of a criminal kind, explains his experiential, narrative method to Watson: " ... if you have all the details of a thousand [cases] at your finger ends, it is odd if you cannot unravel the thousand and first" (Doyle, 1893, p. 24).

Nevertheless, the knowledge of abstractions and general rules plays its part in practical reason. Whether as literature, history, or the evening news, narrative provides the arena in which the reasoner tests not only intermediate moral formulations and ethical judgments but also the general principles themselves, working out their implications in the concrete particulars of human lives. The abstractions – in this instance, bioethical principles – test and are tested by experience, both in the moment and through the stories that human beings hear and create to reflect upon it. Rather than something amusing human beings have learned to do with language, Jerome Bruner believes the construction of narrative accounts of life-events is a fundamental way of thinking, even the motive for the acquisition of language in early childhood (1990). Stories are not merely individual: they are culturally shared. We are Hatfields or McCoys, shy persons who care about cats, survivors of Auschwitz, and cowboys. Even the most personal narratives – courtship stories, for example, or accounts of chronic illness – take their shape from the body of tellable story forms, from plots and a shared sense of their importance and meaning (Hawkins, 1993). Whether fiction, history, life story, or gossip (Spacks, 1985), narrative is thus the nexus of culture (including ethics) and individual psychology (Rosaldo, 1984). The construction and the interpretation of stories are central to practical reason, the means by which individuals and cultures make sense of their circumstances and work out – even in situations of tragic choice – what is, on the whole, the better thing to do.

Clinical Judgment

In medicine, practical reason manifests itself as clinical judgment, and narrative is an essential part of it. The same physicians who claim that medicine is not only science-using but itself a science nevertheless are likely to speak of clinical judgment as the crowning quality of the expert clinician. Neither book-learning nor simple experience, clinical judgment is the *je ne sais quoi* of medical practice. Physician educators disagree about how to teach it; they even debate whether it might not be innate and unteachable (AAMC, 1984). But during the long clinical apprenticeship designed to inculcate it, individual professors feel perfectly able to say which of the young physicians in their charge possess it and to what degree. Residents are likely to resent it as a trump card – "in my clinical judgment" – played by elders who do not have recently published clinical studies at their fingertips, but good clinical judgment remains the goal of their professional training.

What expert physicians possess, with or without the facts from the latest journal article, is an immense and well stored stock of clinical cases. Many of these cases are their own; others they have acquired through observation, reading, and reflection. This store of clinical narrative is various and extensive enough so that the general rules which the cases collectively embody are hedged and qualified, layered in memory with skepticism about their applicability to any particular patient. Solid attempts have been made in computer science to codify clinical expertise, but expert systems in medicine perform only at the level of a good intermediate practitioner and are no match for the expert. Patricia Benner's study (1984) of expertise suggests the reason: the acquisition of clinical skill is a process that goes beyond mastery of the rules to a stage where the rules are no longer recalled; each case is comprehended wholistically. Drawing on her work, Hubert Dreyfus and Stuart Dreyfus have argued that experts do "just what [AI theorist Edward] Feigenbaum (1983) feared [they] might be doing—recognizing thousands of special cases" (1987, p. 340).

Third-year medical students, as they begin their clinical education, take a step toward the acquisition of clinical judgment as they recast the science they have spent years learning into clinically relevant cases. It is a confusing time, and clinical teachers can be heard to complain that, though their apprentices may be the cream of the U.S. educational process, they don't know any science at all. But somehow, always, in the process of observing the care of patients, they learn very quickly. Chief among their discoveries is the lesson that, although much in diagnosis and treatment is replicable and therefore predictable, much is not. Treatment is always to some degree experimental; diagnosis is necessarily a retrospective reconstruction of events. Even the most reliable patient with clear-cut symptoms is a potentially uncertain field of knowledge. The taxonomy of clinical knowledge is replicated for each learner through the observation of phenomena and their alteration over time. As they gather details, they learn to make medical sense of signs and symptoms and to record and report their cases; they resemble naturalists rather than bench biologists. They construct narrative accounts of what they observe and invoke biological science for explanation as needed. They learn, above all, to start as nearly as possible from the beginning with each patient and to put the evidence together with only conditional certainty. The skepticism they absorb about knowledge in medicine is integral to medicine's practical epistemology of clinical care. It is part of the profession's "phronesiology," even though this practical reason has little resemblance to the cool and objective replicable guarantor of certainty that medicine takes as the model for its knowledge.

The principal tool of practical reason in the care of patients for both beginner and expert is the case, the narrative organization of clinical observation whether written or oral. The case records and re-presents the process by which the physician reached a recognizable diagnosis; there are rewards for speed and directness, but there is no substitute for accuracy. Although knowledge in clinical medicine is derived from biological science and epidemiology, it is narrative in its organization and, very probably, in its storage in memory (Schank and Abelson, 1981; Schank, 1990; Kolodner, 1993). Like practical reason in fields such as jurisprudence and moral theology, clinical knowing is interpretive, a matter of making sense of what is going on at a particular place and time. The reasoner relies on skill in the interpretation of signs, practical familiarity with the customary way things work, and a thorough knowledge of the taxonomy of the possible in order to construct a retrospective account of what is going on for this patient at this time. Narrative is thus the principle medium of reasoning in medicine; it is not only the form taken by the expert's stock of clinical experience, it represents the process of clinical reasoning itself. This goes far to explain the suspicion with which clinical judgment is often regarded in the medical profession. Those clinicians who over-ride the recommendations of residents with an appeal to clinical judgment are using anecdotal rather than scientific evidence. The single case is subjective, partial, as likely as not to be skewed, even possibly a singular irreplicable (but never negligible) instance. Clinical education is organized to defeat such bias, and it regularly scrutinizes and excoriates the case narratives upon which it depends (Hunter, 1994). Thanks to biological and clinical research, the borders of the narratable are always shifting—witness the medical accounts of HIV or peptic ulcer or even heart disease over the last 15 years. Case narrative nevertheless does not, cannot, disappear from medicine.

Narrative knowledge in scientific medicine owes its tenacity to the profession's duty to make sense of the presentation of illness by a particular patient. With a full grasp of human biology, clinical epidemiology, and medical decision making, a physician is finally (as Stephen Toulmin [1993] has pointed out) that person who takes the patient's history—and, he might have added, transforms it into a medical case. This act of narrative perception and construction at its richest and most skilled requires a willingness to understand the patient and an ability to recast his or her story of illness into a medical narrative that accords with the prevailing diagnostic taxonomy and leads to appropriate treatment. It includes the ability to elicit useful information from the patient, perform a good physical examination, order tests with precision and restraint, prescribe efficacious therapy with minimal harm to the patient, and discern and address the psychological, moral, and social problems that may arise in connection with the illness. This is the exercise of clinical judgment.

Scientific advance will not change this. In that ideal future, when (some imagine) the pathophysiology of disease is thoroughly known, the epidemiology of every malady established, and both are at the fingertips of the experienced practitioner, the individual case will still be the principal means of knowing and learning in medicine. Richard Rorty's "abnormal discourse" (1979), a consideration of those puzzles that require even the most knowledgeable to focus on the anomalous particulars of a case, will have disappeared. "Normal discourse," however, will still proceed by means of cases. People vary, diseases are expressed in varying ways. The individual patient will still require clinical scrutiny: the history will be taken, the body examined for signs, tests performed, the case constructed. The focus on the particular patient which is the clinician's moral obligation will still demand the exercise of practical reason, and practical reason requires the recollection of experience. Then every clinician will resemble Sherlock Holmes, flawlessly recalling exactly the right knowledge from an impeccable store house of experience, indexed and filed as case narrative; in even the most difficult case every clinician, like Holmes, will readily make of the signs "a single connected narrative" (Doyle, 1901, p. 753).[5] Until that golden day, however, physicians will continue to use narrative not only to store and recall information but as a pattern for observation, a template for thinking through new discoveries, and a primary medium for communicating and teaching both the regularities and the uncertainties of clinical practice.

Literature and Narrative Knowledge

The argument for poetry, drama, and fiction as a source of moral knowledge is well established. Rooted firmly in classical literary theory, the belief that literature cultivates moral sensibility and provides models for behavior and feeling has traditionally existed side by side with the recognition of its aesthetic value. In the *Poetics* Aristotle maintains that drama is a more philosophic form of writing than history precisely because it is not fact (IX, 9, 1451b 5-8). Literature[6] concerns what might be; it engages the moral imagination. Horace's assertion in the *Ars Poetica* that poetry (or imaginative literature) is intended both to teach and to delight was shared by writers and readers through the Renaissance and lasted well into the nineteenth century, when Matthew Arnold argued that literature might substitute for a dying religion. Although this didacticism was opposed for almost a century, from the fin de siecle movement that rejected Victorian literary moralism in favor of "art for art's sake" through the slow erosion (at least to contemporary view) of the New Criticism's apolitical literary formalism, the classical belief in literature as morally edifying was nevertheless a quiet assumption that lay behind the inclusion of literature in medical curricula. The argument is this: from the student's first patient contact through the physician's lifetime struggle against disability and death – struggles that are never but temporarily won – medicine must draw on an understanding of the human condition. Literature is unmatched for the access it gives to the experience of others, especially the inner lives of patients and the meaning of circumstances physicians cannot (or do not yet) share (Coles, 1979; Trautmann, 1981; Jones, 1987; Charon, 1994).

What is true of narrative and practical reason is true *a fortiori* of literature. Imaginative literature represents – indeed it epitomizes – a particularly valuable kind of knowing. As both Wayne Booth (1988) and Martha Nussbaum (1990, especially pp. 54-105) have argued, it is also the agent of moral reason. To read is literally to subject oneself to a different point of view, to the imaginative testing of one's perspective, even to change. Reading fiction and poetry or seeing drama is a model for practical knowing not only in its provision of information about the possibilities of the world but in its encoding of that knowledge. Literature must be read, interpreted. It poses openly the problem of knowing as subjective and situated, more or less reliable. It requires its readers to construct a world that makes truth-claims while simultaneously proclaiming its nonreferentiality. The process of understanding a work of literature replicates the process of making sense of the world, and it inculcates epistemological assumptions as it reinforces procedural habits. Literature thus not only offers its readers a means of acquiring some important information along with the vicarious experience uniquely available through art but also is the medium for cultivating and maintaining the habits and skills of interpretation that are essential to good ethical practice and to good patient care (Charon *et al.*, 1995). That is, literature is a source of moral knowledge

– clinically useful knowledge – and the act of reading, the perception and understanding of what is written, is a model for knowing in both morality and clinical medicine. Reading literature or simply making sense of any narrative entails the reader's retrospective construction of a situated, more or less subjective account of events. Its truths are provisional, uncertain, derived from narrators whose standpoints are always situated, particular, and therefore ultimately uncertain. But literature, like narrative generally, is open both to comparison with the readings of others and, when the situation demands it, to reinterpretation. Thus it not only offers its audiences vicarious experience but skill in interpreting uncertain or ambiguous representations of that experience. Because patients present themselves in words, as stories, both sorts of learning – the more or less factual and the procedural or interpretive – transfer readily to clinical care.

The Role of Literature in Medical Epistemology

Literature is not essential to the consideration of medical epistemology. And just as literature is not the only form narrative takes, literary theory is not the only source of speculation about the status and reliability of knowledge. The preoccupation with "theory" that has overtaken literary study is a philosophical one. The term invokes especially the epistemological controversies that in the second half of the twentieth century have followed the introduction of Russian and "Continental" philosophy into intellectual realms previously dominated by Anglo-American analytic philosophy. It is neither theory in the sense of a set of general principles nor is it unique to literary study. This postmodern epistemology challenges first and foremost the simple, isomorphic notion of representation that had been the foundation of realistic fiction and literary criticism—to say nothing of the philosophy of science (Hesse 1980; Levine, 1993). Since the 1960's literary scholars increasingly have asked whether the reader reads what the writer writes. And if not? What is the perceiver's responsibility to his or her perceptions? Or, to the perceived?

Literature, oddly enough, has been the major importer of post modern epistemological concerns into medicine and the philosophy of clinical practice. This was not inevitable. Philosophers who might have introduced these issues have been called upon instead to think and write about pressing ethical issues, first, in the patient-physician relationship and, then, in public policy.[7] Historians might also have raised the issue of knowledge. Historiographers like Hayden White (1981) and Dominick LaCapra (1987), just to mention North Americans, have wrestled with the epistemology implicit in writing history, borrowing from literary studies many of the questions that inevitably are raised by narrative: the subjectivity of the witness, the reliability of those who create the record, the problem of representation, the indeterminacy of reality, the criteria of truth, the relationship between history and fiction, and how the answers to these questions affect what is understood by "history." Despite their numbers, historians of medicine, have not asked these interesting questions of medical practice. This may be because relatively few historians teach medical students and observe their struggle to move from the science classroom to practical apprenticeship in the hospital, or because those few, far from being scorned by their mainstream colleagues as early philosophers and literary scholars in medicine were, have maintained their customary professional audience and activity. They have written histories of medicine, public health, and medical education much as history is generally written, and their disciplinary success has not led them to an interest in either historiography's epistemological debate or its applicability to the history-writing practiced daily as an integral part of medical care. Instead, the problems of historiography in clinical medicine have been studied by physicians concerned with the problem of medical knowledge (King, 1982; Donnelly, 1988) and by literary scholars interested in the construction of narrative (Poirier *et al.*, 1988). Art history and art theory also might raise questions about realism and representation in clinical knowledge. Indeed, many literary scholars gained their first introduction to these problems from the work of the art theorist, E.H. Gombrich (1960).[8] Such ideas are not strange in medical practice, where x-rays and case presentations are readily understood as partial representations that necessarily eliminate aspects of reality in order to reveal others. This understanding is not inconsistent with treating these representations as "real" information, even grounds for action. While physicians do not spend time on epistemological questions – indeed, unless pressed with examples many would claim to be simple realists – nevertheless, when "the facts" fail to add up, they know that the clinical representations they rely on are maps, potentially skewed, and never the territory. Art historians and art theorists, who might have elaborated on this insight, until recently have been scarce in medical schools.

Anthropology, too, can readily serve as the vehicle for introducing epistemological questions in medicine. The discipline now has a long history of reflexivity, heightened by its complicity in the Vietnam war but enduring in the recurring question of whether it is possible to know another culture—or whether such knowledge must always be a reflection of the observer's predispositions (Myerhoff *et al.*, 1982). As with historians, too few anthropologists work in medical education, and most of these are pressed into service on behalf of patients who hold beliefs about health and illness that differ from those of Western medicine (for example, Hufford, 1993). Where anthropologists study physicians, however, they undertake the difficult task of examining Western assumptions and the culture of medicine that naturalizes biomedical technology (Good, B., 1994; Good, M.-J., 1995). The difficulty is in returning this knowledge to students and clinicians as they learn and practice, inculcating in them the self-consciousness about knowledge that is the strength of anthropology.

In this pedagogical vacuum, literature and literary theory raise questions about the reliability of the narrator, the stability of perceived facts and perceiving selves, the nature of truth, the relativity of concepts, the impossibility of a pure objectivity, the uncertainty of knowing, the difficulty of constructing a narrative and the impossibility of not doing so. These matters are as applicable to bioethics as to the rest of practical reasoning in medicine (Davis, 1991; Chambers, 1994; Chambers, 1995). Literature, along with the other humanities, may have been "parachuted" into medical education (Fox, 1994), but it does valuable work there. As Jerome Bruner writes, "the existence of story as a form is a perpetual guarantee that humankind will 'go meta' on received versions of reality" (1991, p. 55). The reading and interpretation that literature evokes is a paradigm for clinical knowing.

Narrative Ethics and Clinical Judgment

Although our society is too diverse and our options too numerous for bioethics ever to return to its status as solely the province of the physician, moral choice is not and ought not be separated from clinical judgment. It is a part of the practical reason in the care of patients that is part of medical care. There is no difference in the rational method that is essential both to good bioethics and to good clinical practice. Each engages a practical wisdom that, well informed about the generalities that govern the field, draws on experience and habits that have survived reflective scrutiny so as to choose the better action in the present circumstance. Whether in diagnosis, choice of therapy, or moral decision making, narrative is central to practical reason both in its substance and in the process of interpretation that it exemplifies and requires. Clinical judgment and moral discernment are equally a narrative skill or capacity. For each, what is necessary is an accessible store of well-indexed experience. Occasionally, when there is consensus in a particular situation, a general rule or principle will seem to suffice. But the sustained capacity for practical judgment calls for finely honed perception and a flexible capacity for interpretation in an uncertain domain. Timely diagnosis requires a rich taxonomy of diagnostic cases; sound choice of treatment requires a full range of therapeutic ones; and wise ethical reasoning requires a store of narratives about meaning and value in human life. For an attentive and experienced physician, this store could well be accumulated from patients over the course of a career. But for the inexperienced, the hurried, or the disillusioned, imaginative literature – fiction, poetry, drama – offers a rich, vicarious supply. While principles remain essential to bioethics and biological science must always inform good clinical practice, the tendency to collapse morality into principles and medicine into science impoverishes the two practices. In both instances such a reduction takes science as a model for what cannot be purely scientific. It is an attempt to know generally and abstractly what cannot be known except through the particular case—and to be best understood that case must be richly understood.

The clinical exercise of practical reason in the interpretation of illness draws on a knowledge of biology, a store of clinical experience, and a familiarity with the possibilities for meaning in human life. In this endeavor, moral knowledge is scarcely separable from clinical knowledge—and both are more homely endeavors than most physicians and ethicists have been willing to admit. The consequences for medical education are clear: attention to the patient history, careful construction and indexing of the medical case, and the inclusion of patient narratives and imaginative literature in the storehouse of narrative relevant to moral decision making in clinical medicine. Above all, while medical ethics must be open to discussion and interpretation by the community as a whole and individual patients and their families in particular, it nevertheless is substantively and epistemologically an inextricable part of physicians' clinical practice.

Notes

1   Although practical knowing shares much with Vico's "common sense," Hans-Georg Gadamer (1984, pp. 16-17) maintains that it is not (as Vico implied it might be) probabilistic reasoning; he cites as support Helmholtz's description of this mode of knowing as "a kind of tact" that is as judicious in its omissions as in its selection of experiential information. Charles Taylor (1988, pp. 7, 74-75) has argued that modem epistemology's acceptance of a "model of practical reasoning . . . based on an illegitimate extrapolation from reasoning in natural science" is seriously flawed; since so little meets its criteria, the consequence is a widespread skepticism about reason itself.

2   Recent historians and philosophers of science have demonstrated that scientists
    reason contextually and interpretively as well (see, for example, Hesse, 1980).
    This does not alter the ideal that medicine has borrowed, particularly from the
    physical sciences.

3   On the alienation of bioethics from clinical judgment see Rothman (1991). Zuss-
    man (1992) documents the attempts to preserve ethical decisions as an aspect
    of professional expertise by critical care physicians.

4   The ideas and many of the phrases in this and the following paragraph also ap-
    pear in Hunter, 1995.

5   Holmes, like the physicians on whom his expertise is modeled, claims to reason
    scientifically, "deductively" in the practice of his craft, but as in the passage in
    The Hound of the Baskervilles from which this quotation is taken (among many
    other instances), he understands the narrative character of his method. This,
    too, he shares with physicians.

6   As with term "science," I am using "literature" in what could be called an old
    fashioned sense. Barbara Hermstein Smith describes the permeable borders of
    literature in contemporary literary scholarship (1989), Clifford Geertz the ap-
    propriation of its methodologies (1983).

7   Among the exceptions to this very general rule are Schwartz and Wiggins (1985),
    Sundstrom (1987), and many scholars who have written about the definition of
    disease.

8   Gombrich has subsequently repudiated the deconstructionist implications of his
    work (1991).

References

Aristotle, 1952, *Metaphysics*, W.D. Ross (trans.) in *The Works of Aristotle*, Vol. I,
    Encyclopedia Britannica, Chicago, pp. 499-626.

Aristotle, 1952, *Nicomachean Ethics*, W.D. Ross (trans.), in *The Works of
    Aristotle*, Vol. II, Encyclopedia Britannica, Chicago, pp. 339-436

Aristotle, 1952, *Poetics*, I. Bywater (trans.), in *The Works of Aristotle*, Vol. Il,
    Encyclopedia Britannica, Chicago, pp. 681-699.

Association of American Medical Colleges: 1984, 'Physicians for the twenty-
    first century: Study of the general education of the physician [The
    GPEP Report]', *Journal of Medical Education* 59(11), part 2.

Benner, P.: 1984, *From Novice to Expert: Excellence and Power in Clinical Nursing
    Practice*, Addison-Wesley, Reading, Mass.

Booth, W.C.: 1988, *The Company We Keep: An Ethics of Fiction*, University of

California Press, Berkeley.

Bruner, J.: 1990, *Acts of Meaning*, Harvard University Press, Cambridge.

Burrell, D. and Hauerwas, S.: 1977, 'From system to story: An alternative pattern for rationality in ethics,' in S. Hauerwas and L.G. Jones (eds.), 1989, *Why Narrative?: Readings in Narrative Theology*, Eerdmans, Grand Rapids, Michigan, pp. 159-190.

Chambers T.S.: 1994, 'The bioethicist as author: The medical ethics case as rhetorical device,' *Literature and Medicine* 13, pp. 60-78.

Chambers T.S.: 'From the ethicist's point of view: The literary nature of ethical inquiry', *Hastings Center Report*, 26(1), pp. 25-32.

Charon, R. et al.: 1995, 'Literature and medicine: Contributions to clinical practice,' *Annals of Internal Medicine* 122, pp. 599-606.

Charon, R.: 1994, 'Narrative contributions to medical ethics,' in E.R. Dubose et al. *A Matter of Principles? Ferment in U.S. Bioethics*, Trinity Press International, Valley Forge PA, pp. 260-283.

Coles, R.: 1979, 'Medical ethics and living a life,' *New England Journal of Medicine* 301, pp. 444-446.

Davis, D.: 1991, 'Rich cases: The ethics of thick description,' *Hastings Center Report* 21(4), pp. 12-16.

Donnelly, W.: 1988. 'From chronicle to story,' *Journal of the American Medical Association* 260, pp. 823-825.

Doyle, A.C.: 1893, *A Study in Scarlet*, part I, chapter 2, in *The Complete Sherlock Holmes*, Doubleday, New York.

Doyle, A.C.: 1901, *The Hound of the Baskervilles*, in *The Complete Sherlock Holmes*, Doubleday, New York.

Dreyfus, H.L. and Dreyfus, S.E: 1987, 'From Socrates to expert systems: The limits of calculative rationality,' in P. Rabinow and W.M. Sullivan (eds.), *Interpretive Social Science: A Second Look*, University of Chicago Press, Chicago, p. 340.

Eco, U. and Sebeok, T.A. (eds.): 1983, *The Sign of Three: Dupin, Holmes, Peirce*, Indiana University Press, Bloomington.

Elstein, A.S. et al.: 1978, *Medical Problem Solving: An Analysis of Clinical Reasoning*, Harvard University Press, Cambridge.

Feigenbaum, E. and McCorduck, P.: 1983, *The Fifth Generation: Artificial Intelligence and Japan's Computer Challenge*, Addison-Wesley, Reading, Mass.

Feinstein, A.: 1987, *Clinimetrics*, Yale University Press, New Haven, Connecticut.

Forster, E.M.: 1927, *Aspects of the Novel*, Harcourt, Brace, New York.

Fox, R.C.: 1994, The entry of U.S. bioethics into the 1990s: A sociological analysis,' in E.R. DuBose et al., *A Matter of Principles? Ferment in U.S. Bioethics*, Trinity Press International, Valley Forge, Pennsylvania, pp. 21-71.

Gadamer, H.-G.: 1984, *Truth and Method*, 2nd ed., Crossroad Publishing, New York.

Geertz, C.: 1983, 'Blurred genres: The refiguration of social thought,' *Local Knowledge: Further Essays in Interpretive Anthropology*, Basic Books, New York, pp. 19-35.

Gombrich, E.H.: 1960, *Art and Illusion: A Study in the Psychology of Pictorial Representation*, 2nd ed., Bollingen series 24, Pantheon, New York.

Gombrich, E.H.: 1991, *Topics of our Time: Twentieth-Century Issues in Learning and in Art*, University of California Press, Berkeley.

Good, B.: 1994, *Medicine, Rationality, and Experience*, Cambridge University Press, New York.

Good, M.-J.D. 1995, *American Medicine: The Quest for Competence*, University of California Press, Berkeley.

Hawkins, A.H.: 1993, *Reconstructing Illness: Studies in Pathography*, Purdue University Press, West Lafayette, Indiana.

Hesse, M.: 1980, *Revolutions and Reconstructions in the Philosophy of Science*, Indiana University Press, Bloomington, Indiana.

Hufford, D.: 1993, 'Epistemologies in religious healing,' *Journal of Medicine and Philosophy* 18, pp. 175-20.

Hunter, K.M.: 1994, "Don't think zebras": Paradoxical injunctions in clinical medicine,' presented to the University of Chicago Department of Computer Science, November 16, 1994.

Hunter, K.M.: 1995, 'Narrative,' in W.T. Reich (ed.), *Encyclopedia of Bioethics*, rev. ed., Macmillan, New York, Vol. IV, pp. 1789-1794.

Jones, A.H.: 1987, 'Literary value: The lesson of medical ethics,' *Neohelicon* 14, pp. 383-392.

Jonsen, A.R. and Toulmin, S.E.: 1988, *The Abuse of Casuistry: A History of Moral Reasoning*, University of California Press, Berkeley.

King, L.S.: 1982, *Medical Thinking: A Historical Preface*, Princeton University Press, Princeton.

Kolodner, J.: 1993, *Case-Based Reasoning*, Morgan Kaufman Publishers, San Mateo.

LaCapra, D.: 1987, *History, Politics, and the Novel*, Cornell University Press, Ithaca.

Levine, G.: 1993, 'Looking for the real: Epistemology in science,' in G. Levine (ed.), *Realism and Representation: Essays on the Problem of Realism in Relation to Science, Literature, and Culture*, University of Wisconsin Press,

Madison, pp. 1-23.

Macintyre, A.: 1981, *After Virtue: A Study in Moral Theory*, University of Notre Dame Press, Notre Dame.

Myerhoff, B. and Ruby, J.: 1982, 'Introduction,' in J. Ruby (ed.), *A Crack in the Mirror: Reflexive Perspectives in Anthropology*, University of Pennsylvania Press, Philadelphia.

Nussbaum, M.C.: 1990, 'The discernment of perception: An Aristotelian conception of private and public rationality,' *Love's Knowledge: Essays on Philosophy and Literature*, Oxford University Press, New York, pp. 54-105.

Nussbaum, M.C.: 1986, *The Fragility of Goodness: Luck and Ethics in Greek Tragedy and Philosophy*, Cambridge University Press, Cambridge.

Poirier, S. and Brauner, D.J.: 1990, 'Voices of the medical record,' *Theoretical Medicine* 11, pp. 29-39.

Ricoeur, P.: 1984-1988, *Time and Narrative*, 3 vols., (trans.), Kathleen [McLaughlin] Blarney and David Pellauer, University of Chicago Press, Chicago.

Rorty, R: 1979, *Philosophy and the Mirror of Nature*, Princeton University Press, Princeton, New Jersey.

Rosaldo, M.Z.: 1984, 'Toward an anthropology of self and feeling,' in RA Shweder and RA LeVine (eds.), *Culture Theory: Essays on Mind, Self, and Emotion*, Cambridge University Press, Cambridge, pp. 137-157.

Rothman, D.: 1991, *Strangers at the Bedside: A History of How Law and Bioethics Transformed Medical Decision Making*, Basic Books, New York.

Schank, RC. and Abelson, RP.: 1981, *Scripts, Plans, Goals and Understanding: An Inquiry into Human Knowledge*, Erlbaum, Hillsdale, New Jersey.

Schank, R C.: 1990, *Tell Me a Story: A New Look at Real and Artificial Memory*, Scribners, New York.

Schwartz, M.A. and Wiggins, 0.: 1985, 'Science, humanism, and the nature of medical practice: A phenomenological view,' *Perspectives in Biology and Medicine* 28, pp. 334ff.

Smith, B.H.: 1989, 'Breaking up / out/ down: The boundaries of literary study,' in P. Franklin (ed.), *Profession* 89, The Modern Language Association of America, New York.

Spacks, P.M.: 1985, *Gossip*, Knopf, New York.

Sundstrom, P.: 1987, *Icons of Disease: A Philosophical Inquiry into the Semantics. Phenomenology and Ontology of the Clinical Conceptions of Disease*, Linkoping University Press, Linkoping, Sweden.

Taylor, C.: 1989, *Sources of the Self The Making of the Modern Identity*, Harvard University Press, Cambridge.

Toulmin, S.: 1993, 'Knowledge and art in the practice of medicine: Clinical judgment and historical reconstruction,' in C. Delkeskamp-Hayes and M.A.G. Cutter (eds.), *Science, Technology, and the Art of Medicine: European-American Dialogues*, Kluwer Academic Publishers, Dordrecht, The Netherlands.

Trautmann, J. (ed.): 1981, *Healing Arts in Dialogue: Medicine and Literature*, Southern Illinois University Press, Carbondale, Illinois.

White, H.: 1981, 'The value of narrativity · in the representation of reality,' in W.J.T. Mitchell (ed.), *On Narrative*, University of Chicago Press, Chicago, pp. 1-23.

Wiggins, D.: 1980, 'Deliberation and practical reason,' in A.O. Rorty (ed.), *Essays on Aristotle's Ethics*, University of California Press, Berkeley, pp. 221-240.

Zussman, R: 1992, *Intensive Care: Medical Ethics and the Medical Profession*, University of Chicago Press, Chicago.

14

Rita Charon, "Narrative Medicine: A Model for Empathy, Reflection, Profession, and Trust" *The Journal of the American Medical Association* 286 (2001), 1897-1902

Rita Charon is Professor of Clinical Medicine at the College of Physicians and Surgeons of Columbia University and Director of the Program in Narrative Medicine. A graduate from Harvard Medical School in 1978 who trained in internal medicine at the Residency Program in Social Medicine at Montefiore Hospital in New York, she is a general internist in practice. She completed her Ph.D. in the Department of English at Columbia in 1999, writing on the later works of Henry James and on literary analyses of medical texts. Encouraged by mentors Joanna Trautmann and Kathryn Montgomery Hunter, she began focusing attention more closely on the structure and meanings of the narratives revealed by her own patients. Approaching her patients' stories with the same analytical and thoughtful care as she would a work of literature, she gained the confidence that she was understanding better what her patients were experiencing. To encourage the practice, she began asking her medical students and residents to keep what she called a "parallel chart" on the patients in their care, a place where caregivers could write about their feelings, experiences, and understanding of the patients as people and not only their perception of the disease being treated.

Acknowledging the debt her approach owed to the previous genera-tion of literature-and-medicine scholars, Charon dug deeper into certain areas of literary analysis, making conceptual frameworks such as narra-tology (a study of how narrative form affects perception) more integral to her methods. She coined the term "Narrative Medicine" to connect explicitly the grasp of complex narrative structures that are present in the doctor-patient relationship and its bearing on medical practice. As Charon explained,

What narrative medicine offers that the others may not be in a position to offer is a disciplined and deep set of conceptual frameworks – mostly from literary studies, and especially from narratology – that give us theoretical means to understand why acts of doctoring are not unlike acts of reading, interpreting, and writing and how such things as reading fiction and writing ordinary narrative prose about our patients help to make us better doctors. By examining medical practices in the light of robust narrative theories, we begin to be able to make new sense of the genres of medicine, the telling situations that obtain, say, at attending rounds, the ethics that bind the teller to the listener in the office, and of the events of illness themselves.[1]

The piece reproduced here is one of Charon's key articulations of the impact on students, physicians, and patients of the skills of narrative medicine and the effect it can have on the improvement of health care delivery.

---

1   Rita Charon, "Narrative Medicine," *LitSite Alaska*. http://www.litsite.org/index.cfm?section=Narrative-and-Healing&page=Perspectives&viewpost=2&ContentId=985. Accessed February 28, 2015.

Narrative Medicine: A Model for Empathy, Reflection, Profession, and Trust

Rita Charon, MD, PhD

Abstract. The effective practice of medicine requires narrative competence, that is, the ability to acknowledge, absorb, interpret, and act on the stories and plights of others. Medicine practiced with narrative competence, called narrative medicine, is proposed as a model for humane and effective medical practice. Adopting methods such as close reading of literature and reflective writing allows narrative medicine to examine and illuminate 4 of medicine's central narrative situations: physician and patient, physician and self, physician and colleagues, and physicians and society. With narrative competence, physicians can reach and join their patients in illness, recognize their own personal journeys through medicine, acknowledge kinship with and duties toward other health care professionals, and inaugurate consequential discourse with the public about health care. By bridging the divides that separate physicians from patients, themselves, colleagues, and society, narrative medicine offers fresh opportunities for respectful, empathic, and nourishing medical care.

Ms. Lambert (not her real name) is a 33-year-old woman with Charcot-Marie-Tooth disease. Her grandmother, mother, 2 aunts, and 3 of her 4 siblings have the disabling disease as well. Her 2 nieces showed signs of the disease by the age of 2 years. Despite being wheelchair bound with declining use of her arms and hands, the patient lives a life filled with passion and responsibility.

"How's Phillip?" the physician asks on a routine medical follow-up visit. At the age of 7 years, Ms. Lambert's son is vivacious, smart, and the center – and source of meaning – of the patient's world. The patient answers. Phillip has developed weakness in both feet and legs, causing his feet to flop when he runs. The patient knows what this signifies, even before neurologic tests confirm the diagnosis. Her vigil tinged with fear, she had been watching her son every day for 7 years, daring to believe that her child had escaped her family's fate. Now she is engulfed by sadness for her little boy. "It's harder having been healthy for 7 years," she says. "How's he going to take it?"

The physician, too, is engulfed by sadness as she listens to her patient, measuring the magnitude of her loss. She, too, had dared to hope for health for Phillip. The physician grieves along with the patient, aware anew of how disease changes everything, what it means, what it claims, how random is its unfairness, and how much courage it takes to look it full in the face.

Sick people need physicians who can understand their diseases, treat their medical problems, and accompany them through their illnesses. Despite medicine's recent dazzling technological progress in diagnosing and treating illnesses, physicians sometimes lack the capacity to recognize the plight of their patients, to extend empathy toward those who suffer, and to join honestly and courageously with patients in their illnesses.[1,2] A scientifically competent medicine alone cannot help a patient grapple with the loss of health or find meaning in suffering. Along with scientific ability, physicians need the ability to listen to the narratives of the patient, grasp and honor their meanings, and be moved to act on the patient's behalf. This is narrative competence, that is, the competence that human beings used to absorb, interpret, and responded to stories. This essay describes narrative competence and suggests that it enables the physician to practice medicine with empathy, reflection, professionalism, and trustworthiness.[3] Such a medicine can be called *narrative medicine.*[4]

As a model for medical practice, narrative medicine proposes an ideal of care and provides the conceptual and practical means to strive toward that ideal. Informed by such models as biopsychosocial medicine and patient-centered medicine to look broadly at the patient and the illness, narrative medicine provides the means to understand the personal connections between patient and physician, the meaning of medical practice for the individual physician, physicians' collective profession of their ideals, and medicine's discourse with the society it serves.[5,6] Narrative medicine simultaneously offers physicians the means to improve the effectiveness of their work with patients, themselves, their colleagues, and the public.

To adopt the model of narrative medicine provides access to a large body of theory and practice that examines and illuminates narrative acts.[7] From the humanities, and especially literary studies, physicians can learn how to perform the narrative aspects of their practice with new effectiveness. Not so much a new specialty as a new frame for clinical work, narrative medicine can give physicians and surgeons the skills, methods, and texts to learn how to imbue the facts and objects of health and illness with their consequences and meanings for individual patients and physicians.[8,9]

The Turn Toward Narrative Knowledge

Not only medicine but also nursing, law, history, philosophy, anthropology, sociology, religious studies, and government have recently realized the importance of narrative knowledge.[10-13]

Narrative knowledge is what one uses to understand the meaning and significance of stories through cognitive, symbolic, and affective means. This kind of knowledge provides a rich, resonant comprehension of a singular person's situation as it unfolds in time, whether in such texts as novels, newspaper stories, movies, and scripture or in such life settings as court rooms, battlefields, marriages, and illnesses.[14-16] As literary critic R.W.B. Lewis[17] writes, "narrative deals with experiences, not with propositions." Unlike its complement, logicoscientific knowledge, through which a detached and replaceable observer generates or comprehends replicable and generalizable notices, narrative knowledge leads to local and particular understandings about one situation by one participant or observer.[18,19] Logicoscientific knowledge attempts to illuminate the universally true by transcending the particular; narrative knowledge attempts to illuminate the universally true by revealing the particular.

Narrative considerations probe the intersubjective domains of human knowledge and activity, that is to say, those aspects of life that are enacted in the relation between 2 persons. Literary scholar Barbara Herrnstein Smith[20] defines narrative discourse as "someone telling someone else that something happened," emphasizing narrative's requirement for a teller and a listener, a writer and a reader, a communion of some sort.

The narratively competent reader or listener realizes that the meaning of any narrative – a novel, a textbook, a joke – must be judged in the light of its narrative situation: Who tells it? Who hears it? Why and how is it told?[21-23] The narratively skilled reader further understands that the meaning of a text arises from the ground between the writer and the reader,[24,25] and that "the reader," as Henry James writes in an essay on George Elliot, "does quite half the labour."[26] With narrative competence, multiple sources of local – and possibly contradicting – authority replace master authorities; instead of being monolithic and hierarchically given, meaning is apprehended collaboratively, by the reader and the writer, the observer and the observed, the physician and the patient.

Narrative Competence in Medicine

Medicine has never been without narrative concerns, because, as an enterprise in which one human being extends help to another, it has always been grounded in life's intersubjective domain.[27,28] Like narrative, medical practice requires the engagement of one person with another and realizes that authentic engagement is transformative for all participants.

As a legacy of the developments in primary care in the 1960s and 1970s, patient-physician communication, and medical humanities, medicine has become increasingly schooled in narrative knowledge in general and the narrative of patients and physicians in particular.[29-31] This growing narrative sophistication has provided medicine with new and useful ways in which to consider patient-physician relationships, diagnostic reasoning, medical ethics, and professional training.[32-35] Medicine can, as a result, better understand the experiences of sick people, the journeys of individual physicians, and the duties incurred by physicians toward individual patients and by the profession of medicine toward its wider culture.[36-38]

Medical practice unfolds in a series of complex narrative situations, including the situations between the physician and the patient, the physician and himself or herself, the physician and colleagues, and physicians and society. The following sections will summarize the contributions of narrative medicine to each of these 4 situations. Other important narrative situations exist in medicine as well, although they will not be discussed in this essay, such as between the physician and his or her family, between patients and their family members, and among patients.

Patient–Physician: Empathic Engagement

As patient meets physician, a conversation ensues. A story — a state of affairs or a set of events — is recounted by the patient in his or her acts of narrating, resulting in a complicated narrative of illness told in words, gestures, physical findings, and silences and burdened not only with the objective information about the illness but also with the fears, hopes, and implications associated with it.[39] As in psychoanalysis, in all of medical practice the narrating of the patient's story is a therapeutically central act, because to find the words to contain the disorder and its attendant worries gives shape to and control over the chaos of illness.[40-43]

As the physician listens to the patient, he or she follows the narrative thread of the story, imagines the situation of the teller (the biological, familial,

cultural, and existential situation), recognizes the multiple and often contradictory meanings of the words used and the events described, and in some
way enters into and is moved by the narrative world of the patient.[44,45] Not
unlike acts of reading literature, acts of diagnostic listening enlist the listener's
interior resources – memories, associations, curiosities, creativity, interpretive
powers, allusions to other stories told by this teller and others – to identify
meaning.[46] Only then can the physician hear – and then attempt to face, if not
to answer fully – the patient's narrative questions: "What is wrong with me?"
"Why did this happen to me?" and "What will become of me?"

Listening to stories of illness and recognizing that there are often no clear
answers to patients' narrative questions demand the courage and generosity to
tolerate and to bear witness to unfair losses and random tragedies.[47] Accom-
plishing such acts of witnessing allows the physician to proceed to his or her
more recognizably clinical narrative tasks: to establish a therapeutic alliance,
to generate and proceed through a differential diagnosis,[48] to interpret physical
findings and laboratory reports correctly, to experience and convey empathy
for the patient's experience,[49] and, as a result of all of these, to engage the
patient in obtaining effective care.

If the physician cannot perform these narrative tasks, the patient might not
tell the whole story, might not ask the most frightening questions, and might
not feel heard.[50] The resultant diagnostic workup might be unfocused and
therefore more expensive than need be, the correct diagnosis might be missed,
the clinical care might be marked by noncompliance in the search for another
opinion, and the therapeutic relationship might be shallow and ineffective.

Despite – or, more radically, because of – economic forces that shrink
the time available for conversation and that limit the continuity of clinical
relationships, medicine has begun to affirm the importance of telling and
listening to the stories of illness. As practice speeds up, physicians need all
the more powerful methods for achieving empathic and effective therapeutic
relationships. Narrative skills can provide such methods to help physicians
join with their patients, honoring all they tell them.

Physician-Self: Reflection in Practice

Altruism, compassion, respectfulness, loyalty, humility, courage, and trustworthiness become etched into the physician's skeleton by the authentic care of the
sick. Physicians absorb and display the inevitable results of being submerged
in pain, unfairness, and suffering while being buoyed by the extraordinary
courage, resourcefulness, faith, and love the behold every day in practice.

Through authentic engagement with their patients, physicians can cultivate affirmation of human strength, acceptance of human weakness, familiarity with suffering, and a capacity to forgive and be forgiven. Diagnosis and treatment of disease require schooled and practiced use of these narrative capacities of the physician. Indeed, it may be that the physician's most potent therapeutic instrument is the self, which is attuned to the patient through engagement, on the side of the patient through compassion, and available to the patient through reflection.[51]

Reflective practitioners can identify and interpret their own emotional responses to patients, can make sense of their own life journeys, and so can grant what is called for – and called forth – in facing sick and dying patients.[52,53] When sociologists studied medicine in the 1960s, they observed physicians to practice medicine with "detached concern."[54] Somehow, this field observation became a normative prescription, and physicians for decades seemed to consider detachment a goal. Today, relying on newly emerging knowledge from narrative disciplines, physicians are learning to practice medicine with not detached but engaged concern, an approach that requires disciplined and steady reflection on one's practice.[55-57]

As reflective practitioners, physicians have turned to a study of the humanities, especially literature, to grow in their personal understanding of illness.[58] Literature seminars and reading groups have become commonplace in medical schools and hospitals, both for physicians to read well-written stories about illness and to deepen their skills as readers, interpreters, and conjurers of the worlds of others.[59-61] Having learned that acts of reflective narrating illuminate aspects of the patient's story – and of their own – that are unavailable without the telling, physicians are writing about their patients in special columns in professional journals and books and essays published in the lay press.[62-65] Increasingly, physicians allow patients to read what they have written about them, adding a therapeutic dimension to a practice born of the need for reflection.[66] Through the narrative processes of reflection and self-examination, both physicians and patients can achieve more accurate understanding of all the sequelae of illness, equipping them to better weather its tides.

Physician–Colleagues: Profession

The ordinary, day-to-day professional actions of physicians in research, teaching, and collegial life are saturated with narrative work and can be made more effective once recognized as such. It is only with narrative competence that research proceeds, teaching succeeds, clinical colleagueship achieves its goals, and the profession of medicine remains grounded and its timeless, selfless commitment to help.

Scientific research results from the muscular narrative thrust of first imagining and then testing scientific hypotheses, and it relies on narrative inventiveness and imagination as well as scientific training.[67] Like medicine's theoretical knowledge, its practical knowledge is issued in narrative and mastered through time. The student becomes the physician by functioning as a medium for medicine's continuity of knowledge, learning about diseases in the process of living through their passages.[68] No physician mobilizes his or her practical knowledge about a disease without having mastered the sequential stories imagined, over time, to explain its symptoms, from dropsy to the downward limb of the Starling curve to diastolic dysfunction.

In professional life, physicians rely on one another – as audience, witness, reader – for honesty, criticism, forgiveness, and the gusty blend of uncertainty and authority contained in the phrase, "We see this."[69] From interns up all night together to the surgeon and the internist moving through the dark of a patient's illness, physicians grow to know one another with the intimacy and the contention of siblings, affirming one another's triumphs, hearing one another's errors, and comforting one another's grief.[70]

Medicine is considered a profession because of, in part, the strength of these bonds among physicians. Certified to educate and to police one another, physicians accrue responsibility for one another's competence and conscience. Recent urgent calls for professionalism signal physicians' widening failures to accept and enact their commitment to individually and collectively uphold their profession's ideals.[71,72] Instead, physicians seem isolated from one another and from their colleagues in nursing, social work, and other health professions and divided from their ideals and disconnected from their broad professional goals in the face of narrow, competitive drives toward individual distinction or reward.[73]

To profess is a narrative act. Perhaps the most effective methods to strengthen professionalism in medicine are to endow physicians with the confidence required to fulfill their narrative duties toward one another: to envision the stories of science, to teach individual students responsibly, to give and accept collegial oversight, and to kindle and enforce the intersubjective kinship bonds among health care professionals. Only when physicians have the narrative skills to recognize medicine's ideals, swear to one another to be governed by them, and hold one another accountable to them can they live up to the profession to serve as physicians.

Physician-Society: The Public Trust

Physicians are conspicuous members of their cultures, anointed as agents of social control who deploy special powers to rescue, heal, and take command. Granting tonic authority to its physicians while regarding them with chronic suspicion, the public commands physicians to understand and treat disease while doing no harm. While holding physicians accountable to these public expectations, patients also yearn for such private benevolence from their physicians as tenderness in the face of pain, courage in the face of danger, and comfort in the face of death.

Of late, medicine in the United States has experienced highly publicized reversals in public trust with accusations of overbilling for services, withholding from patients the potential risks of research, and deriving financial benefit from professional knowledge.[74,75] Medicine's – if not individual physicians' – trustworthiness has been called into question.[76,77] Yet, patients realize that they cannot explicitly tell physicians how to practice medicine. They must have implicit trust in the virtue and wisdom of those who care for the sick.

The contradictions between a medical system that must be governed from outside and a medical system that has earned the public trust have achieved great urgency. The US culture is now actively and contentiously restructuring its health care system. Having experienced the early phases of a marketplace–driven health care system and having failed in its first attempt at health care system reform, the nation is attempting to open collective discourse in politics and the media about the value to be placed on health and health care.[78,79]

Only sophisticated narrative powers will lead to the conversations that society needs to have about its medical system. Physicians have to find ways to talk simply, honestly, and deeply with patients, families, other health care professionals, and citizens. Together, they must make responsible choices about pain, suffering, justice, and mercy. Not scientific or rational debates, these are grave and daring conversations about meaning, values, and courage. They require sophisticated narrative understandings on all conversationalists' parts of the multiple sources of meaning and the collaborative nature of authority called on to resolve issues of health and illness. With the narrative competence necessary for serious and consequential discourse, patients and physicians together can describe and work toward a medical system undivided in effectiveness, compassion, and care.

Research and Programmatic Implications

Narrative medicine suggests that many dimensions of medical research, teaching, and practice are imbued with narrative considerations and can be made more effective with narrative competence. Already, a spontaneous interest in narrative medicine has germinated from many centers in the United States and abroad, confirming the usefulness and fit of these frameworks and practices for medicine and other health care professions.[80-82] As the conceptual vision of narrative medicine becomes coherent, research agendas and action plans unfold.

The hypotheses to be tested are provocative and wide ranging. It may be that the physician equipped with the narrative capacities to recognize the plight of the patient fully and to respond with reflective engagement can achieve more effective treatment than can the physician unequipped to do so. Medical educators may find that applicants already gifted with narrative skills are better able to develop into effective physicians than are students deficient in them.

Programs have been under way for some time in incorporating narrative work into many aspects of medical education and practice. The teaching of literature in medical schools has become widely accepted as a primary means to teach about the patient's experience and the physician's interior development.[83] Narrative writing by students and physicians has become a staple in many medical schools and hospitals to strengthen reflection, self-awareness, and the adoption of patients' perspectives.[84-87] The practice of bioethics has adopted narrative theory and methods to reach beyond a rule-based, legalistic enterprise toward an individualized and meaning-based practice.[88,89] Certainly, more and more patients have insisted on achieving a narrative mastery over the events of illness, not only to unburden themselves of painful thoughts and feelings but, more fundamentally, to claim such events as parts, however unwelcome, of their lives.[90,91]

Adding to early evidence of the usefulness of narrative practices, rigorous ethnographic and outcomes studies using samples of adequate size and control have been undertaken to ascertain the influences on students, physicians, and patients of narrative practices.[92,93] Along with such outcomes research are scholarly efforts to uncover the basic mechanisms, pathways, intermediaries, and consequences of narrative practices, supplying the "basic science" of theoretical foundations and conceptual frameworks for these new undertakings.

Conclusion

The description of Ms. Lambert at the beginning of this article was written by her physician (the author) after a recent office visit and shown to her on the subsequent visit. As Ms. Lambert read the words, she realized more clearly the anguish she had been enduring. Her sisters had dismissed her concerns, saying she was imagining things about Phillip, and that had added to her own suffering. She felt relieved that her physician seemed to understand her pain, and she told the physician what her sisters had said.

"Can I show this to my sisters?" Ms. Lambert asked her physician. "Then maybe they can help me."

This essay has outlined the emergence of narrative medicine, a medicine infused with respect for the narrative dimensions of illness and caregiving. Through systematic and rigorous training in such narrative skills as close reading, reflective writing, and authentic discourse with patients, physicians and medical students can improve their care of individual patients, commitment to their own health and fulfillment, care of their colleagues, and continued fidelity to medicine's ideals. By bridging the divides that separate the physician from the patient, the self, colleagues, and society, narrative medicine can help physicians offer accurate, engaged, authentic, and effective care of the sick.

References

1. Morris DM. *Illness and Culture in the Postmodern Age.* Berkeley: University of California Press; 1998.
2. Konner M. *Medicine at the Crossroads: The Crisis in Health Care.* New York, NY: Pantheon Books; 1993.
3. Charon R. The narrative road to empathy. In: Spiro H, Curnen MGM, Peschel E, St. James D, eds. *Empathy and the Practice of Medicine: Beyond Pills and the Scalpel.* New Haven, Conn: Yale University Press; 1993:147-159.
4. Charon R. Narrative medicine: form, function, and ethics. *Ann Intern Med.* 2001;134:83-87.
5. Engel GL. The need for a new medical model: a challenge for biomedicine. *Science.* 1977;196:129-136.
6. Laine C, Davidoff F. Patient-centered medicine: a professional evolution. *JAMA.* 1996;275:152-156.
7. Greenhalgh T, Hurwitz B, eds. *Narrative Based Medicine: Dialogue and Discourse in*

Clinical Practice. London, England: BMJ Books; 1998.

8. Kleinman A. *The Illness Narratives: Suffering, Healing and the Human Condition*. New York, NY: Basic Books; 1988.

9. Brody H. *Stories of Sickness*. New Haven, Conn: Yale University Press; 1987.

10. Swenson MM, Sims SL. Toward a narrative-centered curriculum for nurse practitioners. *J Nurs Educ*. 2000;39:109-115..

11. Polkinghorne DE. *Narrative Knowing and the Human Sciences*. Albany: State University of New York Press; 1988.

12. Krieswirth M. Trusting the tale: the narrativist turn in the human sciences. *New Literary History*. 1992; 23:629-657.

13. Mishler EG. Research *Interviewing: Context and Narrative*. Cambridge, Mass: Harvard University Press; 1986.

14. Martin W. *Recent Theories of Narrative*. Ithaca, NY: Cornell University Press; 1986.

15. Brooks P. *Reading for the Plot: Design and Intention in Narrative*. New York, NY: Vintage; 1985.

16. Booth WC. *The Rhetoric of Fiction*. 2nd ed. Chicago, Ill: University of Chicago Press; 1983.

17. Lewis RWB. *The American Adam: Innocence, Tragedy and Tradition in the Nineteenth Century*. Chicago, Ill: University of Chicago Press; 1955:3.

18. Bruner J. *Actual Minds, Possible Worlds*. Cambridge, Mass: Harvard University Press; 1986.

19. Paulos JA. *Once Upon a Number: The Hidden Mathematical Logic of Stories*. New York, NY: Basic Books; 1998.

20. Smith BH. Narrative versions, narrative theories. In: Mitchell WJT, ed. *On Narrative*. Chicago, Ill: University of Chicago Press; 1981:228.

21. James H. *The Art of the Novel: Critical Prefaces*. New York, NY: Charles Scribner's Sons; 1934.

22. Barthes R. *S/Z: An Essay*. Miller R, trans. New York, NY: Hill & Wang; 1974.

23. Kermode F. *The Art of Telling: Essays on Fiction*. Cambridge, Mass: Harvard University Press; 1983.

24. Iser W. *The Act of Reading: A Theory of Aesthetic Response*. Baltimore, Md: Johns Hopkins University Press; 1978.

25. Tompkins JP, ed. *Reader-Response Criticism: From Formalism to Post-Structuralism*. Baltimore, Md: Johns Hopkins University Press; 1980.

26. James H. *The novels of George Eliot*. [First printed in Atlantic Monthly, 1866.] Reprinted in: Stang R, ed. *Discussions of George Eliot*. Boston, Mass: DC Heath & Co; 1960:5.

27. Charon R. Literature and medicine: origins and destinies. *Acad Med*. 2000;75:23-27.

28. Stolorow R, Brandchaft B, Atwood G. *Psychoanalytic Treatment: An Intersubjective Approach.* Hillsdale, NJ: Analytic Press; 1987.
29. Lipkin M, Putnam S, Lazare A, eds. *The Medical Interview: Clinical Care, Education, and Research.* New York, NY: Springer-Verlag; 1995.
30. Society for Health and Human Values. Special issue in humanities and medical education. *Acad Med.* 1995;70:755-813, 822-823.
31. Cassell E. The nature of suffering and the goals of medicine. *N Engl J Med.* 1982;306:639-645.
32. Hunter KM. *Doctors' Stories: The Narrative Structure of Medical Knowledge.* Princeton, NJ: Princeton University Press; 1993.
33. Nelson HL. *Stories and Their Limits: Narrative Approaches to Bioethics.* New York, NY: Routledge; 1997.
34. Jones AH. Literature and medicine: narrative ethics. *Lancet.* 1997;349:1243-1246.
35. Anderson C. "Forty acres of cotton waiting to be picked": medical students, storytelling, and the rhetoric of healing. *Lit Med.* 1998;17:280-297.
36. Hawkins AH. *Reconstructing Illness: Studies in Pathography.* 2nd ed. West Lafayette, Ind: Purdue University Press; 1999.
37. Selzer R. *Letters to a Young Doctor.* New York, NY: Simon & Schuster; 1982.
38. Zabarenko RN. *The Doctor Tree: Developmental Stages in the Growth of Physicians.* Pittsburgh, Pa: University of Pittsburgh Press; 1978.
39. Genette G. *Narrative Discourse: An Essay in Method.* Lewin J, trans. Ithaca, NY: Cornell University Press; 1980.
40. DeSalvo L. *Writing as a Way of Healing: How Telling Our Stories Transforms Our Lives.* San Francisco, Calif: Harper; 1999.
41. Anderson CM, ed. Writing and healing [special issue]. *Lit Med.* 2000;19:1-132.
42. Bolton G. *The Therapeutic Potential of Creative Writing: Writing Myself.* London, England: Jessica Kingsley Publishers; 1999.
43. Anderson CM, MacCurdy MM, eds. *Writing and Healing: Toward an Informed Practice.* Urbana, Ill: National Council of Teachers of English; 2000.
44. Groopman J. *The Measure of Our Days: A Spiritual Exploration of Illness.* New York, NY: Penguin; 1998.
45. Verghese A. *My Own Country: A Doctor's Story.* New York, NY: Vintage/Random House; 1995.
46. Charon R. Medical interpretation: implications of literary theory of narrative for clinical work. *J Narrative Life History.* 1993;3:79-97.
47. Weine SM. The witnessing imagination: social trauma, creative artists, and witnessing professionals. *Lit Med.* 1996; 15: 167-182.
48. Feinstein, A. *Clinical Judgment.* Baltimore, MD: Williams and Wilkins, 1967.
49. Spiro, HM, Curnen MGM, Peschel E, St. James D, eds. *Empathy and the Practice*

of Medicine: Beyond Pills and the Scalpel. New Haven, Conn: Yale University Press, 1993.

50. Toombs SK. *The Meaning of Illness: A Phenomenological Account of the Different Perspectives of Physician and Patient*. Dordrect, the Netherlands: Kluwer, 1993.

51. Novack, DH, Suchman AL, Clark W, Epstein RM, Najberg E, Kaplan C. Calibrating the physician: personal awareness and effective patient care. *JAMA* 1997; 278: 502-509.

52. Miller SZ, Schmidt HJ. The habit of humanism: a framework for making humanistic care a reflexive clinical skill. *Acad Med*. 1999; 74: 800-803.

53. Berger J, Mohr J. *A Fortunate Man*. New York, NY: Pantheon Books, 1967.

54. Fox R, Lief H. Training for 'detached concern.' In: Lief H, ed. *The Psychological Basis of Medical Practice*. New York: NY: Harper & Row, 1963: 12-35.

55. Connelly J. Being in the present moment: developing the capacity for mindfulness in medicine. *Acad Med*. 1999; 74: 420-424.

56. Halpern, J. *From Detached Concern to Empathy: Humanizing Medical Practice*. New York: NY: Oxford University Press, 2001.

57. Risdon C, Edey L. Human doctoring: bringing authenticity to our care. *Acad Med*. 1999; 74: 896-899.

58. Hawkins, AH, McEntyre, MC. *Teaching Medicine and Literature*. New York, NY: Modern Language Association, 2000.

59. Charon R, Banks JT, Connelly JE, et al. Literature and medicine: contributions to clinical practice. *Ann Internal Med*. 1995; 122: 599-606.

60. Coles R. *The Call of Stories: Teaching and the Moral Imagination*. Boston, Mass: Houghton Mifflin, 1989.

61. Skelton JR, Macleod JAA, Thomas CP. Teaching literature and medicine to medical students, part II: why literature and medicine? *Lancet*. 2001;356:2001-2003.

62. Charon R. Reading, writing, and doctoring: literature and medicine. *Am J Med Sci*. 2000;319:285-291.

63. Sacks O. *The Man Who Mistook His Wife for a Hat and Other Clinical Tales*. New York, NY: Summit Books; 1985.

64. Mates S. *The Good Doctor*. Iowa City: University of Iowa Press; 1994.

65. Williams WC. *The Doctor Stories*. New York, NY: WW Norton & Co; 1985.

66. Charon R. Medicine, the novel, and the passage of time. *Ann Intern Med*. 2000;132:63-68.

67. Toulmin S. The construal of reality: criticism in modern and postmodern science. In: Mitchell WTJ, ed. *The Politics of Interpretation*. Chicago, Ill: University of Chicago Press; 1983:99-117.

68. Ludmerer K. Time to Heal: *American Medical Education From the Turn of the Century to the Era of Managed Care*. New York, NY: Oxford University Press; 1999.

69. Bosk C. *Forgive and Remember: Managing Medical Failure.* Chicago, Ill: University of Chicago Press; 1979.

70. Balint M. *The Doctor, His Patient and the Illness.* London, England: Tavistock Publications; 1957.

71. Cruess RL, Cruess SR. Teaching medicine as a profession in the service of healing. *Acad Med.* 1997;72: 941-952.

72. Wynia MK, Latham SR, Kao AC, Berg JW, Emanuel LL. Medical professionalism in society. *N Engl J Med.* 1999;341:612-616.

73. Reynolds PP. Reaffirming professionalism through the education community. *Ann Intern Med.* 1994; 120:609-614.

74. Rodwin MA. *Medicine, Money, and Morals: Physicians' Conflicts of Interest.* New York, NY: Oxford University Press; 1993.

75. Spece R, Shumm D, Buchanan A, eds. *Conflicts of Interest in Clinical Practice and Research.* New York, NY: Oxford University Press; 1996.

76. Rothman D. Medical professionalism: focusing on the real issues. *N Engl J Med.* 2000;342:1284-1286.

77. Anders G. *Health Against Wealth: HMOs and the Breakdown of Medical Trust.* New York, NY: Houghton Mifflin; 1996.

78. Feldman DS, Novack DH, Gracelv E. Effects of managed care on physician-patient relationships, quality of care, and the ethical practice of medicine. *Arch Intern Med.* 1998;158:1626-1632.

79. Morreim EH. *Balancing Act: The New Medical Ethics of Medicine's New Economics.* Washington, DC: Georgetown University Press; 1995.

80. Hurwitz B. Narrative and the practice of medicine. *Lancet.* 2000;356:2086-2089.

81. Harden J. Language, discourse and the chronotope: applying literary theory to the narratives in health care. *J Adv Nurs.* 2000;31:506-512.

82. Heliker D. Transformation of story to practice: an innovative approach to long-term care. *Issues Mental Health Nurs* 1999; 20:513-515.

83. Hunter KM, Charon R, Coulehan JL. The study of literature in medical education. *Acad Med.* 1995; 70:787-794.

84. Charon R. To render the lives of patients. *Lit. Med.* 1986;5:58-74.

85. Branch W, Pels RJ, Lawrence RS, et al. Critical incident reports from third-year medical students. *N Engl J Med.* 1993;329:1130-1132.

86. Reifler DR. "I actually don't mind the bone saw": narratives of gross anatomy. *Lit Med.*1996;15:183-199.

87. Winckler M. *The Case of Dr. Sachs.* Asher L, trans. New York, NY: Seven Stories Press; 2000.

88. Charon R, Montello M, eds. *The Practice of Narrative Ethics.* New York, NY: Routledge. In press.

89. Chambers T. *The Fiction of Bioethics: Cases as Literary Texts.* New York, NY: Rout-ledge; 1999.

90. Bauby JD. *The Diving Bell and the Butterfly.* Leggatt J, trans. New York, NY: Vintage/Random; 1998.

91. Mairs N. *Waist-High in the World: A Life Among the Nondisabled.* Boston, Mass: Beacon Press; 1996.

92. Smyth JM, Stone AA, Hurewitz A, Kaell A. Effects of writing about stressful experiences on symptom reduction in patients with asthma or rheumatoid *JAMA.* 1999;281:1304-1309.

93. Pennebacker JW. Telling stories: the health benefits of narrative. *Lit Med.* 2000;19:3-18.

15

Abraham Verghese, "The Physician as Storyteller,"
Annals of Internal Medicine 135: 11 (2001), 1012-1017

As many of the articles in this volume have illustrated, over the course of the twentieth century a major concern when bringing the humanities into the context of medical education has been to overcome the challenge of interdisciplinary communication. The various meetings and conferences sponsored by the Society for Health and Human Values in the 1960s and 1970s repeatedly confronted questions of how much disciplinary identity – defined by specialized skills, languages, and conceptual frameworks – can be preserved, or must be shed, when interacting with professionals-in-training for another disciplinary pursuit, or engaging in "border crossings" as Delese Wear puts it.[1] By the 1980s and 1990s, the notion of physicians having indoctrination in the humanities was increasingly accepted, and some flourished to garner respect from different disciplines for their achievements. Examples include Jacalyn Duffin, MD, PhD, a hematologist and medical educator at Queen's University in Canada as well as Hannah Chair of History of Medicine; Rita Charon, MD, PhD, who is discussed in the previous chapter in this volume and pioneered an educational program in Narrative Medicine.

Abraham Verghese, MD, Professor of Medicine at Stanford University, is another example. The author of nonfiction and fiction books, including the best-selling novel *Cutting for Stone* and the memoir *The Tennis Partner*, Verghese is often asked in interviews whether he considers himself primarily a doctor or a writer. His answer: a doctor, because to him medicine is "a ministry with a calling," but yet the accolades his writing has received validate to him an effort to produce work that, in his words, "is in that realm of being on the edge of science yet very much about the art." Indeed, if the medical humanities has accomplished anything throughout the twentieth century, it is certainly to have created a space where science and art can come together and suggest new insights to the world of human interactions.[2]

In "The Physician as Storyteller," Verghese reflects on his own development as a writer of stories and how his understanding of character, metaphor, and plot helped him to unravel and accept the complexities of patients' experiences. First delivered as the Nicholas E. Davies Memorial Lecture at the 2000 American College of Physicians – American Society of Internal Medicine Annual Session, Verghese's piece provided timely testimony of the power of stories to allow patients' voices to be heard.

1   Wear D. Border crossings in medical education. *Pharos*. 1997;60:22-6

2   Tracie White writing about Verghese in "Stanford's Abraham Verghese honored as both author and healer" in *Scope* - http://scopeblog.stanford.edu/2014/02/25/stanfords-abraham-verghese-honored-as-both-author-and-healer/#sthash.yms7APni.dpuf (Accessed October 5, 2014)

The Physician as Storyteller

Abraham Verghese, MD

A s physicians, most of us become involved in the stories of our patients' lives. Sometimes we are simply witnesses, chroniclers of the story in the medical chart. But often we become players in the stories. Our actions change the narrative trajectory, or else the patient's or the family's rendering of the story credits us with influencing the story. We may, as Arthur Frank suggests (1), become the "spokesperson" for the disease, and our patients' stories "come to depend heavily on repetition" of what we say. The following excerpt from Troyat's biography of Chekhov illustrates how a physician becomes player and catalyst in a story (2). Anton Chekhov, who was both writer and physician, died young of tuberculosis. In the last days of his life, Chekhov left his home in Russia and went to Germany, to a spa near the Black Forest. As his condition worsened, he sought the aid of the spa physician, Dr. Schwöhrer, who was given the difficult task of caring for a dying physician.

> The windows were wide open, but he could not stop panting; his temples were bathed in sweat. Dr. Schwöhrer arrived at two o'clock. When Chekhov saw him, he sat up, leaned back against the pillows, and in a final reflex of courtesy, mastered his weak German and said, *"Ich sterbe."* [I am dying.] Schwöhrer immediately gave him a camphor injection, but his heart failed to react. He was about to send for an oxygen pillow when Chekhov, lucid to the end, protested in a broken voice, "What's the use? Before it arrives, I'll be a corpse." So Dr. Schwöhrer sent for a bottle of champagne.

> When it came, Chekhov took a glass and, turning to Olga [his wife], said with a smile, "It's been so long since I've had champagne." He emptied the glass slowly and lay down on his left side. A few moments later he stopped breathing. He had passed from life to death with characteristic simplicity.

> It was July 2, 1904, three o'clock in the morning. A large black-winged moth had flown in through the window and was banging wildly against the lamp.

The muffled sound grew maddeningly distracting. Dr. Schwöhrer withdrew after a few words of consolation. All at once, there was a joyous explosion: the cork had popped out of the champagne bottle and foam was fizzing out after it. The moth found its way out of the window and disappeared into the sultry night. Silence returned. When day broke at last, Olga was still sitting and staring into her husband's face. It was peaceful, smiling, knowing. "There were no human voices, no everyday sounds," she wrote. "There was only beauty, peace, and the grandeur of death."

Dr. Schwöhrer's act of ordering champagne and raising a glass with his patient led to a cascade of events (at least in the telling) that ended with the cork popping out of the bottle and the moth escaping. This anecdote summarizes the theses of this paper: 1) *story* helps us link and make sense of events in our lives; 2) we as physicians *create* stories as often as we record them—we are catalysts in stories even if our actions are less dramatic than Dr. Schwöhrer's; and 3) we are characters in various stories, walking on and off the stage in the tales that take place in our hospitals and clinics. Indeed, our lives are seamlessly, mostly unconsciously entwined with the stories we hear and tell, with "those we dream or imagine or would like to tell, all of which are reworked in that story of our own lives that we narrate to ourselves in an episodic, sometimes semiconscious, but virtually uninterrupted monologue" (3).

It may take years of practice for a physician to appreciate and accept his or her role as storymaker and storyteller. John Berger, in his extraordinary book *A Fortunate Man*, captures this development beautifully. Berger followed an English country doctor, Dr. John Sassall, for the better part of 2 years. The author tells us that when Sassall began practice, he saw himself as a sort of mobile, one-man hospital, delivering babies in caravans and operating on kitchen tables.

It would almost be true to say that he sought out accidents.

He had no patience with anything except emergencies or serious illness ... He dealt only with crises in which he was the central character: or, to put it another way, in which the patient was *simplified* by the degree of his physical dependence on the doctor. He was also simplified himself, because the chosen pace of his life made it impossible and unnecessary for him to examine his own motives. (4)

But as the years went on, the doctor began to change. He also noticed that his patients were changing. A girl whom he had treated for measles was now having her first labor. A man who had been in perfect health had shot himself in the head. The doctor's thinking evolved, as shown in the following vivid example:

> One day he was called to a couple of old-age pensioners. They had lived in the Forest for thirty years. Nobody had anything very special to say about them. . . . They usually went to the pub at about eight every Saturday evening. A long time before, the wife had worked as a maid in the big house of a near-by village. The husband had worked on the railway. The husband said that his wife was "bleeding from down below."
>
> Sassall talked to her a little and then asked her to undress so that he could examine her. He went into the kitchen to wait until she was ready. There the husband looked at him anxiously and took the clock from the mantelpiece to wind it. At this age if the wife has to go into hospital, it can be the beginning of the end for them both.
>
> When he went back into the parlour, the wife was lying on the ottoman. Her stockings were rolled down and her dress up. "She" was a man. He examined her. The trouble was severe piles. Neither he nor the husband nor she referred to the sexual organs which should not have been there. They were ignored. Or, rather, he was forced to accept them, as they had done, according to their own reasoning which he would never know.
>
> He became aware of the possibility of his patients changing. They, as they became more used to him, sometimes made confessions for which there was no medical reference so far as he had learnt. He began to take a different view of the meaning of the term crisis. (5)

Later in the book, Berger goes on to say an extraordinary thing.

> An unhappy patient comes to a doctor to offer him an illness—in the hope that this part of him, at least (the illness) may be recognizable. His proper self he believes to be unknowable. In the light of world he is nobody: by his own lights the world is nothing. Clearly the task of the doctor – unless he merely accepts the illness at face value and incidentally guarantees for himself a 'difficult' patient – is to recognize the man. If the man can begin to feel recognized – and such recognition may well include aspects of his

character which he has not yet recognized himself – the hopeless nature of his unhappiness will have been changed: he may even have the chance of being happy. (6)

These excerpts from Troyat and Berger make the point, not by elaborate proofs but in stories themselves, that story is important, that we physicians are inevitably players in other people's stories.

Storytelling Craft and the Internist

Can we become better internists by learning about some of the tools that the writer possesses? Clearly, the opposite is true: It is wonderful training for a writer to be a physician, to be an internist in particular. Aphorisms such as "God is in the details" are staples of both medical training and creative writing classes. Learning how to inspect, to palpate, to percuss, to listen, and to develop skills of acute observation is excellent training for any writer. But are there tools that we can pick up from the writer that might improve our skills as physicians? Or, if a writer's bag of tricks doesn't improve our medical skills, can it improve the quality of our daily lives, our satisfaction in what we do, and – most importantly – can it improve the lives of our patients? This link between reading and writing and empathetic care giving has been the focus of intense scholarly study (7-10) to which the reader is referred for more details. Like all aspiring writers, I read the standard books: E.M. Forster's *Aspects of the Novel* (11); John Gardner's books, *The Art of Fiction* and *On Moral Fiction*; and Dorothea Brande's *Becoming a Writer* (12-14), to name a few. When one reads about the craft of writing, the pillars invariably referred to are *story, character,* and *metaphor,* which are fundamental to good writing in the same way that internal medicine skills rest on understanding the mechanisms behind dyspnea, edema, polyuria, and other cardinal manifestations of disease.

Story

Writing texts commonly state that story is all about conflict, crisis, and resolution. Or that one needs the "Three Ds": Drama equals Desire and Danger (15). For example, if a physician who attended the recent American College of Physicians-American Society of Internal Medicine meeting in Philadelphia wrote a story about her experience, beginning with the flight to Philadelphia and followed by the walk down Market Street, the visit to the Liberty Bell, the meeting with colleagues for breakfast, the sessions she attended, there is no story, no matter how well the physician writes. (Or no *plot* to the story; though for the purposes of this paper, we will not belabor the distinction and use "story" in its broader and commonly used sense.) On the other hand, if during the flight to the convention the physician had a wonderful conversation with his seatmate, who upon landing offered a ride to the convention but then at gunpoint took him to an ATM, emptied his account, stripped him of identity, and left him wandering naked in Philadelphia while the gunman attended the meeting in his place—*now*, we have a story!

Stories need more than conflict and resolution, though. James Joyce spoke of how every story has to have an epiphany, which was the *raison d'être* of the story (16). It is a moment – typically in the head of the protagonist – where a person or an event is seen in such a strange light that it is seen anew, and the viewer is suddenly transformed. Anne Hunsaker Hawkins described the epiphany as "those dimensions of narrative that one might think of as 'vertical,' not horizontal or linear; total, rather than sequential. Narrative, then, whether in literature or in life, could be said to move through nodes of the epiphanic; it moves toward and then away from moments of recognition, insight, and the sudden apprehension of meaning." (17)

Can a story have no resolution? Indeed, yes. Many modern short stories do not have a clear resolution, and yet not having a resolution *is* the resolution. Many a war movie ends with the two combatants still poised on opposing hills and eyeing each other with binoculars, and the epiphany –

> *"The more years I spend as a teacher of medicine, the more I am intrigued by patients with stories that appear to have no conclusions."*

the closure – is the understanding that this battle will never end.

How do these ideas about story relate to internists? I believe that all patients we see, no matter how often we see them or how benign we consider their illnesses to be, are in the midst of a story. For patients, story begins the moment they walk through the portals of the hospital or through the doors of our clinics. When they go to buy groceries, when they drop their children off at school, there's no story. But when they see a physician, the three D's lurk in the background. There is *danger* in the visit, even a "routine" one for, say, a mammogram or a physical; they have the *desire* not to hear bad news; and therefore there is *drama*—and therefore there is *story*.

The more years I spend as a teacher of medicine, the more I am intrigued by patients with stories that appear to have no conclusions. Housestaff often tend to be most comfortable with individuals who come in with very clear-cut stories. Chest pain becomes "Rule Out Myocardial Infarction," or ROMI in my hospital, and a few days later, it becomes MIRO—"MI Ruled Out." Then a few days later a thallium stress test follows, and the patient is channeled to the intervention suites or the bypass factories, or else back to medical treatment. These scenarios are comfortable, at least for the housestaff, because there is a clear road map. (The mere existence of a road map doesn't mean that this is the best path for the patient; elsewhere [18] I have written of the superhighway leading to bypass surgery.) Whenever I hear a certain reluctance on the part of my housestaff to discuss or see a patient or when I hear the words "placement problem," I worry that we are dealing with a story that has not found its epiphany. The challenge is to enter that room despite the magnetic draw of beepers pulling us away and the seemingly more urgent needs of other patients. The challenge is to engage the patient and the family and find the epiphany, even if the epiphany is simply the understanding that there is nothing more to be done medically. The epiphany might simply be a coming to terms with the illness by all concerned— patient, family, and doctors.

When HIV landed in the laps of infectious disease specialists (and many of us were caught up in the "conceit of cure" till that point), it was as if we had been forced to don the mantle of the oncologist. Most of us found out, painfully, that in having no cure to offer, we actually had everything to offer. We discovered what the word "healing" meant and what made the horse-and- buggy doctor of a century ago so effective. By "healing" I simply mean crossing the traditional threshold of a medical–industrial complex and beginning to engage with the patient, with their story, on their turf, in their house, and engaging with their families and loved ones and their stories. A helpful analogy for medical students to understand the distinction between curing and healing is the following: If one day they were to return to their homes and find that they had been robbed of all their valuables, and if the police should in short order find the robber and return all the valuables, the students would be *cured* ... but they would not be *healed*. Their sense of violation would remain for many more days. All illness (particularly AIDS) has these two dimensions: a physical deficit and a spiritual violation. And when there is no cure, the one thing we can offer is to really under- stand the story that is playing out, to aid and abet its satisfactory conclusion. As Charon says, "Paying close attention to language, diction, metaphor, and reader response in texts permits one to pay similarly close attention to the language, mode of speaking, metaphorical content, and allusiveness of patients' histories" (19).

We can be, in other words, like Dr. Schwöhrer, a facilitator of the story. We can order the champagne.

Character

An important lesson a writer learns is that no matter how good his or her story, it is really characters who drive stories. A clever story by itself makes for very dull reading unless a very compelling character makes the story come about.

What ingredients make fictional and real characters compelling and memorable? Part of it is their physical appearance and the accouterments of their profession, hobby, trade, interest, ethnicity, and religion. The rare patient in my county hospital who has fluffy organdy lace bathroom slippers, a sheer silk gown, and a tangerine-colored makeup case on the bedside stand is a different patient from the tattooed prisoner who arrives sans baggage other than chains and handcuffs, even if both patients have the same disease. Physicians are tuned in to appearance, trained to spot physical clues that suggest, say, hyperthyroidism, Marfan syndrome, myxedema, or cirrhosis. But how do we really get to know *character* as opposed to *disease* manifestations? And how do novelists make character come alive?

Novelists create rounded characters mostly through dialogue and by the actions of their characters. What a character says is terribly important, particularly when it is in tension with what the reader (or the doctor) knows about the patient. In medicine, dialogue is the primary means by which we understand the nuances of character. After all, that is how patients approach us, by recounting their story of what happened, which we then translate into the history of the present illness. The patient's account of his or her illness usually is unique and completely different from what we record in the chart. These tales are told in what Mishler calls "the voice of the lifeworld" (20), which includes the voice of the patient. We typically translate this into the "the voice of medicine," which goes something like this: "This-47-year-old-white-male-was-in-his-usual-state-of-health-until-five-days-prior-to-admission-when-he-noticed-acute-onset-of . . . ." Such technical language is necessary and important in diagnosis, but in such translation we might lose our ability to imagine the patient's suffering (21). Medical students, as they learn the voice of medicine, may begin to talk about the "diabetic foot in bed three" and the "MI in bed four." Walker Percy (22) referred to these kinds of habits as the "cowpaths," the increasingly deep ruts that we fall into whenever we take a professional language and adopt it. Any professional language brings with it the risk that it will also put blinders on us, bring about an atrophy of our imagination, a waning of our ability to understand the suffering of the patient.

This dichotomy between the Voice of the Patient and the Voice of Medicine came home to me some years ago when I was asked to see a man in his seventies who had undergone a laminectomy to remove a bulging disc and had developed infection at the operative site caused by an unusual organism, *Corynebacterium xerosis.* The patient made the slow progression from hospital to wheelchair at home, then to walker and then to cane. It took many visits with him to really appreciate the humanity behind that crusty, stoic, Tennessee exterior. I remember that he always used to talk about his Hickman catheter as his "watering hose." (And his wife would say, "Yes, and it's as limp and floppy as your own watering hose!") My office nurses grew to love him. He was excited to know that his illness had been so unique that I had submitted a case report about his illness and the infecting organism. It confirmed for him what most of us want to think about *our* illnesses: that they are unique. I had the opportunity one morning to share the reprint of the paper (23) with him. He sat down to read it with a great deal of excitement. Then his face fell. He looked up and said, "Abraham, there's nothing about me in this paper!" The cold, unimaginative language of science had completely stripped away his story and in the process, it seemed to him, his humanity. It was an important lesson for me on how dissimilar the Voice of Medicine can be from the Voice of the Patient.

Metaphor

Metaphor is at the heart of good literature. Flannery O'Connor, in her story "A Good Man Is Hard to Find," describes the mother as having a face "as broad and innocent as a cabbage." (24) We understand perfectly what she is saying. The great challenge in writing is to come up with original metaphors and not clichés. (We can no longer say that the road was a ribbon of moonlight or talk about the patter of little feet.)

To quote Ozick, "Inspiration is ad hoc and has no history. Metaphor relies on what has been experienced before; it transforms the strange into the familiar." (25) Medicine, based as it is on centuries of experience, has a rich heritage of metaphors, the variety of which astounds secular writers. For example, we can boast the strawberry tongue, the raspberry tongue, the cherry angioma, the cherry red spot, the melon seed body of tuberculous arthritis, the mulberry molar, and the apple core lesion, to name just a few fruit-related metaphors. We could make similar lists referring to vegetables, insects, vertebrates, and beverages.

But metaphors do much more than just portray disease. As Ozick (25) writes, "through metaphorical con- centration, doctors can imagine what it is to be their patients. Those who have no pain can imagine those who suffer. Those at the center can imagine what it is to be outside. The strong can imagine the weak. Illuminated lives can imagine the dark."

Where are the metaphors of modern medicine? It is startling to realize that so few medical metaphors have been coined in the last 70 years. New diseases such as AIDS, Lyme disease, *Legionella* infections, and ehrlichiosis have consumed our attention, but I can't think of too many new metaphors they have generated. Their absence is a sad reflection of our technological times, a suggestion that the romance of medicine has atrophied, that the skills of observation that characterized a William Osler or a Joseph Bell (the real-life inspiration for Sherlock Holmes) are no longer as evident. Perhaps we are not training individuals to think as classically trained internists of old would think. Or perhaps these abilities suffer when students are no longer reading Thomas Wolfe or *Arrowsmith* but instead are watching shows such as *ER* and its clones. Fowles (26) talks about a "prevalent form of blindness, directly caused by the terrible and crippling atrophy of the imaginative faculty (being unable to slip down the magical passage from the little signals we call words into far richer worlds than any film or TV 'version' will ever be able to present)."

Conclusion

A sense for the stories unfolding before us will perhaps allow us to be more conscious of bringing people to the epiphanies that their stories require. By being attuned to character, not just through appearance but particularly through dialogue, we will remember the voice of the patient, even though it is the voice of medicine that we record in the chart. To hear the voice of the patient preserves our capacity to imagine the suffering of the patient. We should be bold with language, willing to recall and to invent new metaphors, willing to write and to think about disease in memorable and metaphorical ways, willing to call up colorful imagery to describe disease (in place of mind-numbing acronyms). We should be not just "doctors for adults" but also ministers of healing, storytellers, storymakers, and players in the greatest drama of all: the story of our patients' lives as well as our own.

References

Berger J, Mohr J. *A Fortunate Man.* New York: Pantheon Books; 1981.

Brande D. *Becoming a Writer.* Los Angeles: Tarcher; 1981.

Brody H. *Stories of Sickness.* New Haven, CT: Yale Univ Pr; 1987.

Brooks P. *Reading for the Plot: Design and Intention in Narrative.* Cambridge, MA: Harvard Univ Pr; 1992:3.

Burroway J. *Writing Fiction: A Guide to Narrative Craft.* 3rd ed. New York: HarperCollins; 1992.

Charon R, Banks JT, Connelly JE, Hawkins AH, Hunter KM, Jones AH, et al. Literature and medicine: contributions to clinical practice. *Ann Intern Med.* 1995;122:599-606. [PMID: 7887555]

Charon R. The narrative road to empathy. In: Spiro H, McCrea Curnen MG, Peschel E, St James D, eds. *Empathy and the Practice of Medicine: Beyond Pills and the Scalpel.* New Haven CT: Yale Univ Pr; 1993:147-9.

Forster EM. *Aspects of the Novel.* New York: Harcourt, Brace & World;

Fowles J. Untitled chapter. In: Fraser A, ed. *The Pleasure of Reading.* London: Bloomsbury Pr; 1992:74.

Frank A. *The Wounded Storyteller.* Chicago: Univ of Chicago Pr; 1995:6.

Gardner J. *On Moral Fiction.* New York: Basic Books; 1978.

Gardner J. *The Art of Fiction.* Notes on Craft for Young Writers. New York: Knopf; 1984.

Hawkins AH. Medical ethics and epiphanic dimension of narrative. In: Nelson H, ed. *Stories and Their Limits.* New York: Routledge; 1997:153-70.

Hunter KM. *Doctors' Stories: The Narrative Structure of Medical Knowledge.* Princeton, NJ: Princeton Univ Pr; 1991.

Jones AH. Reading patients— cautions and concerns. *Lit Med.* 1994;13:190-200. [PMID: 7823627]

Krish G, Beaver R, Sarubbi F, Verghese A. Corynebacterium equis vertebral osteomyelitis. *J Clin Microbiol.* 1989;27:2869-70 [PMID: 2592549].

Mishler EG. *The Discourse of Medicine: Dialectics of Medical Interviews.* Norwood, NY: Ablex; 1984.

O'Connor F. A good man is hard to find. In: *The Complete Stories.* New York: Farrar, Straus & Giroux; 1971:117.

Ozick C. *Metaphor & Memory.* New York: Alfred A. Knopf; 1989:265-83.

Percy W. *Lancelot.* New York: Farrar, Straus & Giroux; 1977:3.

Troyat H. *Chekhov.* New York: Ballantine; 1988:332-3.

Verghese A. Bypass nation. *Talk.* 1999;March:106-9.

Wear D. Border crossings in medical education. *Pharos.* 1997;60:22-6 [PMID: 9038092].

16

Jack Coulehan, "Today's Professionalism: Engaging the Mind but not the Heart," *Academic Medicine* 80:10 (2005), 892-98.

Editor's note: As with other more recently published articles in this volume, I asked authors if they would be willing to reflect on their piece and add introductory comments that would help frame it, or enable them to address issues raised since its original publication. The following remarks are from the author, Jack Coulehan, MD, Senior Fellow, Center for Medical Humanities, Compassionate Care, and Bioethics, Stony Brook University.

I wrote "Today's Professionalism" ten years ago when my medical school, like others around the country, was in the process of developing a new competency-based curriculum that included professionalism as a core element. Professionalism as an essential competency in medical education had only recently been "rediscovered." Professional values, ethics, and traditions had always been present, of course, but the idea of repackaging them under the banner of "professionalism" was relatively new. A major stimulus for this change was the widespread belief that a decline in physicians' professional behavior had contributed significantly to many ills in the health care system: patient dissatisfaction, diminished trust in physicians, excessive and unnecessary testing, economic conflicts of interest, an epidemic of negligence suits, and others. At the time I chaired a faculty task force that drafted a list of professionalism "subcompetencies" students would be required to master; one, for example, was "Exhibits professionalism through compassion, altruism, integrity, respect, responsibility and sensitivity in meeting obligations inherent in the practice of medicine."

The good news was that traditional virtues were being explicitly cited as endpoints of medical education. The bad news: the process seemed to go no further. Virtues were simply listed, much as you would tick off items of medical knowledge, like pathologies of the heart that had to be mastered before graduation. But virtues are habits of the heart, not packets of knowledge about the heart. In what ways would our new curriculum foster these habits? How would we guide students to "exhibit" compassion, altruism, and so forth?

I well understood the power of the "hidden curriculum" to pervert explicit teaching about medical virtue.[1,2] It seemed clear to me that any curricular focus on professionalism that did not address core issues, like character formation and hospital culture, was bound to degenerate into rules of professional etiquette, rather than a becoming a force that nurtured values and decreased the vulnerabilities of our future physicians. So how do we get to the heart of the matter? How can we narrow the gap between the values we "teach" (say) and the values students learn from observing our behavior (do)?[3] Writing "Today's Professionalism: Engaging the Mind but Not the Heart" helped me reflect on these issues.

A decade later, I still enjoy the essay's rhetorical flourishes. More importantly, I think the analysis remains sound, although in recent years I've been impressed by the increasing sophistication of discourse about professionalism. It seems that character formation has come out of the closet. I'm confident that the four initiatives suggested in the essay – major attention to positive role modeling, frequent opportunities for personal reflection, development of narrative competence, and inclusion of service learning – are touchstone components of professional character formation: professionalism that engages the heart, as well as the mind.

1. Hafferty FW, Franks R. The hidden curriculum, ethics teaching, and the structure of medical education. *Acad Med.* 1994;69: 861-71.
2. Hunnert EM, Hafferty F, Christakis D. Characteristics of the informal curriculum and trainee's ethical choices. *Acad Med.* 1996; 71:624-33.
3. Inui TS. *A Flag in the Wind: Educating for Professionalism in Medicine.* Washington, DC: Association of American Medical Colleges, 2003.

Today's Professionalism:
Engaging the Mind but not the Heart

Jack Coulehan, MD

Abstract. Professionalism is *au courant* in medicine today, but the movement to teach and evaluate professionalism presents a conundrum to medical educators. Its intent is laudable: to produce humanistic and virtuous physicians who will be better able to cope with and overcome the dehumanizing features of the health care system in the United States. However, its impact on medical education is likely to be small and misleading because current professionalism curricula focus on lists of rules and behaviors. While such curricula usually refer to virtues and personal qualities, these are peripheral because their impacts cannot be specifically assessed.

The author argues that today's culture of medicine is hostile to altruism, compassion, integrity, fidelity, self-effacement, and other traditional qualities. Hospital culture and the narratives that support it often embody a set of professional qualities that are diametrically opposed to virtues that are explicitly taught as constituting the "good" doctor. Young physicians experience internal conflict as they try to reconcile the explicit and covert curricula, and they often develop non-reflective professionalism. Additional courses on professionalism are unlikely to alter this process. Instead, the author proposes a more comprehensive approach to changing the culture of medical education to favor an approach he calls narrative-based professionalism and to address the tension between self-interest and altruism. This approach involves four specific catalysts: professionalism role-modeling, self-awareness, narrative competence, and community service.

H L. Mencken wrote, "There is always an easy solution to every human problem—neat, plausible, and wrong."[1] This applies to today's project to instill "professionalism" in medical education. I believe the movement to teach and evaluate professionalism in medical training is threatened with failure because the intervention is too simple, too neat, too flimsy, and doesn't engage the problems it attempts to address. These problems, as I conceive them, are both internal and external to the profession. Internally, the medical community suffers from depleted moral imagination, while vast numbers of its individual practitioners suffer from existential conflict and timidity of response. Externally, the profession is beset on all sides by the disappointment, dissatisfaction, and misunderstanding of the people whom it is supposed to serve. So yes, professionalism in medicine does appear to be in bad shape; but no, Professionalism – with a capital "P," indicating the Simple Answer – will not revive it.

In this essay I present a series of reflections on today's culture of medicine and medical education, with particular emphasis on the V-word: virtue. I want to address the issue that Larry Churchill raised more than 15 years ago, "How did we get to this point of not valuing a distinctive professional ethic? A profession without its own distinctive moral convictions has nothing to profess."[2] If indeed we as medical educators have nothing to profess, then an aggressive program to instill and promote a code of professional behavior in physicians-in-training will be artificial and bound to fail. In place of professionalism, I want to suggest a more comprehensive approach to a rebirth of medical morality for the 21st century.

The Recent History of Professionalism

By the early 1970s, biomedical ethics, which focuses mostly on patient rights and the structure and process of shared decision making, had replaced old-fashioned professional ethics in medical education. Many believed that professional ethics, based on virtue and duty, had confined itself to the special interests and obligations of physicians.[2-6] In fact, the discipline had acquired a bad reputation as being more a set of rules to protect the interests of physicians than a code of moral conduct to protect patients. A few biomedical ethicists developed a new approach to morality from the old vantage point of professional virtue,[7-11] but their works tended to lack the edge and bite of "hard" ethics and rarely served as the meat and potatoes of ethics teaching. In teaching about the "good" doctor, we focused on talking the talk (ethics courses) and assumed that walking the walk (following in the footsteps of exemplary physicians) would take care of itself; i.e., physicians-in-training would acquire professional values by osmosis from mentors and role models as they progressed through their training, just as generations of physicians had presumably done in the past.

In 2005, the situation has changed dramatically. Today, the term "professionalism" springs like kudzu from every nook and cranny of medical education. In the last few years, the Association of American Medical Colleges (AAMC), the Accreditation Council for Graduate Medical Education, the

American College of Physicians, and other organizations have generated major initiatives to teach professionalism as a core competency in medicine and also to require that educators measure the outcome of their efforts.[12-17]

Why have we resurrected this explicit focus on "a distinctive professional virtue"? Let me present my own view of the forces that medical educators have been obliged to respond to, in order to meet their goal of producing highly competent and ethical professionals. Over the past several decades, medicine in the United States has evolved into a vast, increasingly expensive technological profit center, in which self-interest is all too easily conflated with altruism. While medical treatment became more efficacious than ever before, it also became potentially more harmful to patients. As technology advanced, patients developed higher expectations of cure, but at the same time they became progressively less satisfied with the personal aspects of medical care. While specialists spent more time wielding the mighty machine, they spent less time listening to or connecting with their patients. Meanwhile, commercialism began to run rampant in medicine, including the rapid development of for-profit hospital systems and managed care organizations and the appearance of a vast array of opportunities for physicians to make money from commercial relationships, especially with pharmaceutical companies. Commercialism set the stage for increasing conflict between the interests of physicians and their patients. The costs of the system skyrocketed, but it nonetheless remained inequitable and inaccessible to significant segments of the population. The evolution of applied science was not accompanied by the evolution of a legal right to health care. Yet our lingering cultural belief in equitable and relationship-based medicine haunts us and casts a pall over today's machine-based medical practice.

As these problems developed, medical educators, far from ignoring them, responded with several generations of well-intended solutions that aimed to integrate the knowledge, skills, and attitudes of good doctoring into this new technological environment. Early innovations included creating the specialty of family medicine, formulating a so-called new paradigm for whole-person medicine (the biopsychosocial model), adding new skills to the curriculum (e.g., courses in communication, humanities, and biomedical ethics), and adopting more creative methods of teaching (e.g., problem-based learning). More recently, the evidence-based medicine movement has provided a means of cutting through the information-dense background to teach physicians to make more scientifically based clinical decisions, and, hence, to make patient care more beneficial. Still, the situation did not appreciably improve; while the *minds* of our students became sharper than ever, their *hearts* appeared to be listless, and their moral compasses adrift. At this juncture, educators adopted an entirely "new" tack, which in essence is a return to pre-1970s professional values; that is, they began insisting that professionalism itself be taught and evaluated.

In medicine, professionalism "requires the physician to serve the interests of the patient above his or her self-interest. Professionalism aspires to altruism, accountability, excellence, duty, service, honor, integrity and respect for others."[18] This definition includes conduct (serving), aims (aspiring), *and* virtues or qualities (altruism, etc.). Note that these terms refer to different but intrinsically related aspects of human functioning. Ideally, conduct arises from aims, which, in turn, are conditioned by qualities. For young physicians to become more humane and effective healers, they must demonstrate professional conduct, which they are unlikely to do unless their education also explicitly nourishes motivation and virtue. My criticism of the professionalism movement is that, in the attempt to render professionalism more quantifiable, it may use skills and practices as surrogates for virtue. Becoming a physician involves *witnessing*, and not just behaving. To the extent that professionalism becomes a list of required practices, it is an example of H.L. Mencken's neat and simple, but wrong, solution.

> "My criticism of the professionalism movement is that, in the attempt to render professionalism more quantifiable, it may use skills and practices as surrogates for virtue."

The State of the Art

The tradition of medical professionalism holds that there are deeply held values internal to the goals of the profession, a commitment to moral behavior grounded in "that which I hold most sacred" (to quote a contemporary version of the Hippocratic Oath), and, as a result of sharing these values and beliefs, a strong sense of community identity in medicine. Values, beliefs, and community are thus essential components of medical professionalism. But unless manifest in the lived experiences – the stories or narratives – of physicians, they are mere academic abstractions, like the bioethical principles of autonomy and beneficence. For medical professionalism to mold the behavior of physicians-in-training, it must be articulated as a meta-narrative that has developed over 2,500 years as a summation of, and reflection upon, many thousands of actual physicians' stories from different times and cultures. Trainees must also experience professionalism as a bundle of contemporary narratives, either observed directly through role-model physicians and other health professionals, or indirectly through stories and film. In other words, to learn professionalism is to enter into a certain kind of narrative and make it one's own.

I will use the term *narrative-based professionalism* to refer to this tradition, contrasting it with *rule-based professionalism*, which is the term I'll use to describe the sets of objectives, competencies, and measurable behaviors that attempt to capture the concept of professionalism, but without focusing on its narrative ethos. I believe this dichotomy has heuristic value, although obviously neither "type" exists in pure form. My claim is that, given the current state of medical education, professionalism curricula are more likely to continue to move in the direction of lists of acceptable behaviors than to embody the full narrative tradition. To explain what I mean by this, let me describe briefly the texture of a medical trainee's experience as it relates human values and professionalism.

Tacit versus Explicit Learning

Many observers have described a conflict between what we think we are teaching medical students and young physicians (the explicit, or formal, curriculum) and a second set of beliefs and values that they learn from other sources (the tacit, informal, or hidden curriculum).[19-29] This conflict begins during students' preclinical education and becomes more pronounced in the hospital and clinic. As students and house officers wend their way through years of training, they gradually adopt the medical culture and its value system as their own. An important aspect of this socialization is the transfer, to trainees from their role models, of a set of beliefs and values regarding what it means to be a "good" physician.

The explicit component of professional development includes courses, classes, rounds, advice, or other teaching designed to instill professional values. Tacit learning, by contrast, includes the learning and socialization processes that instill professional values and identity without explicitly articulating those issues. This hidden curriculum continues throughout medical training. While the explicit curriculum focuses on empathy, communication, relief of suffering, trust, fidelity, and pursuing the patient's best interest, in the hospital and clinic environment these values are largely pushed aside by the tacit learning of objectivity, detachment, self-interest, and distrust—of emotions, patients, insurance companies, administrators, and the state.

The Hospital Narratives

Culture consists of the matrix of stories, symbols, beliefs, attitudes, and patterns of behavior in which we find ourselves. With this in mind, I want to propose a mental experiment and ask the reader to immerse her- or himself in a contemporary teaching hospital. Once there, listen to the conversations among physicians and between physicians and other health professionals. Pay close attention to the texture of hospital practice, in particular to its oral culture, the stories that surround you. What sort of stories are they? How can they be categorized? Which of the narratives appear to be especially meaningful to their narrators and audiences? In what ways do they fit together? What do these stories teach about what it means to be a good physician? In other words, in what moral universe does clinical education take place?

The first surprising observation you may make is that the vitality of this universe is centered outside the patient room. The narrative world is most alive in the teaching hospital's hallways and conference rooms and unit stations. Generally, you discover that physicians enter their patients' rooms as infrequently as possible; and when they do enter, they listen to these patients as little as possible. Instead, they usually have an agenda in mind—a procedure to perform or a parameter to check. Their one-to-one interactions appear to play only a small role in shaping the "received wisdom" of hospital culture. In fact, procedures performed *on* patients are more frequently the starting place for the stories doctors tell one another than are their conversations *with* patients.

The second interesting feature is that stories permeating the hospital ethos don't usually have patients as their active protagonists. Rather, patients serve as clever or frustrating or even stupid plot devices—presenting obstacles or challenges that may impair the story's progress or, alternatively, pleasing foils or surprising twists that facilitate the story's successful resolution. Nonetheless, the *real* protagonists or heroes of these stories are usually doctors, although in an increasing percentage of narratives the doctors may play second fiddle to cyborgs, i.e., machines of one sort or another that figure things out and set them straight.

With regard to villains, hospital narratives are considerably more varied. In some cases, the villain may be an impersonal negative force – a virus or accident, for example – which hardly qualifies as a villain at all. But in more complex cases, other health professionals may play the role of villains; for instance, the arrogant subspecialist, the power-hungry surgeon, the incompetent nurse, the stupid medical student, and so forth. Moreover, the patient's own family may play a malevolent role, either as a result of being present (e.g., the hostile, questioning daughter) or being absent (e.g., the son who never shows up). Finally, patients themselves may take on the role of Bad Guys, with scripts that that demonstrate ignorance, anger, and – above all – noncompliance. In addition, patients play another important role in hospital stories, as the butt of gallows humor.

From an emotional perspective, many hospital stories about patients feel rather flat, even though at the same time these stories are intellectually stimulating. Embedded within them are extraordinarily complex puzzles: diagnostic dilemmas and physiological conundrums. These quandaries share certain characteristics with crossword puzzles (find the correct word), jigsaw puzzles (fit the pieces together), and other games that require speed, endurance, and excellent hand-eye coordination. Nonetheless, the stories are two-dimensional because they contain little emotional resonance.

Yet the lack of emotional resonance in patient-and-doctor stories does not extend to interactions among students and hospital staff. Most of the feelings in medical culture that do get acknowledged are those of doctors or other health professionals, which tend to be expressed in negative attitudes and outbursts: "This place sucks!" "That gomer in 1215 is a real pain in the ass." "I'm so pissed off at that resident I could scream." Although expressions like these are permissible, the physician ethos in general disapproves of emotion and favors stoic acceptance. This, in fact, is one way that doctors demonstrate the superiority they feel over patients, who are often emotional and let subjective perspectives get the best of them.

Finally, as should be obvious, the virtues and values articulated in this thumbnail sketch of hospital culture bear little relationship to the traditional ethos and morality of medicine. If you accept this culture, you say self-interest whereas I say altruism. You say the patient is an object of interest; I say the patient is a subject of respect. You say the bottom line is to free up the bed; I say the goal is to promote healing.

This glimpse that I'm presenting of the world in which medical students and young physicians find themselves is a gross overgeneralization. First, it ignores the narratives of nursing, social work, chaplaincy, and many other professions. These professions, of course, overlap, reverberate with, and influence one another but – and this is quite remarkable – they seem to influence the culture of medicine very little. While physicians in the hospital are completely dependent on multiple other professionals and support personnel, the culture of medicine itself remains rather isolated and uninfluenced by them.

Second, nowadays a substantial proportion of medical education takes place in clinic and office settings, where patient narratives may play a larger role in trainees' overall experiences. Finally, I've overgeneralized about physicians themselves. Fortunately, patients and their physicians also tell vibrant and edifying stories, and many residents and students repeat them and learn from them. Hospital culture is by no means entirely hostile, and many trainees graduate from it having cultivated positive and caring professional identities.

The Varieties of Professionalism

However, the generalizations and value conflicts I have described do exist and do affect the outcomes of medical education. Peter Williams and I have argued elsewhere that such conflict between tacit and explicit values seriously distorts medical professionalism.[26-28] At an experiential level, medical students and house officers relieve or resolve their internal conflict by adopting one of three styles of professional identity.

- A *technical* professional identity, in which young physicians abandon traditional values and adopt a view of medical practice consistent with hospital culture. They become cynical about duty, fidelity, confidentiality, and integrity; and question their own motivation and that of others, thereby narrowing their sphere of responsibility to the technical arena.

- A *nonreflective* professional identity, in which physicians consciously adhere to traditional medical values while unconsciously basing their behavior, or some of it, on opposing values. In this type of self-delusion, a young physician believes that when she acts in accordance with hospital culture, she actually manifests the explicit values she learned in the classroom, although instead it is the hidden, negative values that are being expressed. For example, compassion is best manifested by detachment, and personal interaction is suspect because it lacks objectivity.

- A *compassionate and responsive* professional identity, adopted by a third, substantial group of young physicians, who thereby overcome the conflict between tacit and explicit socialization.

Let me emphasize that these characterizations represent the physician's internalization of what being a good doctor means and the manner in which he or she should behave. As such, they cut-across my rule-based and narrative-based categories, which refer to the manner in which professionalism is conceptualized and taught by medical educators. Williams and I claim that a large percentage of our graduates are best characterized as nonreflective professionals; that is, physicians who believe that they embody virtues like fidelity, self-effacement, integrity, compassion, and so forth, while acting in ways that not only conflict with these virtues, but also contribute to contemporary problems in health care such as rising costs, inadequate physician–patient communication, and widespread dissatisfaction. It is this group of physicians that most clearly exemplifies Albert Jonsen's insight about the core dynamic of professionalism, "The central paradox in medicine is the tension between self-interest and altruism."[30]

A Flag in the Wind

Thomas Inui's report, "A Flag in the Wind: Educating for Professionalism in Medicine," which is based on his experience as scholar-in-residence at the AAMC,[31] presents a systematic and comprehensive analysis of our continued failure to instill professional virtue in medical education. Because Inui's eight conclusions parallel my argument, I want to summarize them here. First, "the major elements of what most of us in medicine mean by professionalism have been described well, not once but many times." (p. 4) This is understandable because these elements are based upon "the attributes of a virtuous person," about which there is widespread consensus. Next he observes, however, that the literature and rhetoric of medicine fail to grasp "the *gap* between these widely recognized manifestations of virtue in action and *what we actually do*" in medical education and practice. (p. 4) Inui acknowledges that physicians "may be unconscious of some of this gap" but when they are conscious of it, they tend to be "silent or inarticulate about the dissonance." (p. 4)

In his fifth conclusion, Inui draws attention to the discrepancy between "what they see us do" (the hidden curriculum) and "what they hear us say" (the formal curriculum). Under these circumstances, "students become cynical about the profession of medicine—indeed, they may see cynicism as intrinsic to medicine." (p. 5) In this context, "additional courses on medical professionalism are unlikely to fundamentally alter this regrettable circumstance. Instead, we will actually have to change our behaviors, our institutions, and ourselves." (p. 5) Finally, Inui indicates that the most difficult challenge of all is for students and educators to understand that medical education is "a special form of personal and professional *formation*" (emphasis added), rather than a species of technical learning. (p. 5)

Inui recognizes that the gap between belief and behavior that characterizes our teaching hospitals is partly unconscious. To the extent that this is true, these physicians manifest nonreflective professionalism; that is, in the formation of their professional identities, they have internalized the belief that certain nonvirtuous behaviors are virtuous, since they are "the way things are in medicine." The term "nonreflective" implies that these physicians rarely, if ever, step back and consider the impact of their behavior on themselves and others, as human beings deserving of care and respect. Inui suggests that another part of the institutional gap between belief and practice is conscious and, therefore, hypocritical. Unfortunately, physicians with little interest in the narrative and value dimensions of medicine may at times be required to serve as teachers – and presumably role models – because of the infrastructure and demands of medical education. When these physicians impart their rote "wisdom," they do so hypocritically. Trainees quickly detect this and respond with cynicism.

Narrative Based Professionalism

To nurture the professional virtue, or narrative-based professionalism, that I am advocating, Inui observes that "we will actually have to change our behaviors, our institutions, and our selves."[31] In the educational culture that I've described, the prospects for such change seem bleak; yet I believe that cultural change is possible, given the right catalyst and sufficient receptivity in the medical community. I believe that receptivity among medical educators is growing, given their dissatisfaction with the processes and products of professionalism education. As to the right catalyst, I will suggest four interrelated educational requirements that could provide a basis for the formation of a new medical morality in the 21st century. In proposing this framework, I am drawing upon the ideas of others, especially my colleagues in the fields of reflective practice and narrative medicine, whom I cite below. Moreover, as a means of evaluating a trainee's performance as he or she progresses through the process of learning professional virtue, I proposed another borrowed idea, the educational portfolio.[32–35] Such a portfolio is a collection of material assembled over time that provides evidence of learning and achievement. A medical trainee's portfolio might be structured to address specific competencies and include, for example, formal papers, case reports, extended patient narratives, descriptions of critical incidents, reflective writing, and self-assessment.[36]

Professionalism Role Modeling

The first requirement for a sea change in professionalism is to increase dramatically the number of physicians who are able to role-model professional virtue at every stage of medical education. By this I mean full-time faculty members who exemplify virtue in their interactions with patients, staff, trainees, and the community at large; who have internalized a broad, humanistic, and narrative perspective; and who are willing to forego high income in order to teach. These physicians eschew commercial entanglements. Because such physicians are reflective, as opposed to nonreflective, in their professionalism, their presence would dilute and diminish the conflict between tacit and explicit values, especially in the hospital and clinic. Such physicians communicate honestly and directly with trainees, who are likely to "get" the message because it comes from the heart. With the incorporation of more such faculty, the teaching environment would contain fewer mixed messages, where, for example, the voice says "engage" while the behavior says "detach." What trainees need is time and humanism. However, such faculty members cannot pay for themselves, and this implies major new financing for medical education.

Self-Awareness

The second prerequisite for developing narrative-based professionalism is to provide, throughout medical school and residency, a safe venue for students and residents to share their experiences and enhance their personal awareness. Doctors need to understand their own beliefs, feelings, attitudes, and response patterns. One of the earliest proponents of this view was the British psychiatrist Michael Balint, who encouraged physicians to meet regularly in small groups to discuss difficulties with patients and their personal reactions to practice.[37] Physicians tend to view emotions as negative or disruptive, and often confuse intellectualizing their responses (naming an "affect") with genuine emotion.[38] Physicians are particularly vulnerable to anxiety, loneliness, frustration, anger, depression, and helplessness when caring for chronically or terminally ill patients.[39] They often try to cope with these emotions by suppressing or rationalizing them. The more effectively physicians reverse this process by developing self- awareness, the more likely they will have the resources to connect with, and respond to, their patients' experiences.

In addition, the trainee's moral development may be hindered by every-day learning situations. These include conflicts between the requirements of medical education and those of good patient care, assignments that entail responsibility exceeding the student's capabilities, and personal involvement in substandard care. Once again, the opportunity to discuss, analyze, critique, and sometimes repair these situations allows students to find their own voice and may eventually empower them to develop that voice effectively.[40–43]

Narrative Competence

Medical practice is structured around narrative—between physician and patient, teacher and student, and the like. However, as a result of the tension between explicit and tacit values, students learn to objectify their patients and devalue subjectivity. In part, they learn to conceptualize their patients in terms of flow sheets, rather than personal stories. At the same time, they internalize hospital narratives, which tend to be cynical, arrogant, egotistic, self-congratulatory, and highly rationalized, but nonetheless become influential in the formation of the trainee's professional persona. Moreover, students immersed in these stories have little time to listen to, and may also lack the skill to understand and respond to, their patients' stories, or to experience themselves as characters in the larger narrative of professionalism in medicine.

Accordingly, *the third prerequisite for fostering narrative-based professionalism is the development of narrative competence.* This can be understood as "the ability to acknowledge, absorb, interpret, and act on the stories and plights of others."[44] The narrative medicine movement provides a way of reframing the knowledge, skills, and attitudes of good doctoring under the aegis of language, symbol, story, and the cultural construction of illness.[45–50] It draws upon the centrality of clinical empathy in establishing and maintaining therapeutic relationships, and also upon the broader, more imaginative empathy that allows observers to "connect with" the experience of persons not immediately known to them, such as the uninsured in Appalachia, HIV-infected children in South Africa, or refugees in Sudan.[51–55]

The trainee's own life experience, molded by positive role-modeling and reflective practice, serves as the basic material from which narrative competence may develop. However, students may enhance their repertoires of life experience by exposure to the written, filmed, and oral narratives of real and fictional physicians; and they may increase awareness of their own developing professional identities by writing personal and professional narratives consistently and with discipline.[56–61]

Community Service

Finally, in order to teach narrative-based professionalism, the medical curriculum must include socially relevant service- oriented learning. Interaction with patients in the hospital or office setting is insufficient to provide students and young physicians with narrative of interdisciplinary practice, biopsychosocial modeling, and social responsibility. The American Medical Association's Code of Ethics specifies in section VII that "A physician shall recognize a responsibility to participate in activities contributing to an improved community."[62] In section III, the Code of Ethics indicates that "A physician shall . . . recognize a responsibility to seekchanges in (legal) requirements which are contrary to the best interests of the patient."[62] These manifestations of professional virtue need to be addressed in medical education.

Service learning may operate on many different geographic and social levels, from activities that take place locally to those on a national or international level. Moreover, the focus may include students contributing to clinical care (e.g., working at free clinics, doing clinical work in third-world countries), public health work (e.g., vaccinating migrant workers, assisting in "Stop Smoking" campaigns), health education (e.g., participating in HIV education in local high schools, speaking at church groups and community organizations), community service (e.g., volunteering in local agencies or with groups that provide direct assistance to third-world countries), and political action on health and welfare issues.[63–70] Whatever the specific tasks involved, the minimal required "dose" of community service must be sufficiently large for students to view it as integral to the culture of medical education, rather than an unconnected add-on.

Conclusions

Professionalism is *au courant* in medicine today, but the movement to teach and evaluate professionalism presents medical educators with somewhat of a conundrum. Its intent is laudable: to produce humanistic and virtuous physicians who will be better able to cope with and overcome the dehumanizing features of the health care system in the United States. However, the impact of this movement on medical education is likely to be small and misleading unless it directly confronts the "central paradox in medicine," which is the "tension between self-interest and altruism."[30]

In many ways, today's culture of medicine tends to be hostile toward altruism, compassion, integrity, fidelity, self-effacement, and other traditional qualities. In fact, hospital culture, and the narratives that support it, implicitly identify a very different set of professional qualities as "good," and sometimes these qualities are diametrically opposed to the virtues that we explicitly teach. Students and young physicians experience internal conflict as they try to reconcile the explicit and covert or hidden curricula, and in the process of their professional character formation they often develop nonreflective professionalism. Additional exercises in or courses on professionalism as it is currently taught are, in themselves, unlikely to alter this dynamic, even if they are supplemented by lists of competencies that trainees are required to demonstrate. This rule-based approach to professionalism does not alter the tension or conflict between tacit and explicit values.

Instead, I propose promoting narrative-based professionalism as a more comprehensive approach to changing the culture of medical education and addressing its central paradox. This involves immersing students and young physicians in a wide array of narratives, drawn from their own experiences as well as those of others, that display professional virtue. In essence, this approach would provide a counterculture of virtuous practice that may gradually displace the more negative elements of contemporary medical culture and allow students to bear witness to their profession, not just symbolically through oaths and White Coat ceremonies, but in the ways they conduct themselves in their day-to-day practice. Each component of this approach – professionalism role-modeling, self-awareness, narrative competence, and community service – overlaps with and reinforces the others. Moreover, each lends itself to longitudinal evaluative processes, such as the creation of narrative-based professionalism portfolios by students and residents.[32–36]

Many of the elements for this development are already present, but in most medical schools dispersed too thinly and/or integrated too sparsely to produce a significant impact on the culture of medical education. I don't know what critical mass might be required to initiate a chain reaction in medical education in favor of narrative-based professionalism. Presumably, however, it would not require that every faculty member and attending physician pass a litmus test for virtue and empathy. Nor would it mandate that commercialism disappear. The concept of a catalyst is important here because I believe that cultural change can take place if a relatively small number of well-placed faculty members, curricula, faculty development programs, and institutional supports are brought together with an aggressive treatment plan not only to alleviate the symptoms of an ailing professional culture, but also to set that culture on the road to recovery.

References

1   Mencken HL. The divine afflatus. In: *A Mencken Chrestomathy*. New York: Vintage Books, 1949 (reissued 1982), p. 442.

2   Churchill LR. *Reviving a distinctive medical ethic*. Hastings Cent Rep. 1989;19:28-34, p. 34.

3   Jonsen A. *The New Medicine and the Old Ethics*. Cambridge: Harvard University Press, 1990.

4   Beauchamp TL, Childress JR. *Principles of Biomedical Ethics*, 5th ed. New York: Oxford University Press, 2001.

5   Veatch RM. Against virtue: a deontological critique of virtue theory in medical ethics. In: Shelp EE (ed). *Virtue and Medicine: Explorations in the Character of Medicine* (Philosophy and Medicine series, No. 17). Dordrecht: D. Reidel Publishing, 1985:329-45.

6   Jonsen AR, Siegler M, Winslade WJ. *Clinical Ethics*. New York: Macmillan, 2002.

7   Pellegrino ED, Thomasma DC. *The Virtues in Medical Practice*. New York: Oxford University Press, 1993.

8   Pellegrino ED. Character, virtue and self-interest in the ethics of the professions. *J Contemp Health Law Policy*. 1989;5:53-73.

9   Pellegrino ED. The virtuous physician and the ethics of medicine. In: Shelp EE (ed). *Virtue and Medicine: Explorations in the Character of Medicine* (Philosophy and Medicine series, No. 17). Dordrecht: D. Reidel Publishing, 1985:243-55.

10 Drane JF. *Becoming a Good Doctor. The Place of Virtue and Character in Medical Ethics*. Kansas City: Sheed & Ward, 1988.

11 Coles R. *The Call of Stories: Teaching and the Moral Imagination*. Boston: Houghton Mifflin, 1989.

12 Accreditation Council for Graduate Medical Education. ACGME Outcomes Project (http://www.acgme.org/Outcome/). Accessed 7 July 2005.

13 American Association of Medical Colleges. Project Professionalism, Assessment (http:// www.aamc.org/members/gea/professionalism.pdf). Accessed 7 July 2005.

14 American Board of Internal Medicine. Project Professionalism (http://www. abim.org/pdf/ profess.pdf). Accessed 7 July 2005.

15 Barry D, Cyran E, Anderson RJ. Common issues in medical professionalism: room to grow. *Am J Med*. 2000;108:136-42.

16 Epstein RM, Hundert EM. Defining and assessing professional competence. *JAMA*. 2002;287:226-35.

17 Medical Professionalism Project. Medical professionalism in the new millennium: a physicians' charter. *Lancet*. 2002;359:520-22.

18 American Board of Internal Medicine. Professionalism in medicine: issues and opportunities in the educational environment. Project Professionalism, p. 5

(http://www.abim.org/pdf/profess.pdf). Accessed 7 July 2005.

19   Bloom SW. The medical school as a social organization: the sources of resistance to change. *MedEduc.* 1989;23:228-41.

20   Hafferty FW, Franks R. The hidden curriculum, ethics teaching, and the structure of medical education. *Acad Med.* 1994;69: 861-71.

21   Hunnert EM, Hafferty F, Christakis D. Characteristics of the informal curriculum and trainee's ethical choices. *Acad Med.* 1996; 71:624-33.

22   Stephenson A, Higgs R, Sugarman. Teaching professional development in medical schools. *Lancet.* 2001;357:867-70.

23   Swick HM, Szenas P, Danoff D, Whitcomb ME. Teaching professionalism in undergraduate medical education. *JAMA.* 1999;282:830-32.

24   Wear D, Castellani B. The development of professionalism: curriculum matters. *Acad Med.* 2000;75:602-11.

25   Wear D. On white coats and professional development: the formal and hidden curricula. *Ann Intern Med* 1998;129:734-37.

26   Coulehan J, Williams PC. Professional ethics and social activism: where have we been? Where are we going? In: Wear D, Bickel J (eds). *Educating Physicians: Medical Student Professional Development and Social Change.* Iowa City: University of Iowa Press, 2001:49-69.

27   Coulehan J, Williams PC. Vanquishing virtue: the impact of medical education. *Acad Med.* 2001;76:598-605.

28   Coulehan J, Williams PC. Conflicting professional values in medical education. *Camb Q Healthc Ethics.* 2003;12:7-20.

29   Rothman DJ. Medical professionalism—focusing on the real issues. *N Engl J Med.* 2000;342:1284–86.

30   Jonsen AR. Watching the doctor. *N Engl J Med.* 1983;308:1531-35.

31   Inui TS. *A Flag in the Wind: Educating for Professionalism in Medicine.* Washington, DC: Association of American Medical Colleges, 2003.

32   O'Sullivan PS, Reckase MD, McClain T, Savidge MA, Clardy JA. Demonstration of portfolios to assess competency of residents. *Adv Health Sci Educ Theory Pract.* 2004;9:309-23.

33   Carraccio C, Englander R. Evaluating competence using a portfolio: a literature review and web-based application to the ACGME competencies. Teach Learn Med. 2004 Fall;16:381-87.

34   Jarvis RM, O'Sullivan PS, McClain T, Clardy JA. Can one portfolio measure the six ACGME general competencies? *Acad Psychiatry.* 2004;28:190-96.

35   Driessen E, van Tartwijk J, Vermunt JD, van der Vleuten CP. Use of portfolios in early undergraduate medical training. *Med Teach.* 2003 Jan;25:18-23.

36   Challis M. AMEE Medical Education Guide No. 11 (revised): portfolio-based

learning and assessment in medical education. *Med Teach.* 1999;21:370-86.

37   Balint M. *The Doctor, His Patient, and the Illness.* New York: International Universities Press, 1972.

38   Novack DH, Suchman AL, Clark W, Epstein RM, Najberg E, Kaplan MD. Calibrating the physician: personal awareness and effective patient care. Working Group on Promoting Physician Personal Awareness, American Academy on Physician and Patient. *JAMA.* 1997;278:502–9.

39   Meier DE, Back AL, Morrison RS. The inner life of physicians and care of the seriously ill. *JAMA.* 2001;286:3007-14.

40   Branch WT Jr., Pels RJ, Calkins D, et al. A new educational approach for supporting the professional development of third year medical students. *J Gen Intern Med.* 1995;10: 691-94.

41   Branch WT Jr, Kern D, Haidet P, et al. The patient-physician relationship: teaching the human dimensions of care in clinical settings. *JAMA.* 2001;286:1067-74.

42   Pololi L, Frankel RM, Clay M, Jobe A. One year's experience with a program to facilitate personal and professional development in medical students using reflection groups. *Educ Health.* 2000;14:36-49.

43   Suchman AL, Williamson PR, Litzelman DK, Frankel RM, Mossbarger DL, Inui TS. Relationship-Centered Care Initiative Discovery Team. Toward an informal curriculum that teaches professionalism. Transforming the social environment of a medical school. *J Gen Intern Med.* 2004;19(5 Pt 2):501-4.

44   Charon R. Narrative medicine. A model for empathy, reflection, profession, and trust. *JAMA.* 2001;286:1897-902.

45   Morris DB. Narrative, ethics, and thinking with stories. *Narrative.* 2001;9:55-77.

46   Charon R. Narrative medicine: form, function, and ethics. Ann Intern Med. 2001; 134:83-87.

47   Frank AW. *The Wounded Storyteller: Body, Illness, and Ethics.* Chicago: University of Chicago Press, 1995.

48   Greenhalgh T, Hurwitz B (eds). *Narrative Based Medicine: Dialogue and Discourse in Clinical Practice.* London: BMJ Books, 1998.

49   Montgomery K. *Doctors' Stories: The Narrative Structure of Medical Knowledge.* Princeton: Princeton University Press, 1991.

50   Morris DB. *Illness and Culture in the Postmodern Age.* Berkeley and Los Angeles: University of California Press, 1998.

51   Bennett MJ. *The Empathic Healer: An Endangered Species?* New York: Academic Press, 2001.

52   Coulehan J. An alternative view: listening to patients. *Lancet.* 1999;354:1467-68.

53   Coulehan J. Tenderness and steadiness: Emotions in medical practice. *Lit Med.* 1996; 14:222-36.

54   More ES, Milligan MA (eds). *The Empathic Practitioner: Empathy, Gender, and Medicine*. New Brunswick: Rutgers University Press, 1994.

55   Connelly J. Emotions, ethics, and decisions in primary care. *J Clin Ethics*. 1998;9:225-34.

56   Bolton G. Stories at work: reflective writing for practitioners. *Lancet*. 1999; 354:243-45.

57   DasGupta S, Charon R. Personal illness narratives: using reflective writing to teach empathy. *Acad Med*. 2004;79:351-56.

58   Charon R. Narrative and medicine. *N Engl J Med*. 2004;350:862-64.

59   Williams CM, Wilson CC, Olsen CH. Dying, death, and medical education: student voices. *J Palliat Med*. 2005;8:372-81.

60   Pitkala KH, Mantyranta T. Feelings related to first patient experiences in medical school. A qualitative study on students' personal portfolios. *Patient Educ Couns*. 2004;54: 171-77.

61   Coulehan J, Clary P. Healing the healer: poetry in palliative care. *J Palliat Care*. 2005;8: 382-89.

62   AMA Council on Ethical and Judicial Affairs. Code of Medical Ethics (http://www.ama- assn.org/ama/pub/category/2512.html). Accessed 7 July 2005.

63   Elam CL, Sauer MJ, Stratton TD, Skelton J, Crocker D, Musick DW. Service learning in the medical curriculum: developing and evaluating an elective experience. *Teach Learn Med*. 2003;15:194-203.

64   Haq C, Grosch M, Carufel-Wert D. Leadership Opportunities with Communities, the Medically Underserved, and Special Populations (LOCUS). *Acad Med*. 2002;77:740.

65   Albritton TA, Wagner PJ. Linking cultural competency and community service: a partnership between students, faculty, and the community. *Acad Med*. 2002;77:738-39.

66   Sidelinger DE, Meyer D, Blaschke GS, et al. Communities as teachers: learning to deliver culturally effective care in pediatrics. *Pediatrics*. 2005;115(4 supl):1160-64.

67   Clark DL, Melillo A, Wallace D, Pierrel S, Buck DS. A multidisciplinary, learner-centered, student-run clinic for the homeless. *Fam Med*. 2003;35:394-97.

68   Davidson RA. Community-based education and problem solving: the Community Health Scholars Program at the University of Florida. *Teach Learn Med*. 2002;14:178-81.

69   O'Toole TP, Kathuria N, Mishra M, Schukart D. Teaching professionalism within a community context: perspectives from a national demonstration project. *Acad Med*. 2005;80:339-43.

70   Coulehan J, Williams PW, McCrary SV, Belling C. The best lack all conviction: biomedical ethics, professionalism, and social responsibility. *Camb Q Healthc Ethics*. 2003; 12:21-38.

17

Gretchen A. Case and Guy Micco, "Imagination Takes the Stage:
Readers' Theater in a Medical Context," *Journal for Learning through
the Arts*, 2(1) Publication Date: 2006.

Editor's note: As with other more recently published articles in this
volume, the authors updated their introductory comments to help set
the stage for their piece reproduced here.

Every teacher knows the value of a good story. Students at all levels
respond to the pleasures and challenges of listening to a narrative
that illustrates an important lesson. Both authors have long-standing
interests in literature as it intersects with the medical realm. We
came together from two different academic disciplines, performance
studies (Case) and clinical medicine (Micco), through a shared interest
in expanding our students' knowledge of the lived experience of aging
and old age. We were familiar with many prose, poetry, and nonfiction
texts that raise important issues surrounding this topic and had
already used some of those texts to advantage in classroom settings.
As we talked about the importance of empathy (and the difficulty of
teaching it), we planned a new course that we hoped would foster in
each of our participants curiosity and what has been variously called
the moral, empathic, or narrative imagination.[1-3] What is it like to be
this particular other person in his or her particular circumstances? For
our medical professional students, we sought to generate new ideas for
opening conversations with patients and new perspectives on aging. For
our theater and performance students, we hoped to reinforce existing
interests in the performing arts as an important conduit for building
community. We wanted all our students to experience the value of
telling and listening carefully to stories. Thus, in 2005 and 2006, we
developed and taught a course at the University of California, Berkeley
titled, "Readers' Theater in a Medical Context: On old age and aging."

Imagination Takes the Stage:
Readers' Theater in a Medical Context

Gretchen A. Case, PhD and Guy Micco, MD

Abstract: In this article, we describe an elective course using readers' theater with students in the health care professions and the arts. Readers' theater is a technique used for the performance of literature in which texts are staged with minimal production values and scripts are not fully memorized. These techniques are drawn upon more commonly in theater and performance studies classrooms, but we found them to be effective as tools for connecting future health care providers with their local communities. With a central theme of age and aging, we chose non-dramatic works of literature and adapted them for dramatic readings at retirement communities in Berkeley and Oakland, California.

The Tradition of Readers' Theater

Our decision to create this course, which would move beyond the classroom and into the community, was inspired by Dr. Todd Savitt's example at the Brody School of Medicine at East Carolina University (ECU), where he has directed a successful readers' theater program since 1988. Readers' theater is a technique used in the performance of literature in which texts are staged with minimal production values and scripts are not fully memorized. Literature not necessarily intended for dramatic interpretation is presented by performers who read aloud but do not wear costumes, use props, or move about the room. A formal theatrical stage is not necessary. Poems, short stories, novels, memoirs, and many other forms of fiction and nonfiction have been successfully adapted for the stage through this technique. Readers' theater allows the audience to experience a live performance of the texts while significantly shortening the rehearsal and preparation time necessary. Readers' theater makes performance available to communities with fewer resources and opens the text to performers who cannot commit to the six to eight weeks of nightly rehearsal traditionally necessary for a fully staged production. Live performance helps bring new interpretation and new meaning to the written word. Listening to a story or poem as it is read and then discussing it with others is quite a different experience than reading silently to oneself.

Savitt and his students perform in the Greenville, North Carolina, community using their adapted texts to open post-performance discussions on a variety of health-related issues. Savitt's book, Medical Readers Theater: A Guide and Scripts, provided us with both performance material and an example of the sort of work that can be done once such a program is well established. During our first "pilot" course at UCB in the spring of 2005, we invited Savitt to Berkeley to participate in rehearsals, workshops, and performances. His collaboration proved valuable as we completed our 2005 course and planned for our 2006 course.

"Readers' Theater in a Medical Context" has linked UCB students with elder residents of local continuing care retirement communities. Health professional students and students in the arts and humanities interested in issues concerning old age and aging performed selections from literature intended to open conversations between themselves and elders living in continuing care retirement communities in the San Francisco Bay Area. We chose stories that deal with the pleasures as well as the problems and concerns of aging in our society. We presented both on-campus and off-campus performances, each followed by an audience discussion with the performers.

The Readers, Young and Old

In spring 2005, our course had eight medical students from the UC Berkeley-UC San Francisco Joint Medical Program and one graduate student from the UC Berkeley Department of Theater, Dance, and Performance Studies. The students worked together in weekly meetings over a period of nine weeks. Early on, we discussed readers' theater and performance of literature techniques for those who were unfamiliar with the terms; we also worked on very basic aspects of performance (such as breathing exercises and vocal projection) for those students who did not have experience on stage. At each of our meetings, all in ordinary classroom spaces, we discussed a number of texts and the issues they raised and then rehearsed them for potential inclusion in our performances. As noted above, one major benefit of readers' theater is that it does not require the resources or time commitment of a fully-staged production. This limited time commitment fit the needs of our student performers very well, as both medical students and other graduate students are perpetually short on time. We managed two off-campus performances at retirement communities and an on-campus workshop during this nine week period, which included Todd Savitt's residency.

In spring 2006, we enrolled five medical students, one graduate student in optometry, and one graduate student in Performance Studies. We also decided to grant admission to three advanced undergraduates who were either applying or already admitted to graduate programs in the health sciences; two of these undergraduates also held minors in theater. With the cooperation of both departments, our 2006 students had the choice of enrolling in the course as an elective in either the Joint Medical Program or in Theater, Dance, and Performance Studies. We were delighted with the additional diversity in our 2006 students and in the variety of perspectives they brought to our discussions and performances.

After our first set of student performances, we considered the possibility that there might be educational value and enjoyment in having elders from the community perform and lead discussions for the students (some of whom may one day be their health care providers). So, in 2006, we expanded our course by inviting residents from one particular retirement community to perform with us. The community's activities director found many eager volunteers, eight of whom stayed on throughout the process. This group was modest about their theatrical accomplishments at first, but slowly and slyly let us know that they were "ringers"; all of them had extensive stage or public speaking experience. One of the elder performers admitted with a coy smile that she had done a lengthy stint on Broadway as a young woman. (This should have come as no surprise, as retirement communities are a treasure trove of elders with a plethora of rich life experiences.) For practical reasons, the elder performers and the student performers had entirely separate rehearsals. While this made for some unknowns on the day of our public performance, it also enhanced the delicious elements of surprise and unpredictability that are inherent in any live performance.

In both 2005 and 2006, students enrolled in the course for many different reasons. Some of the health sciences students were attracted to the course, because they were already interested in working with elders and wanted to develop further their communication skills and interactions with this group of future patients. At least one student, however, remarked that she took the course precisely because of her discomfort and uncertainty around "older people." The students from theater and performance studies were interested in the impact that theater can have in a community and also found value in fostering interdisciplinary thinking about the arts and the sciences. Most of the students at some point remarked on their attraction to the course, because it represented something different in their school day: a break from study-ing; a chance to interact with the off- campus world; the opportunity to read, analyze, and interpret good literature.

Satisfactions and Surprises

Some of the outcomes of this course, while not necessarily predictable, were exactly as we had hoped. Our students found themselves intrigued by the literature we presented and brought in further texts for consideration. At least one student (spring 2006) became interested in the process of adapting litera-ture for readers' theater and tried her hand at it. Classroom discussion—on which texts we would perform and how we would perform them—were lively. The students gave honest, sometimes blunt, assessments of the merits of each text and argued congenially with us and one another as we planned each performance. Post-show discussions were similarly animated. Aided by one of us as a designated facilitator, the students participated actively in conversa-tions with the elders in our audiences. The elders, for their part, were equally participatory and critical: they told us precisely what they liked and disliked about the texts and our performances; they questioned the students about their goals as healthcare practitioners and community- oriented artists; and did not shy away from difficult issues raised by the stories and poems.

The frankness of these discussions was quite unimaginable before the fact. A particular text in 2005 raised the issue of a life supported entirely by medical technology and the protagonist's wish to end her life under those terms. Some of our students expressed concerns about the feelings of audi-ence members who might know someone in this position, or who may have been called upon to "pull the plug." One student stated that she did not think this text was at all appropriate. However, we put it to a vote and decided to perform the story. The post-performance discussion was one of our fin-est. Indeed, one audience member did report her distress at listening to our performance; she had just completed power of attorney and medical directive documents for herself and her spouse. Other audience members discussed their fears of losing their current quality of life and of making life-and-death decisions for loved ones. The discussion was tender and respectful, and we were all moved by the evening's events.

The greatest surprises came when the elders entered into the performances with us during the 2006 course. At our first performance at a retirement com-munity, a woman in the audience, urged on by her peers, spontaneously recited "Daffodils" by William Wordsworth. The prompt for this recitation seemed to be a sense of friendly competition; the elders wanted the younger performers to see that there were performers among them too. This woman's audience, including our performers, was delighted, especially when she gamely waited out a brief memory lapse, recalled the lines she had missed, and finished with aplomb. This event had occurred before we asked for volunteer performers from this retirement center, but it was fortuitous in showing us that we were not mistaken to think there would be interested parties. The memory lapse during her performance was also instructive. One of the main reasons we work with readers' theater techniques is because it does not require memorization, meaning it is a good match for both forgetful elders and overtired (and forgetful) students. Our choice to adapt and perform non- dramatic literature was also validated in this moment of performance; clearly, our audience of elders was comfortable with – and nostalgic for – the oral performance of poetry and prose. Many of them grew up memorizing and reciting canonical works in school.

These routine recitations of best-loved works from earlier years seemed also to be preserved in the memories of some of our elders. Hearing a familiar poem during one of our performances set off a chorus of nods, smiles, and whispered accompaniment. Another 2006 performance by our students at a retirement center included William Shakespeare's well-known Sonnet 73. The student performers gave a lovely and sincere rendition of the text, which we had divided to be read by four voices in order to emphasize the logic of each quatrain and the final couplet. During the post-performance discussion, a woman raised her hand and indicated that the quiet gentleman next to her could recite this same sonnet from memory. Without preamble, and in a fragile but urgent voice, he leaned into the microphone and gave a performance that eclipsed ours with an intensity coming from decades of rehearsal and contemplation. This same man had his name and his room number clearly written on a tag pinned to his sweater, no doubt to keep him from getting lost if he should forget his way home. Although we did not discuss his performance other than to congratulate him, the persistence of his ability to perform Shakespeare's words – and their emotional impact – through the challenge of a fogging memory was instructive.

At our on-campus public performance toward the end of the 2006 course, both elders and students performed the same poems, one after the other, so that we could discuss the difference in each group's reading. One of these poems was "Unending Love," by Indian mystic poet and Nobel Laureate Rabindranath Tagore. The students did not like this poem, finding it too sentimental and clichéd and resisted including it in the performance. The elders, on the other hand, unanimously voted to perform this piece when we offered it for their consideration. They found the poem's themes of eternal love, spiritual ecstasy, and love that changes but endures over time to be reflective of their own experiences. They spoke of lost (and found) spouses, children who grew up or apart, even a high school prom date couple who meet again fifty years later. Because of the elders' enthusiasm for "Unending Love," we prevailed upon the reluctant students to perform it as well. With separate rehearsals, neither group heard the other perform until they were onstage together in front of an audience. Again, our students gave a lovely, thoughtful reading despite their earlier reservations. Everyone in the theater heard the difference, however, when the elders took their turn. Their lived experience of lasting love was present not only in the emotional inflections they gave to the words but also in the rich, mellow quality of their older voices. Their gravitas seemed hard-earned and undeniable.

Practical Concerns

When we began planning for the course in the spring of 2004, we recognized the need for funding and other material support to offset costs such as photo-copying, travel to performance sites, and small props and other supplies for the performers. In spring 2005, we received modest support from the Joint Medi-cal Program; the Center for Medicine, the Humanities, and Law; the Resource Center on Aging; and the Department of Theater, Dance, and Performance Studies, all at UCB. In spring 2006, we received additional funding from UCB's Consortium for the Arts, which allowed us to record some of our rehearsals and performances and create a short DVD to be used in classrooms. (Please contact the authors for more information about the DVD.)

Because our audience was drawn almost exclusively from a population of elders, we faced a few age-related challenges. For one, many of the people attending our performances had some hearing impairment. This meant that vocal projection, whether aided or unaided, was a key responsibility of our performers. We spent a good deal of time in rehearsals working on techniques for voice projection, with some performers having more success than others at increasing their volume without sounding strained. While we made the best possible use of the microphones and sound systems available at each venue, we never found an ideal configuration within our limited budget.

We also needed to pay attention to accessibility and accommodations for our elders during their rehearsals and performance. Rehearsals were limited by the retirement community's activity schedules and by the energy of the performers. Large-print scripts with clearly marked lines were crucial. We required a wheelchair-accessible stage, with comfortable chairs, bottled water, and nearby accessible restrooms. Further, we had to rehearse knowing that one or more of our performers might not be well enough to participate on a given day; we planned to step in ourselves as understudies, if need be. Luckily, all our performers remained in good health throughout the process.

We also had to deal with copyrighted texts and permissions for performance. Savitt's book, *Medical Readers' Theater: A Guide and Scripts* (University of Iowa Press, 2002) offers fourteen scripts adapted from texts for which general permission to perform has been granted or which fall into the public domain by virtue of their publication date. In seeking to expand our texts beyond Savitt's book, we sought performance permission for some, but also found a wealth of good material in the public domain. One of our texts, "Poem for Wei Ba" by Chinese poet Du Fu, dates to the 8th century AD, but proved timely in its enduring sentiments. In this poem, friends reuniting after years of separation muse on their children, their gray hairs, their lost acquaintances, and their sadness at the inevitable end of their visit.

Concluding Thoughts

Each of the pieces we performed provided a scenario of aging that could be used to explore the problems and questions at hand for our elder audience members. For example, what would it be like to lose one's life-long partner and have to leave one's home of 40 years to move into a one-room apartment with an unknown roommate? What would it be like to be this 87 year-old woman, living in a nursing facility since her stroke two years ago, whom no one comes to visit? What is it like? Some of the answers might well come from someone who sat beside or in front of our students, watching them perform. The otherness of aging and old age – laden as it is with stereotypes and prejudices – is an ideal problem to place before our young students for whom the word "old" might be nothing but pejorative. This is true for our performance students as well as for our medical professional students. All of them have an interest in working with the elders in their communities. All of them have parents and, likely, grandparents who are aging. All of them, though they may not yet appreciate it fully, are themselves aging.

Finally, there is the question of whether a performance studies PhD and a medical educator MD can work together in harmony to develop a successful interdisciplinary course. The answer is a resounding yes. The rewards for both of us were clearly manifested and includes a better understanding of each others' disciplines, the pleasure of stretching into unfamiliar academic territory, and the excitement of working with a variety of new students.

Our performers, their audiences, and we took great pleasure in these endeavors. However, we also had a serious intent: to develop the moral imagination of everyone involved. We stress that the strength of readers' theater, for us, is in the complete process rather than in the individual performances, and that the performance of unrehearsed, unexamined texts would have far less impact. The full range of activities in our readers' theater course – from critically discussing and selecting the texts through the audience-student interactions at our performances – proved essential to its success. Ethical queries and textual analyses occurred at every stage and invited not only our students, but also members of the wider community to develop their curiosity and imaginations. We believe in stimulating these qualities, for they are not only necessary to a fulfilling career in the medical professions, they are an essential part of a reflective, satisfying life.

Sonnet 73[5]
By William Shakespeare

That time of year thou mayst in me behold
When yellow leaves, or none, or few, do hang
Upon those boughs which shake against the cold,
Bare ruin'd choirs where late the sweet birds sang.
In me thou see'st the twilight of such day
As after sunset fadeth in the west,
Which by and by black night doth take away,
Death's second self, that seals up all in rest.
In me thou see'st the glowing of such fire
That on the ashes of his youth doth lie,
As the death-bed whereon it must expire,
Consum'd with that which it was nourish'd by.
  This thou perceiv'st, which makes thy love more strong,
  To love that well which thou must leave ere long.

Poem for Wei Ba[6]
By Du Fu

Often a man's life is such
that he seldom sees his friends,
like the constellations Shen and Shang
which never share the same sky.
If not this evening, then what evening
should we share this lamp light?
How long can our youth and vigor last?
The hair at our temples is already gray.
We inquire about old acquaintances
to find that half are ghosts—
shocked cries betray
the torment of our hearts.
How could I have known
that it would be twenty years
before I again entered
your honored home.
When we parted last
you were yet unmarried;
now your sons and daughters
line up in a smiling row
to greet their father's friend.
They ask whence I have come
but before I can answer all questions
you chase them off
to bring wine and cups.
In the night rain, chives are cut
for the freshly steamed rice
mixed with yellow millet.
Saying how difficult it has been
for us to meet at last,
you pour ten cups in a row!
But even after ten cups
I'm not drunk, being so moved

by your lasting friendship.
Tomorrow we will be separated
by the peaks of mountains,
each of our worldly affairs
lost to the other's sight.

Unending Love[7]
By Rabindranath Tagore

I seem to have loved you in numberless forms, numberless times,
In life after life, in age after age forever.
My spell-bound heart has made and remade the necklace of songs
That you take as a gift, wear round your neck in your many forms
In life after life, in age after age forever.

Whenever I hear old chronicles of love, its age-old pain,
Its ancient tale of being apart or together,
As I stare on and on into the past, in the end you emerge
Clad in the light of a pole-star piercing the darkness of time.
You become an image of what is remembered forever.

You and I have floated here on the stream that brings from the fount
At the heart of time love of one for another.
We have played alongside millions of lovers, shared in the same
Shy sweetness of meeting, the distressful tears of farewell—
Old love, but in shapes that renew and renew forever.

Today it is heaped at your feet, it has found its end in you,
The love of all man's days both past and forever:
Universal joy, universal sorrow, universal life,
The memories of all loves merging with this one love of ours—
And the songs of every poet both past and forever.

References

1   Scott, PA. Imagination in Practice. *Journal of Medical Ethics.* 1997;23:45-50.

2   Momeyer, RW. What conception of moral truth works in bioethics? *Journal of Medical Philosophy.* 2002;28:244-8.

3   Hall K. (2002). "Medical decision-making: an argument for narrative and meta-phor." *Theoretical Medicine and Bioethics* 2002;23;1:55-73.

4   Savitt, Todd (Ed.). *Medical readers theater: a guide and scripts.* Iowa City: University of Iowa Press, 2002.

5   <http://rpo.library.utoronto.ca/poem/1864.html>

6   Trans. by David Lunde. <http://www.chinapage.org/poet-e/dufu2e.html>

7   Tagore, Rabindranath. *Selected poems.* Trans. by William Radice. New York: Penguin Books, 1987.

18

Johanna Shapiro, Jack Coulehan, Delese Wear, Martha Montello, "Medical Humanities and their Discontents: Definitions, Critiques, and Implications," *Academic Medicine* 84:2 (2009), 192-198

Editor's note: As with other more recently published articles in this volume, I asked authors if they would be willing to reflect on their piece and add introductory comments that would help frame it, or enable them to address issues raised since its original publication. The following remarks are from contributing author Johanna Shapiro.

Health Humanities and Its Satisfactions

It is always a mixed blessing to revisit old work. On occasion, you are struck by how smart you used to be. More commonly, you regret turns of phrase, perhaps a lack of nuance or subtlety of argument, even entire conceptualizations. In the case of "Medical Humanities and Its Discontents," the article is an accurate reflection of the authors' personal intersections with medical humanities at the time of its publication. However, upon rereading, I'm struck by its pessimism. Even its recommendations fall more within the realm of wish fulfillment than actuality. Fortunately, in the past 5 years, from my perspective the field has taken great strides toward addressing our earlier concerns and implementing our idealistic vision. Given the chance, I would modify the article in several ways.

I would start by calling it, "Health Humanities..." (1). This may seem mere semantics, but in fact, as has been argued, this term represents a broader, more inclusive approach than the earlier designation, one that welcomes a range of health professionals even as it shifts the focus to embrace health and wellbeing as well as a more pathological orientation.

Second, while definitions of health humanities remain fuzzy, my view is that today there is more comfort with this big, admittedly at times unwieldy, tent and less need for precision definition. This is due to the fact that the conversation about the goals of health humanities has become clearer, crisper, and also more flexible. It is also because it has become de rigeur that scholars and professionals from many backgrounds and diverse training and worldviews can beneficially work in pursuit of these ends (2).

The definitional elements we included then still have merit. These include a focus on suffering and healing (today I would add positive wellbeing), and on the significance of therapeutic relationship; a critical self- and other-awareness (and here I would stress even greater critical interrogation of systemic and institutional assumptions in healthcare), simultaneously skeptical and humane, grounded in close attention and reflection; an inarguable interdisciplinary emphasis (which over the last 5 years has grown even more essential and fortunately more common); and a continued highlighting of the "moral function" of health humanities that comes from deep immersion in suffering, marginalization, and personhood. As Jack Coulehan, one of the authors on the original article observes, there are encouraging signs among medical educators of renewed interest in addressing the issues of character formation and compassionate care (3,4).

Our first main concern in the article focused on the skepticism among medical students toward health humanities instruction, especially required instruction. My own experience is that such skepticism has softened (although not vanished), mercifully replaced by a refreshing openness and eagerness among learners to explore any avenue that might help them become better doctors. It is hard to know whether this is a result of the recent broadening of the MCATS, the selection of medical school applicants more broadly grounded in the liberal arts (5), or other factors, but it is a joy regardless.

In terms of the content critique our original article identified (the humanities are tangential, nice but not essential), nowadays the relevance of humanities and arts to clinical practice is much less called into question. What is practical and relevant seems to be defined more generously and more flexibly. Snow's two cultures have a fuzzier boundary, so coursework in the humanities feels like less of an intellectual bait-and-switch. Students are receptive to the idea that the artist and the scientist are no longer so far apart.

The article also discusses the teaching critique, in which many students (6) and humanities scholars (7) felt humanities teaching in medical schools contained an implicit (or explicit) effort to "improve" their humanism or "make" them more compassionate and empathic. Since our writing, pedagogical approaches have been nuanced, so that there is more emphasis on horizontality, less emphasis on teaching/ making/prescribing, and more on open exploration and curiosity. Even instructors embedded in very traditional curricula now recognize that the humanities are not about character formation, but about inviting students to think about how they wish to shape their own characters. On the learner side, students appear to feel safer reflecting on themselves, and less likely to rebel at introspection. They engage more comfortably with uncertainty (8), and are less disconcerted when no one (not even instructors) has all the answers.

Further, our article addressed the structural critique regarding whether humanities curricular offerings should be elective or required. In contemporary curricula, we are seeing more integrated courses; more required health humanities material; and more interest in integrating health humanities in the clinical years. There has also been a flourishing of reflection activities, such as reflective writing (11) and original creative projects (10). As well, we are seeing increasing integration of the humanities not only within medical education, but also downward into the undergraduate years (medical/health humanities minors or majors) (9) and upward into residency (12). All these developments have the immensely beneficial effect of normalizing and legitimizing the health humanities as a valued and expected part of medical education. Importantly, as Jack Coulehan notes, the real issue is not humanities courses per se, but integration of humanities perspectives and skills into medical education.

One of our recommendations for improvement in the health humanities was to incorporate ongoing cross-disciplinary reflective practice throughout the medical school curriculum and beyond. Again, while much more needs to be achieved in this regard, my sense is that the intellectual tools of the humanities are more widely in use at all levels of medical education from undergraduate to faculty development. It is no longer primarily humanities scholars and a handful of intrepid physicians talking about reflection, parallel process, and critical inquiry (13). More and more learners and practicing physicians recognize the value of thinking about the profession as well as "doing" the profession. There is a growing awareness that the study of humanities provides ways to help students contemplate medicine in all its messy complexity rather than a tidy version of what some think it should be.

One of the stickiest wickets in navigating the relationship between health humanities and medical education remains the ways in which health humanities contribute to and challenge professional identity formation (14) and educational milestones and competencies (15). Our original article argues in favor of thoughtful conceptualizations of these terms that go beyond checklists and that seek to develop habits of mind (and heart) rather than mere behaviors. In this domain in particular we have the potential to expand our thinking by listening attentively and respectfully to each other. Under our capacious interdisciplinary umbrella we have not only the expertise of humanities scholars and qualitative researchers but also that of quantitative investigators from the medical and social sciences. The methods of the latter cannot be easily or simplistically applied wholesale to disciplines such as arts and humanities. But the potential creativity from all disciplinary perspectives that can be brought to bear on this thorny question is at once impressive and exciting.

Our article also called for a more pervasive attention to narrativity in medicine (16) which, in its most basic form, simply refers to a valuing of patients' stories as well as their symptoms and diagnoses. Five years later, narrativity is still more often mentioned in the professional literature than practiced at the bedside. Nevertheless, I detect a growing reappreciation for the importance of knowing patients' (and physicians') stories, while at the same time recognizing the risks of appropriating and misrepresenting the stories of vulnerable others (17).

Finally, we planted the seed of developing "applied humanities scholars." To be honest, at the time of writing, we did not have a detailed understanding of what this might mean – and still don't! However, it remains an exciting possibility to be fleshed out. The humanities have developed increasing interest in practical, translational approaches that bring humanities from the academy into the community (18,19), or in our case, to the bedside or clinic (20). We envision humanities scholars as part of ward team, participant-observers who might provide harried physicians with the illuminating metaphor to understand their patient in different ways; or active in the clinic, facilitating encounters between medical students and patients not only around symptoms but around poetry.

In conclusion, my impression today is that there is much to be excited about regarding the health humanities. The vision is not nearly fulfilled. Much hard work lies ahead, both within the field itself and in interfacing with medical school and residency leaders. In particular, the relationship of the health humanities to professionalism and competencies or milestones, and the ways in which we demonstrate the value of the humanities to administrators and medical educators remain contentious. Overall, however, we are moving in a positive direction. I have always believed that the ultimate goal of teaching and scholarship in the health humanities is to help change the face of medical education, and through this process, to help influence medicine and healthcare itself, so that the healing arts become a truly interdisciplinary enterprise balanced between the technicalness of doing and the wisdom of being. As a culture changes, its metaphors change, and I take it as a hopeful sign that in medical education, we hearing more about growth and healing, meaning-making and perspective-taking. Today while the anchors of our article remain, the work has proceeded, and that is something about which we can all feel hopeful as well as curious to see, five years from now, what the future will hold.

References

1. Crawford P., Brown.B, Tischler V, Baker C. Health humanities: The future of medical humanities? *Mental Health Review Journal* 2010; 1(3): 4-10.
2. Jones T. (ed) Health humanities reader. Rutgers University Press, 2014
3. Coulehan J. "A gentle and humane temper": humility in medicine. *Perspect Biol Med.* 2011;54(2):206-16.
4. Bryan CS, Babelay AM. Building character: a model for reflective practice. *Acad Med.* 2009;84(9):1283-8.
5. Muller D, Kase N. Challenging traditional premedical requirements as predictors of success in medical school: the Mount Sinai School of Medicine Humanities and Medicine Program. *Acad Med.* 2010;85(8):1378-83.
6. Brainard AH, Brislen HC: Learning professionalism: a view from the trenches. *Acad Med* 2007, 82:1010-1014.
7. Bishop JP: Rejecting medical humanism: Medical humanities and the metaphysics of medicine. *J Med Humanit* 2008, 29:15-25.
8. Kumagai A, Wear D. "Making strange": a role for the humanities in medical education. *Acad Med* 2014;89:973-977.
9. Wald H, Borkan JM, Taylor JS, Anthony D, Reis SP. Fostering and evaluating

reflective capacity in medical education: developing the REFLECT rubric for assessing reflective writing. *Acad Med.* 2012;87(1):41-50. d

10.   Kumagai AK. Perspective: acts of interpretation: a philosophical approach to using creative arts in medical education. *Acad Med.* 2012;;87(8):1138-44.

11.   Baylor http://www.baylor.edu/medical_humanities/index.php?id=88442

12.   Winter RO Happy healers. Journal for Learning through the Arts 2011; 7(1). Retrieved from: http://www.escholarship.org/uc/item/81q4s277

13.   Krasner MS, Epstein RM, Beckman H, Suchman AL, Chapman B, Mooney CJ, Quill TE. Association of an educational program in mindful communication with burnout, empathy, and attitudes among primary care physicians. *JAMA* 2009;302(12):1284-1293.

14.   Doukas DJ, McCullough LB, Wear S, et al.: Perspective: The challenge of promoting professionalism through medical ethics and humanities education. *Acad Med* 2013;88:1624-1629.

15.   Brooks MA: Medical education and the tyranny of competency. *Perspect Biol Med* 2009, 52(1):90-102.

16.   Miller E, Balmer D, Hermann N, Graham G, Charon R. Sounding narrative medicine: studying students' professional identity development at Columbia University College of Physicians and Surgeons. *Acad Med* 2014; 89:335-342.

17.   Baruch J. The story always comes first. Literature, Arts, and Medicine Blog. http://www.medhum

18.   Lubar S. Applied, translational, open, public humanities http://steven-lubar.wordpress.com/2014/06/05/applied-translational-open-digital-public-new-models-for-the-humanities

19.   Rumsey AS. Creating value and impact in the digital age through translational humanities. http://www.clir.org/pubs/ruminations/03smithrumsey

20.   Shapiro J. Toward the clinical humanities: How literature and the arts can help shape humanism and professionalism in medical education. Posted January 6th, 2014 in Humanities in Medicine, http://humanism-in-medicine.org/toward-the-clinical-humanities-how-literature-and-the-arts-can-help-shape-humanism-and-professionalism-in-medical-education/

Medical Humanities and their Discontents: Definitions, Critiques, and Implications

Johanna Shapiro, PhD, Jack Coulehan, MD, MPH, Delese Wear, PhD, and Martha Montello, PhD

Abstract: The humanities offer great potential for enhancing professional and humanistic development in medical education. Yet, although many students report benefit from exposure to the humanities in their medical education, they also offer consistent complaints and skepticism. The authors offer a pedagogical definition of the medical humanities, linking it to medicine as a practice profession. They then explore three student critiques of medical humanities curricula: (1) the content critique, examining issues of perceived relevance and intellectual bait-and-switch, (2) the teaching critique, which examines instructor trustworthiness and perceived personal intrusiveness, and (3) the structural/placement critique, or how and when medical humanities appear in the curriculum. Next, ways are suggested to tailor medical humanities to better acknowledge and reframe the needs of medical students. These include ongoing cross-disciplinary reflective practices in which intellectual tools of the humanities are incorporated into educational activities to help students examine and, at times, contest the process, values, and goals of medical practice. This systematic, pervasive reflection will organically lead to meaningful contributions from the medical humanities in three specific areas of great interest to medical educators: professionalism, "narrativity," and educational competencies. Regarding pedagogy, the implications of this approach are an integrated required curriculum and innovative concepts such as "applied humanities scholars." In turn, systematic integration of humanities perspectives and ways of thinking into clinical training will usefully expand the range of metaphors and narratives available to reflect on medical practice and offer possibilities for deepening and strengthening professional education.

As any medical educator will tell you, it is in the nature of medical students to complain about their curriculum.[1-3] The medical humanities receive more than their fair share of students' critiques in terms of both quantity and virulence. Although the majority of students' comments are supportive and positive, many refer to humanities teaching as pointless, boring, worthless, or just plain stupid.[4] Even otherwise favorably disposed students are sometimes adamant about not making medical humanities required coursework. This situation leads us to ask, Why does humanities teaching regularly engender not just legitimate criticism, but outpourings of anger and contempt?

In this article, we offer a pedagogical definition of medical humanities, describe their potential contributions to the medical education enterprise, identify major critiques of the medical humanities from learners' perspectives, and offer suggestions for systemic pedagogical responses to address these critiques.

A Pedagogical Definition of the Medical Humanities

Despite ongoing lack of clarity on what exactly the medical humanities comprise, and how they should be integrated into medical education,[5] medical humanities teaching activities share several characteristics:

1. They use methods, concepts, and content from one or more of the humanities disciplines to investigate illness, pain, disability, suffering, healing, therapeutic relationships, and other aspects of medicine and health care practice.

2. They employ these methods, concepts, and content in teaching health professions students how to better understand and critically reflect on their professions with the intention of becoming more self-aware and humane practitioners.

3. Their activities are interdisciplinary in theory and practice and necessarily nurture collaboration among scholars, healers, and patients.

Conditions 1 and 2 imply that medical humanities have a significant *moral* function.[6-9]* That is, an important goal of medical humanities is to reconceptualize health care, through influencing students and practitioners to query their own

---

* Following Friedman,[10] we see medical humanities and bioethics having equally valuable but essentially different ways of analyzing information, viewing the world, confronting dilemmas, and teaching students.

attitudes and behaviors, while offering a nuanced and integrated perspective on the fundamental aspects of illness, suffering, and healing. In Aristotelian terms,[11] medical humanities aim to improve health care (*praxis*) by influencing its practitioners to refine and complexify their judgments (*phronesis*) in clinical situations, based on a deep and complex understanding (*sophia*) of illness, suffering, personhood, and related issues. In this respect, medical humanities have a more applied function than the humanities as they are traditionally defined in the academy.

Nevertheless, despite the substantial promise of the medical humanities during the past 35 years and compelling evidence of their significance for medical education,[12–14] the incorporation of medical humanities in medical training has not proceeded smoothly. By and large, medical humanities remain an intriguing sideline in the main project of medical education.[15] Below, we consider major critiques of medical humanities curricula that we have heard from learners and those critiques' implications for the relationship between the humanities and medical education.

Learners' Critiques of Medical Humanities Curricula

Critiques of medical humanities may be grouped as responses to three broad questions: (1) Is the content irrelevant? (2) Are humanities teachers and their methods the problem? (3) Is the positioning of humanities coursework within the curriculum inappropriate?

Is it the content?

The relevance critique. This critique acknowledges that the humanities may be important to future physicians in some indirect way, but it asserts that the material is impractical. The humanities can't provide student physicians with concrete skills (such as learning how to start an IV) that are useful in clinical practice. How does reading a poem help the student measurably improve the treatment of patients? When one of us (J.C.) first introduced topics such as interviewing, clinical ethics, and medical humanities, some students found the material simplistic, commonsense, uninteresting, and – worst of all – irrelevant.[16]

At the medical school of another one of us (M.M.), first- and second-year students were polled after their courses to assess, among other things, whether the humanities material presented in lecture, readings, and small-group discussion was "clinically relevant." Results showed that almost half of the students gave the humanities material moderately low ratings for "clinical relevance";

the remainder of the students gave the material more positive ratings. A study examining possible outcomes of students' exposure to poetry reading during an interstation break of a third-year OSCE indicated little or no effect in up to one third of respondents in terms of influencing treatment, increasing empathy, or improving stress.[17] A kinder, gentler version of the relevance critique affirms the "niceness" of the humanities, as in "It's a nice change of pace from pathophysiology" or "It's very relaxing." This modification assumes that the medical humanities are enjoyable but not crucial to the education of physicians. In either case, both anecdotal and investigational data suggest that medical humanities faculty have failed to adequately convince students that the medical humanities really matter to them as future physicians.

Intellectual bait-and-switch. Most students enter medical school having internalized the view that medicine is an objective, scientific pursuit based almost exclusively on factual knowledge and technical skills. This perspective is understandable because it reflects the prevalent image of medicine in American culture[18] and is reinforced by the narrow prerequisites of premedical majors and entry requirements for medical school that prioritize quantitative and scientific performance. In medical training, it is reinforced by basic science courses and, later, a hospital culture that often eschews patient-centered or relationship-based medicine in favor of technical expertise.[19,20] One of us (M.M.) recalls a student complaining bitterly about a narrative writing assignment about patients. Why should he be "forced to write a story?" He "didn't come to medical school to be a writer." This young man and students like him feel a sense of grievance: it's unfair to be evaluated in an area they hadn't expected to be part of their curriculum.

The preference for "elective" humanities. One of the symbolic manifestations of "irrelevance" and "intellectual bait-and-switch" complaints is the persistent resistance to required curriculum in the humanities. One of us (D.W.) recounts a typical incident:

> A student and I were talking about a required. Reflections on Doctoring class that focuses on topics most often illuminated by a short story, poem, or essay. The young man told me how much he liked the class, that is, *really* liked it, but that "a lot" of students did not and wondered if it wouldn't be better as an elective. "Of course, I'd take the course if it were elective and I know a lot of students would, but it would relieve those who aren't interested or who are too busy to come to class.... We're all so busy."

Because medical humanities are a domain outside the basic and clinical sciences, some students believe that one must have an interest in or affinity for them, a bit like the elective system in the final year of medical school. This assumption guarantees a peripheral role for the humanities in the curriculum.

Is it the teachers and their methods?

The trustworthiness critique. In medical education, the current process of socialization encourages a reliance on insiders (physicians) and distrust of outsiders (nonphysicians). There is a widespread perception that nonphysicians do not comprehend clinical realities. Students object that humanities instructors lack professional training or experience in medicine. They aren't doctors, and only doctors can train medical students in clinical skills. Thus, to many students, medical humanities teachers seem to talk the talk without walking the walk.

The therapeutic critique. Humanities-based exercises frequently ask students to reflect on their own values, attitudes, and behavior, as well as on issues of subjectivity, multiple truths, and ambiguity through the filters of poems, stories, artwork, or music.[21-25] Students often resist this personal engagement as excessively intimate and intrusive.

Indeed, the very "softness" of the humanities can pose a threat to students by forcing them to examine their own vulnerability and uncertainty. Being asked to write, either about their own experiences or about those of patients, or even being asked to offer opinions about a poem or painting, can generate anxiety because no universally agreed-upon right answer exists. Instead, they must use their own powers of observation, insight, and intellectual and emotional connections as the bases for their responses. Equally disconcerting, humanities instructors often say, "I don't know, what do you think?" thus questioning the foundational expertise that medical students have learned to expect from their teachers. Perhaps most alarming, "real" teachers, such as basic science faculty, overworked residents, and multitasking attending physicians seem to studiously avoid such subjectivity and lack of uncertainty.

Along these lines, some students perceive that humanities courses attempt character formation, and they believe their own characters not to be in need of further formation. One of us recently carried out a study[26] in which a quarter of participating fourth-year students believed that their medical education had little or no effect on their conceptions of and capacity for compassion, altruism, and respect for patients. Such students feel pressured by humanities courses to somehow become more humanistic when, in fact, they believe qualities of humanism are already formed and unchangeable.

Is it the placement in the curriculum?

The structural critique. Medical humanities are often criticized for inefficiency and improper placement in the curriculum. With regard to inefficiency, students seem to adopt the Rule of Halves: however many hours or seminars are assigned to the humanities, they say the program would be more effective (and more highly rated by students) if it were taught in half the time. Students make a compelling argument that the less humanities teaching they are exposed to, the more they would learn. Another version of the structural critique is the Content Catch 22. In this case, if the humanities curriculum includes high content (dense lectures, lots of reading), it is criticized for overwhelming students. On the other hand, if it includes low content (small groups, process oriented), it is criticized for being vague, open ended, and too personal.

A related argument is that the humanities are not properly positioned in the curriculum. Appearing in the first year, they are too far removed from the clinical setting. In the second year, they compete with preparation for the boards (on which they are not represented). In the third year, students are overwhelmed trying to master basic clinic medicine and, therefore, are less responsive to humanities teaching. In the fourth year, students frequently disappear to away-rotations. It may seem that the best place to introduce medical humanities is nowhere.

A Meaningful Conceptual Response

Underlying all of these specific student criticisms is the larger problem of how certain biomedical narratives are privileged,[27] which in turn influences what can be legitimately incorporated in the curriculum and what can be excluded. The prevailing metaphors of medical education continue to be heavily mechanistic (the body is a machine), linear (find the cause, create an effect), and hierarchical (doctor as expert),[28,29] while its dominant narrative tends to be a story of restitution (patient becomes ill; patient is cured by physician expert; patient is restored to preillness state).[30] Exclusive reliance on these metaphors and narratives, with little space to acknowledge or explore others,[31,32] marginalizes the humanities, which don't neatly conform to this cultural model. So, how can we work to change such elusive abstractions as metaphor and narrative?

Training cross-disciplinary reflection about medicine

Surprisingly, little curricular time currently is devoted to training students to think about the practice of medicine, to help them examine the process of doctoring as well as its outcomes. What is it that doctors do? What *should* doctors do? How do different people experience the same illness? How do doctors learn to care for patients as persons? How do doctors interface with the larger society?[10] Doctors – and students – tend not to ask such meta-questions, as if by and large they consider medicine a-theoretical, a permanent "Truth" with a capital T, a constant reality that simply *is*. Of course, this is not to say that medicine has not been extensively and insightfully theorized, from biopsychosocial,[33] phenomenological,[34] postmodern,[14,35] feminist,[36,37] and narrative[38–40] perspectives. Nonetheless, such theorizing seems to bear little relationship to day-to-day medical education or clinical practice. We believe that this needs to change.

Despite the dominance of technical, rational, and efficiency-based priorities in contemporary medicine and medical education, the culture of medicine is not a monolithic entity and no longer speaks with a single voice. For example, a recent study[41] concluded that although many physicians responded to the term "medical humanities" with reactions of uncertainty or even contempt, in fact the goals of medical humanities – particularly those involving increased personal and professional awareness and self-critique – and the goals of the physicians interviewed in terms of fostering professionalism and professional identity, were very similar. This suggests an underlying commonality of interest uniting medical humanities and medicine. Within our own and other institutions of medical learning, many reflective physicians and other medical educators are eager, and indeed have already been working, to engage in activities to promote an expanded vision of medicine and medical education beyond the instrumental. These nascent changes in conceptualizing and contextualizing medicine, if embraced by educational structures, should be nurtured and enlarged.

What we hope future educational initiatives will acknowledge in a substantive, systematic way is just how close to the heart of medicine the humanities lie. Essentially, the humanities focus on the study of those subjects that lead to a better understanding of the human condition.[42] Medicine necessarily engages with almost every aspect of the human condition. In this respect, the humanities are not *additive* to medicine, which implies that medicine has become somehow *deficient*.[43] Rather, as Bishop[44] suggests, we should be working toward abandoning the instrumental thinking that humanities inquiry is *compensatory* to the "biologism of the scientists." It may be more accurate to say that the humanities can offer medical students additional intellectual tools to help recontextualize their profession in a way that more fully honors its complexity, nuance, ambiguity, and possibility.

In the past decade or so, the concept of reflective practice has penetrated the medical school curriculum through sessions in which humanities scholars, physicians, and medical students interact to more critically understand their own and patients' experiences in health care.[45–47] Reflective writing and journaling further supplement discussion as a reflective exercise.[48] Engendering self-reflection in students will likely legitimate multiple ways of identifying and evaluating medical knowledge and skills beyond the purely technical.[49,50] In particular, it can help medical humanities educators focus their efforts on three crucial aspects of medical education, namely developing medical professionalism, understanding the narrative dimension of doctoring, and critically questioning the current emphasis on competency-based education.

Professionalism. The humanities have important implications for the concept of medical professionalism or, in lay terms, what matters in the making of a physician or, to return to an earlier point, what constitutes authentic relevance to *praxis*. Epstein and Hundert[51] offer a comprehensive definition of professionalism that extends far beyond conventional competency checklists.

They include criteria identified more closely with the humanities than with biomedical sciences, such as tolerance of ambiguity and anxiety, observations of one's own thinking, emotions, and techniques, recognition of and response to cognitive and emotional biases, and integrating judgment from multiple sources including the scientific, the clinical, and the humanistic. Of special interest is their inclusion of relational, affective, and moral components, including attentiveness, critical curiosity, self-awareness, and presence, dimensions that legitimize introspective, emotional labor as well as instrumental work[52] and that increasingly are recognized as valuable by other scholars.[53,54] The humanities' recognition of multiple perspectives, priorities, and truths requiring "practice in the negotiation of meanings"[55] as well as the moral implications accompanying this recognition can provide valuable approaches—for example, through supplemental monthly reflection sessions that accompany required clerkships to further develop such habits of mind.

"Narrativity." Medical humanities should play an even larger role in teaching *narrativity*, which Charon[56] defines as "the ability to acknowledge, absorb, interpret, and act on the stories and plights of others." The narrative medicine movement reframes many core doctoring skills under the aegis of language, culture, and story.[56,57] In furthering comprehension of the narrative component of medicine, literary and cultural scholars could contribute to case conferences and other exercises in which students present verbal narratives that explore their developing professional identities. Likewise, they might help design and facilitate curricular opportunities for medical students to write their patients' stories and/or their personal reactions to patients, families, colleagues, and teachers. Medical humanities faculty could also coordinate curricula in which students enhance their narrative understanding through exposure to memoirs, essays, fiction, poetry, and film. Stories about physicians may also contribute to developing professional identity by expanding the student's repertoire of positive and negative physician role models.[58]

"Humanistic" competencies? Looking beyond the narrow instrumental focus of medicine would also lead to natural and organic ways of address-ing certain recognized clinical competencies that have common sensical links to the medical humanities. Because much of medical education is currently framed in terms of competencies,[59] there is no reason for medical humanities to reflexively resist examining what the profession is trying to achieve through this system of outcomes and measurement. However, such curiosity does not imply that the humanities should unquestioningly further the agenda of the current medical culture. Rather, serious inclusion of medical humanities in conceptualizing the educational process can help the profession think more broadly and creatively about what exactly it is pursuing through its compe-tency orientation.

For example, until now, competencies in areas such as empathy and communication have been defined almost exclusively in checklist-, product-oriented ways (i.e., measurable, observable, and quantifiable behaviors). One contribution to emerge from a mutually respectful dialogue between humanities and medicine would be possibilities for enlarging how to more meaningfully investigate the goals and pursuits that "humanistic" competen-cies symbolize. Specifically, the humanities can contribute an understanding of attitudes, knowledge, and behaviors as dialogical, things that come about between human beings in ways that are always incomplete, partial, and inevita-bly biased. The humanities' tradition of critical inquiry and intellectual skepti-cism can help medicine move beyond checklists and algorithms to advance analytical and reflective habits of mind in students so that they are better able to think from the perspectives of others, move toward a greater humility, and focus on the values and vision that they brought to medicine in the first place.[60,61] This approach could incorporate the building of student portfolios[62] to provide textured, depth exploration, and demonstration of humanistic values through methods such as critical incident reports[63] and creative projects,[64] as well as the use of "humanistic connoisseurs"[65] to mentor and formatively evaluate learners.

Pedagogical and Structural Implications

Integrated, required curriculum. A broader context within which to understand medicine, to conceptualize and develop professionalism, to appreciate the narrative, story-making component of illness and its treatment, and to revisit the concept of humanistic competencies would also logically lead to an integrated curricular role for the humanities. This approach already has been tried successfully with large numbers of cross-cutting areas, such as behavioral health, communication skills, cultural awareness, palliative care, and geriatrics.[66] Disciplinary divisions still form the underpinnings of the academic community, and this is especially true in medical schools. Nevertheless, at the higher echelons of administration, deans of schools of medicine and schools of humanities and the arts might profitably open dialogues that eventually could lead to shared and funded positions that bridge the arts/science divide.

Locations abound throughout the four-year medical curriculum where humanities-based learning can occur alongside the basic and clinical sciences. Moving away from purely elective formats would be a huge step in diminishing the perception that medical humanities are an add-on, separate from the "real" curriculum. For a significant systemic change in the culture of academic medicine, faculty allies of the medical humanities must take advantage of the ample and substantive opportunities for meaningful integration in the basic sciences (e.g., end-of-life inquiry in anatomy; film, art, and literary representations of depression, schizophrenia, or autism in neuroscience) and in each of the clinical clerkships (e.g., arts-based sessions to hone observational skills; narrative medicine seminars integrating poetry and prose stories of illness; popular media representations of physicians and patients; relevant historical perspectives in each required specialty; ethical issues from the perspectives of patients as well as physicians and bioethicists).

To some extent, these opportunities already exist in lecture, small-group, and electronic formats. The key emphasis, however, should be on *systemic* application: all these suggestions require buy-in from the leadership on basic science and clinical curriculum committees to prevent the sporadic, in- the-margins enactment of humanities inquiry, which often gives such inquiry its irrelevant, frivolous, why-are-you- wasting-my-time feel for so many students. If humanities analysis can genuinely become part of the everydayness of learning medicine, endorsed by well-positioned, respected faculty, little by little the ubiquitous divide between scientific/clinical medicine and all other domains may be lessened. In such a changed culture, students may begin to recognize and appreciate how meaning making is a lush, complex, and often contradictory undertaking rarely tied to evidence and efficiency in scientific ways, one that honors rather than dismisses subjectivity.

Integrated role modeling. It is well established in the research literature that role modeling is among the strongest influences on medical students' learning.[67] Medical humanities faculty can play a key role in helping interested physicians become more effective in manifesting humanistic skills and values in their teaching.[68] Humanities educators can accomplish this informally by serving as role models for clinical faculty, especially in large, required multi-disciplinary "patient-doctor" courses, where we coteach or cofacilitate group sessions, and more formally through medical humanities workshops and retreats for physician faculty. We could consider developing mini- fellowships that focus not only on pedagogy but also on selected knowledge and skills in medical humanities. Even further, we can promote the concept that medical humanities teachers *themselves* serve as role models for students in terms of listening, thinking, resonating emotionally, and being fully present.

Applied humanities? It is beyond the scope of this article to address the debate as to whether the humanities should properly focus only on training modes of critical thinking and analysis or whether they should also aim to encourage certain "narrow behaviors or mental attitudes," such as compassion or empathy.[69] However, wading into the shallows of these waters, we offer the concept of the *applied humanities scholar* as a further extension of curricular integration. Evans[70] has usefully distinguished various functions of the medical humanities, including the analysis of the practice of medicine, the moral suasion of medicine, and medical education. Certainly, not all medical humanities educators need to develop applied skills, but like their counterparts in anthropology,[71] some might consider becoming more deeply immersed in the world of illness and its treatment that they study. An applied humanities scholar conceivably could be part of a ward team, whose role would be to ask questions, for example, about the stories being told (or not told), the exercise of power, the way the interaction between doctor and patient might be understood as a kind of dramatic performance, or the aesthetic aspects of the encounter.

Concluding Thoughts

Our approach to medical humanities teaching addresses students' critiques in a number of ways. First, our call for across-disciplinary, collaborative recontextualization of medicine places medical humanities close to the core rather than on the periphery of the profession, and it makes perceptions of irrelevance much more difficult to sustain. Similarly, because professionalism, narrativity, and competencies are concepts currently acknowledged as critical in medical education, focused attention in these domains from the medical humanities will help these disciplines be seen not only as "nice" but also as essential. Taking seriously the scholarly traditions of the humanities will quickly demonstrate their intellectual challenge, toughness, and rigor and would make students less likely to succumb to intellectual bait-and-switch grievances.

In addition, regular collaboration in teaching, clinical correlates, grand rounds, and other pedagogical exercises, such as those suggested here, need not entail major curricular battles or changes in time allocation. It would also reduce the prevailing insider-outsider distinction that exists between physician and nonphysician faculty and would improve the perceived fidelity and credibility of medical humanities educators. Further, rather than somehow attempting to "produce" humanistic attributes widget-fashion, the kind of mechanical attempts at character formation that students so resent, this approach would instead stimulate thoughtful and disciplined investigation of and dialogue about these concepts and values and perhaps help to stem the moral stagnation and erosion that can occur over the course of training.[72] Required medical humanities curricula would reinforce all these dimensions of relevance, intellectual rigor and value, pedagogical trustworthiness, and moral inquiry.

New metaphors and storylines about the nature of doctoring would also emerge in conjunction with this proposed teaching model. For example, we would likely see inclusion of more types of narratives as acceptable,[73] even desirable, in the practice of medicine. Rather than exclusive reliance on restitution narratives (always welcome when you can get them), with all other narratives seen as synonymous with failure, curiosity about other narrative typologies might begin to surface. Doctors and patients might explore and, in the right circumstances, even welcome *journey narratives*, in which they embark on a rite of passage together. They might become curious about *witnessing narratives*, where the physician accepts that bearing witness to a patient's suffering or final days is a valuable contribution to healing, or even about *transformational narratives*, in which the encounter between doctor and patient changes both of them in multiple ways. Instead of metaphors that revolve only around mechanical function and its repair, we will begin to hear health profession-als—and their ever-attentive students—also using metaphors of growth, organicity, and healing (and other metaphors not yet imagined). In short, we will be able to use the humanities' intricate and sympathetic knowledge about the human condition (*sophia*) as well as its ability to examine particularistic, experiential knowledge (*phronesis*) to help ensure a morally sensitive, narratively sound, and deeply professional clinical practice (*praxis*).

References

1   Miles S, Leinster SJ. Medical students' perceptions of their educational environ-ment: Expected versus actual perceptions. *Med Educ.* 2007;41:265-272.

2   Schwartz PL, Loten EG. Effect of year in school on medical students' percep-tions evaluated with the Cognitive Behavior Survey, Attitudes Toward Social Is-sues in Medicine Survey, and Learning Environment Questionnaire. *Teach Learn Med.* 2004;16: 333-344.

3   Brainard AH, Brislen HC. Learning professionalism: A view from the trenches. *Acad Med.* 2007;82:1010-1014.

4   Wear D, Zarconi J. A humanities-based capstone course in medical education: An affirming and difficult look back. *Journal for Learning through the Arts: A Re-search Journal on Arts Integration in Schools and Communities* [serial online]. 2006;2(1): Article 8. Available at: ⟨http://repositories. cdlib.org/clta/lta/vol2/iss1/art8⟩. Accessed August 10, 2008.

5   Campo R. A piece of my mind. "The medical humanities," for lack of a better term. *JAMA.* 2005;294:1009-1011.

6   Charon R, Montello M, eds. *Stories Matter: The Role of Narratives in Medical Ethics.* New York, NY: Routledge; 2002.

7   Coles R. *The Call of Stories: Teaching and the Moral Imagination.* Boston, Mass: Houghton Mifflin; 1989.

8   Pellegrino ED, Thomasma DC. *The Virtues in Medical Practice.* New York, NY: Oxford University Press; 1993.

9   Lindemann H, ed. *Stories and Their Limits: Narrative Approaches to Bioethics.* New York, NY: Routledge; 1997.

10   Friedman LD. The precarious position of the medical humanities in the medical school curriculum. *Acad Med.* 2002;77:320-322.

11   Tyreman S. Promoting critical thinking in health care: Phronesis and criticality. *Med Health Care Philos.* 2000;3:11-124.

12   Mattingly C, Garro LC. *Narrative and the Cultural Construction of Illness and Healing.* Berkeley, Calif: University of California Press; 2000.

13 Charon R. The patient–physician relationship. Narrative medicine: A model for empathy, reflection, profession, and trust. *JAMA.* 2001;286:1897-1902.

14 Morris DB. Narrative, ethics, and thinking with stories. *Narrative.* 2001;9:55-77.

15 Special theme: Humanities education. *Acad Med.* 2003;78:973-1075.

16 Block MR, Coulehan JL. Teaching the difficult interview in a required course on medical interviewing. *J Med Educ.* 1987;62: 35-40.

17 Shapiro J, Duke A, Boker J, Ahearn CS. Just a spoonful of humanities makes the medicine go down: Introducing literature into a family medicine clerkship. *Med Educ.* 2005;39:605-612.

18 Morris D. *Illness and Culture in the Postmodern Age.* Berkeley, Calif: University of California Press; 1998.

19 Coulehan J, Williams PC. *Vanquishing virtue: The impact of medical education.* Acad Med. 2001;76:598-605.

20 Coulehan J. Viewpoint: Today's professionalism: Engaging the mind but not the heart. *Acad Med.* 2005;80:892-898.

21 Levine RB, Kern DE, Wright SM. The impact of prompted narrative writing during internship on reflective practice: A qualitative study. *Adv Health Sci Educ Theory Pract.* September, 21 2007. Available at: ⟨http:// www.springerlink.com/ content/ n8tg852142u12t49/⟩. Accessed November 30, 2008.

22 Shapiro J, Rucker L, Beck J. Training the clinical eye and mind: Using the arts to develop medical students' observational and pattern recognition skills. *Med Educ.* 2006;40: 263-268.

23 Case GA, Micco G. Moral imagination takes the stage: Readers' theater in a medical context. *Journal for Learning through the Arts: A Research Journal on Arts Integration in Schools and Communities* [serial online[. 2006;2(1):Article 12. Available at: ⟨http:// repositories.cdlib.org/clta/lta/vol2/iss1/art12⟩. Accessed August 10, 2008.

24 Hatem D, Ferrara E. Becoming a doctor: Fostering humane caregivers through creative writing. *Patient Educ Couns.* 2001;45:13-22.

25 Van Roessel P, Shafer A. Music, medicine, and the art of listening. Journal for *Learning through the Arts: A Research Journal on Arts Integration in Schools and Communities* [serial online]. 2006;2(1):Article 14. Available at: ⟨http://repositories.cdlib. org/clta/lta/vol2/ iss1/art14⟩. Accessed August 10, 2008.

26 Wear D, Zarconi J. Can compassion be taught? Let's ask our students. *J Gen Intern Med.* 2008;23:948-953.

27 Epstein J. *Altered Conditions: Disease, Medicine, and Storytelling.* New York, NY: Routledge; 1995.

28 Sontag S. *Illness as Metaphor and AIDS and Its Metaphors.* New York, NY: Picador; 2001.

29   Coulehan J. *Metaphor and medicine: Narrative in clinical practice.* Yale Biol Med. 2003;76:8-95.

30   Frank AW. Asking the right question about pain: Narrative and phronesis. *Lit Med.* 2004; 23:209-225.

31   Hunsaker-Hawkins A. *Reconstructing Illness: Studies in Pathography.* 2nd ed. West Lafayette, Ind: Purdue University Press; 1999.

32   Frank AW. *The Wounded Storyteller: Body, Illness, and Ethics.* Chicago, Ill: University of Chicago Press; 1995.

33   Engel GL. The need for a new medical model: A challenge for biomedicine. *Science.* 1977; 196:129-136.

34   Schwartz MA, Wiggins O. Science, humanism, and the nature of medical practice: A phenomenological view. *Perspect Biol Med.* 1985;28:231-261.

35   Lewis B. *Moving Beyond Prozac, DSM, & the New Psychiatry: The Birth of Postpsychiatry.* Ann Arbor, Mich: University of Michigan Press; 2006.

36   Shildrick M. *Leaky Bodies and Boundaries: Feminism, and (Bio)ethics.* New York, NY: Routledge; 1997.

37   Grosz E. *Corporeal Bodies: Toward a Corporeal Feminism* (Theories of Representation and Difference). Purdue, Ind: Indiana University Press; 1994.

38   Charon R. *Narrative Medicine: Honoring the Stories of Illness.* Oxford, UK: Oxford University Press; 2006.

39   Greenhalgh T, Hurwitz B, eds. *Narrative Based Medicine: Dialogue and Discourse in Clinical Practice.* London, UK: BMJ Books; 1998.

40   Hunter KM. *Doctors' Stories: The Narrative Structure of Medical Knowledge.* Princeton, NJ: Princeton University Press; 1991.

41   Knight L. A silly expression: Consultants' implicit and explicit understanding of medical humanities. A qualitative analysis. *J Med Ethics Med Humanit.* 2006;32:119-124.

42   Kidd MG, Connor JTH. Striving to do good things: Teaching humanities in Canadian medical schools. *J Med Humanit.* 2008;29: 45-54.

43   Peterson A, Bleakley A, Bromer R, Marshall R. The medical humanities today: Humane health care or tool of governance? *J Med Humanit.* 2008;29:1-4.

44   Bishop JP. Rejecting medical humanism: Medical humanities and the metaphysics of medicine. *J Med Humanit.* 2008;29:15-25.

45   Branch WT Jr, Pels RJ, Calkins D, et al. A new educational approach for supporting the professional development of third year medical students. *J Gen Intern Med.* 1995;10:691-694.

46   Pololi L, Frankel RM, Clay M, Jobe A. One year's experience with a program to facilitate personal and professional development in medical students using reflection groups. *Educ Health.* 2000;14:36-49.

47 Belling C, Coulehan J. The teachable moment: Ethical and social issues in the obstetrics and gynecology clerkship. *Teach Learn Med.* 2006;18:326-329.

48 Bolton G. Stories at work: Reflective writing for practitioners. *Lancet.* 1999;354:243-245.

49 Novack DH, Suchman AL, Clark W, Epstein RM, Najberg E, Kaplan MD. Calibrating the physician. Personal awareness and effective patient care. *JAMA.* 1997;278:502-509.

50 Meier DE, Back AL, Morrison RS. The inner life of physicians and care of the seriously ill. *JAMA.* 2001;286:3007-3014.

51 Epstein RM, Hundert EM. Defining and assessing professional competence. *JAMA.* 2002;287:226-235.

52 Larson EB, Yao X. Clinical empathy as emotional labor in the patient-physician relationship. *JAMA.* 2005;293:1100-1106.

53 Dobie S. Reflections on a well-traveled path: Self-awareness, mindful practice, and relationship-centered care as foundations for medical education. *Acad Med.* 2007;82:422-427.

54 Epstein R. Mindful practice. *JAMA.* 1999;282: 833-839.

55 Belling C. Metaphysical conceit? Toward a harder medical humanities. *Atrium.* Fall 2006:1-5.

19

G. Thomas Couser, "What Disability Studies Has to Offer Medical Education," *Journal of Medical Humanities* 32 (2011), 21-30.

Editor's note: As with other more recently published articles in this volume, I asked authors if they would be willing to reflect on their piece and add introductory comments that would help frame it, or enable them to address issues raised since its original publication. The following remarks are from the author G. Thomas Couser.

I was very gratified to learn that this article had been selected for reprinting here because I have a particular investment in it: if anything I've ever written could make a difference in the lives of disabled people, this is it. I welcomed the opportunity to reflect on it from my current perspective, but I found myself putting off rereading what I had written. My procrastination was a function of my discouragement about the reception of the article to date: had I been too critical of biomedicine and its approach to disability?

The original stimulus to this piece was Hofstra's establishment of a medical school in 2008. As the founder and director of Hofstra's undergraduate Disability Studies program, I thought I might have an opportunity to influence the new school's curriculum, so I tried to show how it might benefit from the perspective of critical disability studies. But despite my efforts to engage the relevant administrators, that has not happened, as far as I can tell.

In preparing these reflections, I came across an earlier article, "Medical Education and Disability Studies," which looks at the issues more empirically (Fiona Kumari Campbell (*JMH* [2009] 30:221-235). From it, I learned that the integration of Disability Studies into the medical curriculum had been attempted as early as the 1990s, but with little success—apart from a flagship program at Bristol University in the United Kingdom.

It is troubling that biomedicine seems so resistant to the insights of disability studies. But perhaps this response is understandable. The crux of the matter may be, as Campbell suggests, that medical professionals' sense of themselves as healers and carers makes it difficult for them to acknowledge that healthcare may be hostile to disability (p. 225).

But in its advocacy of "health," biomedicine sometimes conflate illness and disability, thus pathologizing conditions that may be merely anomalous and not inherently unhealthy. By hailing disabled people as sick, the medical paradigm constructs their conditions as requiring medical intervention, which is not always helpful or desired. This approach effectively devalues those who are disabled, projecting a desire for cure where it may not exist. Many disabled people are surprisingly well adjusted to their conditions, especially if their impairments are congenital or acquired early. In contrast, nondisabled people, *especially medical professionals*, typically estimate the quality of life of disabled people as quite poor. Hence the danger of the medical "bias" in favor of health.

In reviewing my article, I felt I had been fair. I give biomedicine credit for saving and improving the lives of many disabled people. I note that the medical and the social paradigms of disability should be regarded as complementary rather than opposed. At the same time, I remain concerned that my critique of biomedicine — which is not original with me — has not had a more favorable reception. There is much work to be done to ensure that our healthcare system treats disabled people fairly and respectfully. It will require more than (misguided) disability simulations and the occasional workshop: it will require some rigorous conceptual work, some new thinking. I hope the republication of the essay here will be of service in that endeavor.

What Disability Studies Has to Offer Medical Education

G. Thomas Couser

Abstract: Disability studies can be of great value to medical education first, by placing the medical paradigm in the broad context of a sequence of ways of understanding and responding to disability that have emerged in the last two thousand years or so; second, by reminding medical professionals that people with disabilities have suffered as well as profited from medical treatment in the last two hundred years; finally, by providing access to a distinctive point of view from which the experience of disability looks very different than it may from the outside.

I had been writing about narratives of illness and disability for about fifteen years and teaching disability studies for about ten years when, in 2007, my university, Hofstra, announced its decision to create a brand new medical school. This announcement caught me quite by surprise, but it prompted me to think seriously about what our program in disability studies, which I had founded five years earlier, might have to contribute to the new medical curriculum. I began by reviewing the syllabus of my Introduction to Disability Studies, a course I teach every year to undergraduates (few of whom seem to be "premed," in the sense of aspiring to attend medical school). To my gratification, I came to believe that the course – and disability studies, generally – has much to offer to medical students because (1) it addresses matters necessarily of interest to medical professionals, and (2) it does so from a distinctive and valuable angle.[1]

The course description reads as follows:

> This course approaches disability not as an individual tragedy or medical problem but as a cultural construct – akin to gender and race – that undergirds social practices and cultural representations in various media. It is thus intended to complement the more service-oriented approaches to disability that might be emphasized in courses offered by the School of

Education, Health, and Human Services. It seeks to illuminate the broad and complex topic of disability from various distinct disciplinary angles—primarily literary, historical, philosophical and ethical, and political. History furnishes an account of the experience and treatment (or mistreatment) of disabled people; literary analysis addresses the cultural representation of disability (primarily but not exclusively by nondisabled persons); philosophy interrogates the crucial notion of the "normal"; ethics addresses questions of justice; politics explores current issues on which disability impinges (such as welfare, euthanasia, and abortion).

The broadly interdisciplinary nature of the disability studies is no accident; one of the deep lessons of this relatively new field is that disability can be fully understood only when examined from multiple perspectives and with consideration of its impact in so many areas of life.

In disability studies today, a distinction is made among three major models, or paradigms, of disability – the symbolic, the medical, and the social – as they emerge in a historical sequence as Western culture develops. This sequence locates medicine's distinctive approach to disability in a broad framework, highlighting not only its power but also its limits. Under the symbolic paradigm, which is characteristic of traditional faith-based cultures, a particular condition is considered a sign of a moral or spiritual condition. Under the medical paradigm, which is characteristic of modern fact-based cultures, a particular condition is seen solely as a dysfunction of a particular body that which may be prevented, cured, corrected, or rehabilitated. And under the social paradigm, which is characteristic of post-modern culture, particular conditions are seen as socially constructed in the manner of race and gender; thus, how they are understood varies from time to time and from place to place.[2]

The key feature of the symbolic paradigm is that some anomaly in the body represents a legible and reliable sign of a moral condition or divine disfavor. The outer appearance of the body reveals the moral or spiritual status of the person. This paradigm maps the supernatural onto the natural, the metaphysical onto the physical, the intangible onto the tangible. Present in both the Hebrew Bible and the New Testament, the symbolic paradigm is *deeply* embedded in Western culture from very early on.

For example, in the book of Leviticus, 21:18-2 (King James), restrictions are placed on those high priests who perform certain ritual ceremonies. As they are to be in proximity with the deity, they are required to be without "blemish"—where blemishes are enumerated as a long list of what we would consider disabilities: blindness, disfiguration, lameness, dwarfism, and so on.

In the gospels, Jesus is at pains to disassociate holiness from strict observance of the Law and to associate it, rather, with being in a right relation to God. He demonstrates this by using his power to heal people whom we would regard today as diseased or disabled. The most dramatic are the cases of those who are explicitly described as possessed by evil spirits—as found in the Gospel according to Mark 1–3, 5, 7–8. This is presumably the origin of the Christian practice of faith healing. The good news is that the diseased and disabled may be healed; the bad news is that they are characterized as in need of spiritual cleansing. Thus, this paradigm adds moral insult to physical injury.

Although the symbolic paradigm has been largely discredited, it cannot be totally discounted. Faith healing is still practiced and continues to harm vulnerable people. For example, one newspaper recounts the inadvertent suffocation of a teenager with epilepsy who was beaten, then crucified, in a gruesome attempt to exorcise him.) But the symbolic paradigm may also infiltrate mainstream understandings of disease and disability, undergirding what some observers believe is a contemporary "moral panic" over obesity. Obesity does entail significant health risks, of course, but the widespread public concern over the "epidemic" of obesity seems to reflect, in part, moralistic concern about over-consumption and self-control. Many people believe that obesity is primarily a function of poor selfcontrol—in effect, that it reveals an individual's moral failing. In any case, the symbolic paradigm continues to thrive in cultural representations of illness and disability; consider the cliché of the maimed or scarred villain in popular fiction and film.

The advent of the medical paradigm is associated with the birth of the clinic, usually assigned to the eighteenth century. But it is adumbrated in the Renaissance, notably in Sir Francis Bacon's seventeenth-century essay, "Of Deformity." There Bacon argues that deformity is not, contrary to popular belief, an index of bad character: "Therefore, it is good to consider of Deformity, not as a *Signe*, which is more Deceivable; But as a *Cause*, which seldome faileth of the Effect."[3] According to Bacon, people with deformed bodies react to others' scorn in ways that lead them to be either overachievers or crooks. Bacon suggests that any correlation between character and body shape is not divinely ordained but rather a defensive human response to negative attitudes. The slippage from sign to cause marks a crucial step toward a modern, empirical view of physical anomaly.

The medical paradigm tends to demystify and naturalize somatic anomaly, stripping away any supernatural or moral significance and characterizing physical variation solely as a matter that science may investigate and attempt to remedy. Compared to the symbolic paradigm, the medical paradigm offers much benefit for people with anomalous bodies. People who once might have been persecuted, prosecuted, even executed (as witches) because of conditions like Tourette syndrome, epilepsy, and schizophrenia might now be regarded as candidates for medical treatment and be absolved of responsibility for their conditions.

Biomedicine offers much to people with many impairments; for starters, it offers some of them life itself, making it possible for people to survive impairments that once would have been fatal. Thus, while wars have always numbered amputees among their veterans, only in the latter half of the 20th century have there been paralyzed veterans—thanks to modern antibiotics. Yet the reach of biomedicine reach always exceeds its grasp. And its commendable ambition to explain mysterious medical conditions sometimes leads it to reinscribe prejudicial tropes. Typically, this takes the form of the discovery – which is really the invention – of an "X syndrome personality." For all his early modern skepticism, Bacon in effect limits people with deformities to two variants of what we might call "the deformed personality syndrome": (1) the overachiever, known today as the superpcrip, and (2) the angry, devious cripple. Similarly, as Oliver Sacks has pointed out, for most of the twentieth century, migraine was explained away as a function of a personality type.[4] When medical science confronts anomalous somatic conditions that elude definitive explanation, it sometimes psychologizes them in a way that falls back on the symbolic paradigm. And when biomedicine remystifies disability in this way, its tropes may be more insidious than those of the earlier paradigm; backed by the authority of science, they may be accorded undeserved credence.

The social paradigm was developed by disabled scholars and advocates in the U.K. and the U.S. in the last quarter of the 20th century. It has several variants, but common and essential to all is the notion that, like race and gender, disability is a social construct which varies both from culture to culture and over time. Indeed, this is not just one more paradigm but a meta-paradigm that exposes both of the previous paradigms as constructions of particular cultures or mindsets. In this poststructuralist approach, a crucial distinction is made between *impairment*, which is located in the body, and *disability*, which is located in the body's social and cultural context. This is, admittedly, confusing, since these terms are commonly used synonymously. And it is somewhat counterintuitive to use the term, disability, for the extrinsic disadvantages of impairments (sometimes referred to as handicaps). But this distinction, which is at the heart of the new disability studies, allows us to recognize, analyze, and alleviate disadvantages, like discrimination and exclusion, that may appear to be, but are not, intrinsic to particular impairments.

The classic illustration of this distinction is the difference between being unable to move one's limbs (a physiological fact) and being unable to negotiate one's wheelchair through a built environment that lacks ramps or elevators (a socially created constraint). Thus, the social paradigm emphasizes the way in which culture (in all its dimensions, not just material) enables and empowers individuals with "normal" bodies and dis-enables and disempowers those with "deviant," or "abnormal," bodies. In contrast to the medical paradigm, this one places the onus on society to accommodate anomalous bodies. The key move made by disability studies scholars is thus a conceptual figure-ground reversal: whereas the medical paradigm locates the problem in the figure, the social paradigm locates it in the ground—or in the relation of figure and ground. In this model, of course, medicine is part of the context, or ground. As such, it comes under considerable scrutiny.

The distinction between impairment and disability helps explain why many disabled people were so disappointed by Christopher Reeve's disability advocacy after his injury: in their view, Reeve was overinvested in a cure for spinal-cord injury and insufficiently attentive to the many ways in which paralyzed people are disadvantaged by social and cultural restrictions. Even if research does find a cure for spinal cord injury, which is certainly to be desired, it will not make ramps obsolete, because paralysis has many causes. Biomedicine will always be playing catch up; the need to modify the environment and ensure access is all the more urgent given the inevitable lag between research and cure.

The shift of emphasis from body to environment has far-reaching implications. A powerful illustration can be found in American disability rights laws culminating in the Americans with Disabilities Act (ADA) of 1990, which, after having been eviscerated by court decisions, was restored to its original scope by the ADA Amendments Act (ADAAA) just a year ago—an historic event that passed with hardly a ripple in the mainstream media. Like laws barring discrimination on the basis of race and gender, the ADA bans discrimination on the basis of somatic difference. *Unlike* other civil rights laws, however, the ADA actually calls for *unequal* treatment: the law explicitly requires public institutions, public transportation, businesses and employers to make "reasonable accommodation" for people with disabilities and to treat them *differently* from others. As the social paradigm mandates, the law calls for modification of the environment rather than of the impaired body. As places designed for use by injured people, hospitals ought to be paragons of accessibility. When it comes to *physical* accessibility (accommodating those who travel on wheels rather than on foot and those who cannot manipulate doorknobs), this seems to be the case. But when it comes to accommodating those with communication or cognitive disorders, architectural accessibility is not enough; accommodation needs to go much further.

The medical and social models are often characterized as conflicting with, or opposed to, each other. And it is true that the first cohort of disability studies scholars, a group of white male professionals in Britain, was somewhat hostile to medicine. Most of them were paraplegics who did not require much medical attention or benefit much from it; their lives were limited more by social and cultural obstacles than by their inability to walk. Their overriding concern, at that time, was with equal rights, with access to public life and economic opportunity. Hence their strong preference for the social model over the medical, which they characterized as patronizing and marginalizing. (Bear in mind that, in the 1970s, the practice of medicine was quite paternalistic.)

Today, however, there is considerable debate among disability scholars over whether the social paradigm has had the unfortunate, and ironic, effect of effacing the body, of deflecting attention from the painful realities of some impairments, particularly degenerative conditions. A leading British disability scholar, Tom Shakespeare, has aggressively challenged the orthodoxy of the social model, which he sees as gravely flawed and needing to be replaced. In *Disability Rights and Wrongs*, Shakespeare has criticized the social model for undermining political organization along the lines of particular impairments and for generating counterproductive suspicion of medical research and development. And the field is now reckoning with the fact that the minority model (the idea of disabled people as an oppressed group) does not adequately address the needs of those with conditions like serious mental illness and cognitive deficiencies. Removing barriers, or offering accommodation, is less helpful for people with these conditions than for the iconic wheelchair user.

It seems to me that choosing between the models is not a matter of choosing between the empowering and the oppressive. In fact, I am unsure that it is always *necessary* to choose between them. Ideally, they are complementary; the social model picks up where the medical leaves off. Each attends to a different dimension of a common goal: ensuring optimal functioning and quality of life for those with anomalous bodies. Each has a necessary and valuable function, and both may need to be deployed to maximize human capability. But medical professionals need to be aware that, and why, some disabled people will favor the social over the medical paradigm. As Martha Nussbaum writes:

> People with physical disabilities want medical care for their needs, the way we all
> do. But they also want to be respected as equal citizens with options for diverse

> forms of choice and functioning in life, comparable to those of other citizens....
> Thus making care available when people want and need it should be sharply
> distinguished from forcing people into a situation in which they have to depend
> on others, even if that is not what they want.[5]

It is important for medicine not to prejudge or devalue people with disabilities
so as to deprive them of autonomy.

In addition to placing the medical model in this broad, but abstract, historical sequence, disability studies can also supply concrete detail, putting flesh, so
to speak, on the skeletal outline. Lennard Davis has memorably characterized
the historical plight of disabled people as follows: "For centuries, people with
disabilities ... have been isolated, incarcerated, observed, written about, oper-
ated on, instructed, implanted, regulated, treated, institutionalized, and controlled to a degree probably unequal to that experienced by any other minority
group."[6] Much of this treatment has been benevolent in intention, but much
of it has also been constraining and even destructive in its effects. And much
of it, of course, has been carried out by medical professionals. So disability
studies also offers to medical education an important historical reality check.

Disability history offers a salutary perspective on the power that has
accrued to biomedicine even before it has attained much curative effect. A
good place to start is with Davis' essay, "Constructing Normalcy: The Bell
Curve, the Novel, and the Invention of the Disabled Body in the Nineteenth
Century." He analyzes how several historical factors came together to generate a quantitative sense of normal human somatic traits. Among those factors were the rise of the middle class in post-feudal and post-revolutionary
Europe; the Industrial Revolution, which relocated rural laborers to urban
settings and introduced them to harsh and rigid factory regimens; the development of statistics, which produced the normative bell curve; and the interest
of democratic governments in gathering data about their citizenry, the body
politic. Seemingly a neutral objective practice, the quantitative norming of
human traits inevitably assigns value: it tends to characterize the abnormal,
the *statistically* deviant, as inferior, even potentially dangerous to public health.
Further, it tends to encourage the *normalizing* of the population, the impulse
to eliminate or minimize outliers. And its close relative, ranking, which obtains
when the valued position is at one end of the continuum rather than in the
center (as with IQ), can have even more insidious effects, as well. In any case,
the advent of norming really puts the *power* in what Michel Foucault referred
to as biopower: modern states' regulation of citizens' bodies by various practices and institutions, some medical, some quasi-medical.

An effective illustration is the increasing use of human growth hormone, at the present time, to "treat" extreme shortness in children who have no underlying pathology. In "The Short of It," Stephen Hall shows how simply being at the wrong end of the bell curve has been pathologized on the basis of ill-founded stereotypes about short people. The power of the pharmaceutical industry is crucial here: once HGH had been synthesized and was more affordable, the inclination to prescribe increased. In any case, extreme shortness has been treated, medically, as a pathological condition. The same can now be said for shyness, which is diagnosed and treated as "social anxiety disorder."

As this last example suggests, biomedicine may unnecessarily pathologize what appears to be abnormal or deviant human *behavior*. The ongoing revision of the *Diagnostic and Statistical Manual of Mental Disorders* offers real-time access (as filtered through mass media, of course) to the process by which certain behaviors – like compulsive shopping – are officially determined to be disabilities and thus reassigned from the category of moral failings to that of minor mental illness. Useful by analogy here is the example of homosexuality, which was once seen primarily as a moral evil, then pathologized as a mental disorder, then depathologized and ultimately dropped from the *DSM* in 1974. All too often when an effective treatment is available for a particular anomaly, whether physiological or behavioral, modern medicine tends to declare that variation pathological, even if it is functionally harmless, like being short or being shy.

One of the prime targets of ranking, of course, has been I.Q., and consideration of the consequences of the ranking of intelligence takes us into the zone of eugenics. In "Carrie Buck's Daughter," Stephen Jay Gould has detailed the misdiagnosis of Carrie Buck and her illegitimate daughter as mentally retarded and the involuntary sterilization of Carrie and her sister, who thought she was undergoing an appendectomy. It was the Buck family, of course, who elicited Oliver Wendell Holmes's now infamous comment: "Three generations of imbeciles are enough" (Buck v. Bell, 1927). My only reservation about that essay is that Gould's energy goes almost exclusively into showing that Carrie and her daughter were not, in fact, intellectually deficient; rather, Carrie was a victim of rape who was subsequently institutionalized largely out of class prejudice masked as concern for public health. Unfortunately, establishing that Carrie was no imbecile dodges the issue of the reproductive rights of people who *are* cognitively disabled, but the essay provides a bridge from the emergence of the bell curve to its eugenic applications.

As is now increasingly well known, the Nazi T4 program to euthanize people with physical and mental impairments was, in effect, the culmination of American and British eugenic philosophy. In their powerful documentary, *A World without Bodies*, disability studies scholars, David Mitchell and Sharon Snyder, give an incisive, vivid account of the program. Part of the film is narrated by Mitchell as he wheels his chair through a gas chamber once used to execute the disabled. It was then "mothballed" and now is part of the campus of a psychiatric hospital in Bernberg. The Nazis did not destroy the evidence of the killing of diseased and disabled people, unlike the extermination of other groups of victims. The point for medical education, of course, is that in both Carrie Buck's Virginia and in Hitler's Germany, it was medical personnel who carried out the policies in question. Those trained to care somehow rationalized sterilizing and executing those deemed not genetically healthy. Thus, one of the lessons of disability studies for medical education is that with regard to people with disabilities medicine has, again and again, violated its own injunction to "do no harm."

The disability critique of the nineteenth-century invention of norming is instrumental to the creation in the twentieth century of the "minority model" of disability, which undergirds legislation like the ADA. This variant of the social paradigm suggests that some seemingly pathological differences should be accepted as valuable in their own terms—as valid, if atypical, ways of being. The most obvious and compelling example of such a condition is hereditary deafness. Deaf people (with a capital D) consider sign language their first language and their community a distinct linguistic and cultural entity. Thus, in a postcolonial era, they have strongly opposed the use of cochlear implants as having ethnocidal implications.

Less obviously, some people with autism now argue that their condition is not a pathology but rather a valuable neurological variant. A readily available testament to this effect is a mesmerizing eight-minute YouTube manifesto called "In My Own Language." It begins with startling footage, shot by the subject herself, of a young woman at home where she is absorbed in telltale autistic behaviors in her apartment. She rocks back and forth, hums tunelessly and waves her hands; she bangs household objects together rhythmically; she moves her hand back and forth under running water from a tap; she holds a book open in front of her, but instead of reading it, she rubs her face in it. Eventually, one hears a synthesized voice reading a text typed at lightning speed by the subject. Contrary to the standard characterization of autistic people as being trapped in their own private worlds, the author of this manifesto, A. M. Baggs, proclaims that she interacts with her environment more fully than "neurotypicals," who pay attention only to each other and not to the sights, sounds, and textures of their immediate surroundings. What looks deficient, she claims, is not unhealthy but merely different. Even less obviously, but more significantly, the same stance has been taken by individuals with some mental illnesses.

In practice, disabled people are not a monolithic group. They can be divided along many lines—according to their particular impairments, according to whether those impairments are mental or physical, formal or functional, visible or not, stable or "progressive," and so on. But the most consequential division may have to do with the time and circumstances of the onset of the condition in question. People with congenital conditions or early-onset conditions are far more likely than those with conditions acquired in maturity to (1) rate their quality of life highly, (2) identify as "disabled," (3) declare they don't want to be fixed or cured, and (4) invest mainly, if not exclusively, in the social paradigm.

Historically, disabled people have challenged, and thus frustrated, medicine by presenting conditions that medicine *cannot* cure or correct. But today, some of those who have been disabled all their lives may present bodies that *defy* medicine to fix them, even if it can. I believe that we will continue to see these sorts of challenges as the power of biomedicine grows with new technologies and the decoding of the human genome. Here the medical and social paradigms actually *are* in conflict.

This last acknowledgment brings me to a consideration of areas in which disability studies has most to offer, in a practical way, to medical professionals today, for it provides an indispensable perspective on some very important issues in health care. One of these has to do with the beginning of life, another with its

> *"Historically, disabled people have challenged, and thus frustrated, medicine by presenting conditions that medicine cannot cure or correct. But today, some of those who have been disabled all their lives may present bodies that defy medicine to fix them, even if it can."*

end: selective abortion and physician-assisted suicide, respectively. On these two issues, disability advocacy groups have taken positions that are outside the mainstream of bioethical thinking. Their concern is that both practices are rooted in ignorance or prejudice about living with disability; both practices are considered to devalue lives that many disabled people live with considerable gratification. When it comes to eugenics and euthanasia, disabled people are like canaries in the coal mine, the first to be threatened with harm. But unlike canaries, they are aware of their vulnerability, and in recent decades, they have come together to resist threats to their welfare and their survival.

The mission of medicine, its raison d'être and professional imperative, is to heal and make whole, and its power to do so will continue to increase. But the flip side of that orientation may be a tendency to turn away from that which can't be corrected, that which frustrates, or embarrasses, medicine. (This is a problem, I understand, in treating terminal and chronic illness.) Disability studies can help here through its crucial distinction between impairment and disability. One often hears disabled people referred to as "suffering from" X. Sometimes this is the case, of course, but conditions that are inherently painful or causes of constant suffering are rarer than many think. The phrase is really a speech formula that assigns or *presumes* suffering in the absence of testimony. More important, many disabled people claim that they suffer more from the stigma, marginalization and exclusion of disability than they do from their impairment itself.

This bears directly on choices regarding which children should be born and under what conditions assisted suicide should be permissible. One of the virtues of disability studies is that it has encouraged the creation of a growing repository of testimony by people living with disability, most recently, in the form of numerous memoirs. The deep subtext of this body of literature, taken as a whole, is that living with disability, though rarely easy and always challenging, is not only possible but also gratifying. I suspect that such testimony is an underutilized resource in medicine. For testimony regarding mental disability and selective abortion, I recommend Michael Bérubé's memoir of having a son with Down syndrome, *Life As We Know It*. Some 90% of prospective parents terminate a pregnancy when a fetus tests positive for Down syndrome, which is, and should be, their right. However, too many do so without a real sense of what a child with Down syndrome might be like—*who* such a child might become; thus they might benefit from the testimony of parents like Michael and his wife, Janet Lyons. In his blog, Michael periodically updates readers on Jamie's accomplishments. Now a teenager, he knows the words to a large number of Beatles' songs, and as a professor of English who was never any good at memorizing poetry, I view this achievement with envy and even awe.

For testimony on living with a severe neuromuscular impairment, I would recommend Harriet McBryde Johnson's memoir, *Too Old to Die Young*. Many parents would abort a fetus if they knew would their child would be as disabled as Johnson. Indeed, complete strangers have approached her on the street to say that if they had to be like her, they'd kill themselves. If one has never been disabled, it's easy to *think* that a condition like hers is intolerable, that death would be better. But we can't really know that until and unless it becomes our fate, which is the value of memoir as vicarious experience, personal testimony of what it's like to live with a compromised body.

As it happened, Johnson lived far longer than expected, hence the title, *Too Old to Die Young*. In 2008, she died suddenly and unexpectedly—at the age of fifty (still quite young, from my perspective). But she wrote lyrically and compellingly about the distinctive pleasures afforded her by her shriveled and helpless body. These were things she enjoyed not *despite* her condition but *because* of it: being bathed from head to toe by her personal assistant each morning, enjoying the refreshing breeze caused by her effortless movement through the hot humid air as she commuted to her law office in Charleston in her motorized wheelchair. Her longevity was presumably, in part, a function of good medical care, but what made her life so gratifying was her environment, broadly construed to include the right to attend public school, college, and law school; wheelchair access to theaters, concert halls, restaurants, stores, and so on. Thus, many of her pleasures were activities also cherished by non-disabled people, and not being segregated from them was crucial.

It is all too easy for nondisabled people to underestimate the quality of life that many people with disabilities experience. And where there is suffering, it is critically important to distinguish that which is intrinsic to the condition from that which is extrinsic. While the alleviation of extrinsic suffering is not the business of medicine, life-and-death decisions made in medical venues may be distorted by the failure to make this distinction. This is where disability studies has a critical and very practical role to play. Many disabled people fear the advent of a stealth eugenics—a kinder, gentler eugenics carried out by supposedly free agents, pregnant women and elderly and disabled people. Until the world truly welcomes and fully accommodates those with disabilities, these choices are not truly free. These concerns are not only understandable but legitimate; ultimately they affect us all, and the medical profession needs to take them seriously.

In conclusion, I have tried to demonstrate that disability studies can be of value to medical education in several ways: first, by placing the medical paradigm in the broad context of a sequence of ways of understanding and responding to disability that have emerged in the last two thousand years or so; second, by reminding medical professionals that people with disabilities have suffered as well as profited from medical treatment in the last two hundred years; finally, by providing access to a distinctive point of view from which the experience of disability looks very different than it may from the outside.

I tell the students who take my courses for various reasons – some career-related, some personal – that I consider "disability literacy" an important attribute of an educated citizenry today because so many public policy issues have a disability dimension. I hope it is obvious by now why I consider disability literacy even more critical as an attribute of contemporary medical professionals: because they operate where theory meets practice, where thinking about human variation is powerfully brought to bear on bodies and minds at risk.

Notes

1   I refer to disabled people (or people with disabilities) collectively, when they are hardly a monolithic group. Similarly, I will use the term, medicine, as a kind of shorthand for the medical-industrial complex, which is also not monolithic. Finally, I will be describing disability studies as though it were more cohesive than it is.

2   The discussion of these paradigms draws on chapter two, "Paradigms Cost,"of my *Signifying Bodies: Disability in Contemporary Life Writing* (Ann Arbor: University of Michigan Press, 2009), 16-30.

3   Sir F. Bacon, "Of Deformity," in *The Essayes or Counsels, Civill and Morall*, ed. Michael Kiernan (Cambridge: Harvard University Press, 1985), 133-34.

4   O. Sacks, *Migraine: Understanding a Common Disorder*, rpt. (Berkeley: University of California Press, 1985, 140.

5   M. Nussbaum, *Frontiers of Justice: Disability, Nationality, Species Membership* (Cambridge: Harvard University Press, 2006), 189; I have reordered her sentences.

6   L J. Davis, *Introduction, Disability Studies Reader*, 2nd ed. (New York: Routledge, 2006), xv. 26 J Med Humanit (2011) 32:21-30

References

Bacon, F. "Of Deformity." In *The Essayes or Counsels, Civill and Morall*. Edited by M. Kiernan, 133–34. Cambridge: Harvard University Press, 1985.

Baggs, A M. "In My Own Language." http://www.youtube.com/watch?v=JnylM1hI2jc (accessed September 24, 2009).

Bérubé, M. *Life as We Know It: A Father, a Family, and an Exceptional Child*. New York: Vintage, 1998.

Couser, GT. *Signifying Bodies: Disability in Contemporary Life Writing*. Ann Arbor: University of Michigan Press, 2009.

Davis, LJ. "Constructing Normalcy." In *Enforcing Normalcy: Disability, Deafness, and the Body*, 23–49. London: Verso, 1995.

———. Introduction. *Disability Studies Reader*, xv–xviii. 2nd ed. New York: Routledge, 2006.

Gould, SJ. "Carrie Buck's Daughter." In *The Flamingo's Smile: Reflections in Natural History*, 306–18. New York: Norton, 1985.

Hall, SS. "The Short of It." *New York Times Magazine*, October 16, 2005.

Johnson, HM. *Too Late to Die Young*. New York: Holt, 2005.

Mitchell, DT., and SL. Snyder. *A World without Bodies*. Brace Yourselves Productions, 2002.

Nussbaum, M. *Frontiers of Justice: Disability, Nationality, Species Membership*. Cambridge: Harvard University Press, 2006.

Sacks, O. *Migraine: Understanding a Common Disorder*. Reprint. Berkeley: University of California Press, 1985.

Shakespeare, T. *Disability Rights and Wrongs*. London: Routledge, 2006.

20

Paul Ulhas Macneill, "The Arts and Medicine: A Challenging Relationship," *Medical Humanities* 37 (2011), 85-90.

Editor's note: As with other more recently published articles in this volume, I asked authors if they would be willing to reflect on their piece and add introductory comments that would help frame it, or enable them to address issues raised since its original publication. The following remarks are from the author, Paul Ulhas Macneill.

For many years, I have been responsible for teaching ethics to medical students: both in Australia and Singapore (and with some teaching in the UK, the USA, Canada and New Zealand). My concern is that medical education, in all these places, emphasises medicine as a science rather than an art. Any effective practitioner of medicine knows better however: medicine is equally — if not more so — an art. The science is relatively easy to grasp. But the art is more challenging, and the art is difficult to teach. It is complex and lacks the simplicity and clarity of the 'biomedical model' and its attendant metaphor of the 'body as a machine'.

There have been many attempts to 'humanise' medicine by adding courses to medical degrees including communication skills, ethics, history of medicine, and the medical humanities. My concern however is that the medical humanities — along with all the recent additions to medicine — are not taken seriously by students. As a consequence, the response has been to justify the medical humanities by their instrumental effectiveness. The effect of this approach — as I argue in the following essay — is to pacify and domesticate the humanities. It strips the humanities of their power to shock and transgress, to shake certitudes and confront difficult complexities. Ultimately it is to demean art and each of the arts and it deprives medical education of the full power of the arts as a critical and expansive force.

This essay is part of a broader exploration, for me, of the arts on their own terms, and the power of the arts to challenge and refine our understanding in other disciplines. In my own field I have been exploring a relationship between ethics the arts and I have recently published a book entitled *Ethics and the Arts* (Springer, 2014). In that book, I explore the potential for art and ethics to be mutually challenged and changed in that meeting. Similarly, in the following essay, I argue that the arts should be presented in all their power and ambiguity. In that context also, there is a potential for both medicine and the arts to be challenged and changed in that meeting.

My dad was an oil painter and I was fortunate to grow up surrounded by art and music. I imbibed an understanding that meaning is to be found in each of the arts — whether or not that can be reconciled with other sources of knowledge. To me, good art is complex — not confined to the simple beat of pop, or scientism. A good movie — such as 'Winter's Sleep' (by Turkish filmmaker Nuri Bilge Ceylan) — may appear simple, but it captures complexity. Life too is complex. Ideally medical educators will make use of simple models, but they will also also introduce students to the complexities of life. My essay is a challenge to present the arts on their own terms, not just for their instrumental effectiveness. When we take the arts seriously they potentially shake the simplistic certitudes of medical education and the models and metaphors on which it is (currently) founded.

The Arts and Medicine: A Challenging Relationship

Paul Ulhas Macneill

Abstract: This paper discusses various justifications for including medical humanities and art in healthcare education. It expresses concern about portrayals of the humanities and art as benign and servile in relation to medicine and the health professions. An alternative is for the humanities to take a more active role within medical education by challenging the assumptions and myths of the predominant biomedical model. Another is to challenge quiescent notions of the arts by examining examples of recent provocative work and, to this end, the paper considers the work of performance artists Stelarc and Orlan who have subjected their bodies to modifications and extensions. Their work challenges, and potentially undermines, conceptions of the body, medicine, and humanity's relationship with technology. Similarly, other artists, working with biological cultures, have raised controversial issues. Recent work of this kind defies easy understanding and resists being pressed into the service of medicine and other health professions for educational purposes by opening up topics for exploration and discussion without providing unitary explanatory frameworks. The paper goes on to discuss the implications for medical education if this is the approach to the arts and humanities in healthcare education. It suggests that there needs to be a shift in the foundational assumptions of medicine if the arts and humanities are to contribute more fully.

The medical humanities includes a broad spectrum of disciplines and different ideas about the place of the arts and humanities in medicine.[1,2] Two of the major rationales for including the humanities in medical, nursing and other health professional courses are that they provide instrumental benefits to students, and they are enriching for individual health professionals.[3-8] These are benign portrayals of the humanities in relation to medicine and the health professions more generally. Recent critical reviews propose that the humanities take a more active role within medical education by challenging the assumptions of the predominant biomedical model and by engaging more critically with the myths of medicine and the overstatement of medical competency.[1,6] This is an appealing strategy because it draws on the interrogative and analytical strengths of the humanities and puts them in a different position of power in relation to medicine. Another approach is to challenge the depiction of the arts as benign and passive. To this end, the paper discusses the artists Stelarc and Orlan, whose performances dramatise and draw attention to assumptions about the human body within both medicine and society. This highlights a need to move away from purveying the arts and the humanities as materials to service medical and other healthcare courses, and towards accepting them on their own terms. A discussion along these lines inevitably leads (again) to the value of the humanities and the arts in healthcare education.

Instrumental Benefits from the Humanities

A number of educational benefits are said to result from studying the humanities, including broader perspectives on medicine and the health professions, and an understanding of the patient within her particular circumstances and milieu.[9] The humanities are occasionally spoken of as 'humanising' medicine,[10,11] although the term has a variety of meanings including that the humanities "provide a different viewpoint" and a "critical and questioning attitude",[11] broaden the medical curriculum,[10] and bring patients being back into focus "as unique persons living with an illness" within "particular cultures or communities."[9] The expression also refers, on occasion, to developing self-awareness within the trainee health practitioner by giving attention to their own human-ness in the sense of feelings for others and understanding of their own limitations, concerns and prejudices.[11] However, the notion of the arts 'humanising medicine' has been criticised more recently.[6,9,12] It is also noted that the reference to "humanities related to medicine" in *Tomorrow's Doctors* published in 2003 by the General Medical Council in the UK, was not included in the revised 2009 document.[13,14] Perry observes an underlying assumption in the medical humanities that the "arts can assist in the development of the student as a communicative doctor."[15] Macnaughton suggests that literature, drama and painting offer insight into the "nuances of communication between people, both verbal and non-verbal."[4] Downie claims that the humanities provide "transferable skills" such as "sensitivity to nuances, ambiguities, and hidden meanings."[5] Chen *et al* consider that the "attitudes and behaviour of a holistic and compassionate practitioner " can be "experienced vicariously through the medical humanities."[16] Some claim that studying the humanities promotes empathy,[15] although many commentators are sceptical about this claim[8,17-20] (also see p. 216 in Downie[5]). Little argues, for example, that the arts only influence those already open to them.[8,17] From a review of the literature, Perry *et al* found some evidence that arts programs in medical courses lead to changes of attitude and the acquisition of some skills but no evidence to indicate whether these changes are long lasting and bring about behavioural change.[15]

There is a more general concern about instrumental justifications for the medical humanities. Gillis describes the approach as "product oriented" and presents it as an argument that "through the humanities we make physicians more understanding peopledand by extension, more effective physicians. and for this reason [the humanities] should be a part of the medical curriculum."[18] This highlights a concern that the humanities and the arts are used as *mere* instruments to the end of producing effective practitioners.

The allusion here to Kant's categorical imperative (that we should not use another human being 'merely as a means' to our own ends) is deliberate as it helps to isolate what it is about the instrumental justification that is troubling (Kant, p. 37).[21] The concern is that we may be treating the arts as *mere* instruments to effect an end—a point that Macnaughton and Downie also address.[4,5] While the humanities and the arts may provide an instrumental benefit to medical education, they are more than this in that they potentially offer benefits to individuals beyond their capacities as medical students.[4]

Macnaughton, and Downie and Macnaughton, are careful to note that the medical humanities "also have an intrinsic *value* in their own right" and they consider that this value is itself essential to "what it means to be 'educated' as distinct from simply 'trained'" (Macnaughton, p. 192).[4,22] This provides a further justification for including the humanities because, without them, a course in medicine is an insular vocational 'training' rather than an education.[4] Warner observes that this idea has been a "persistent refrain" since the early 1900s when some leaders of the USA medical establishment "warned that the allegiance to science driving the profession's technical and cultural success was endangering humanistic values fundamental to professionalism and the art of medicine." Many of these leaders argued for teaching the history of medicine as an antidote in order to maintain the "liberal education, civility and moral wisdom" of the profession and as a means for attaining the "ideal of the 'gentleman-physician' well versed in the classic liberal arts."[23]

Personal Development and Enrichment

'Personal development' and 'personal enrichment' are broader justifications for teaching medical humanities.[4,8] Unlike the instrumental rationale, the humanities are justified, even if they do not make people better doctors, because they enrich and bring greater pleasure to their lives and because "the education process touches the student more deeply at a personal level" (Macnaughton, p. 195).[4] Little (a surgeon and published poet), for example, writes that the "humanities offer an experience of the world of feelings and values, which can be as profound as people allow it to be" (Little, p. 170).[17] He cautions however, that "[t]hose who hope to make better clinicians by teaching poetry may make some of their students into better or happier people, but I doubt that they will enhance their clinical skills"[8] (see also p. 38 in Scheper-Hughes[24]). For 'teaching poetry' we could equally read 'music', 'theatre', 'film' or 'dance.'

Marcel Proust appears to agree:

> This mysterious gift [flair in diagnosis] does not entail any superiority in the other departments of the intellect, and a creature of the utmost vulgarity, someone who admires the worst pictures, the worst music. may perfectly well possess it. (Proust, p. 380)[25]

While personal enrichment may justify electives drawn from the medical humanities, this is not sufficient reason to institute a compulsory course, especially as "there are some who will always be indifferent to aesthetics, and yet be competent physicians" (Little, p. 164).[17]

The instrumental and the enriching depictions of the relationship treat the arts and humanities as providing support to medicine and comfort to practitioners. If this was the extent of the relationship, then the medical humanities would be solely justified by a health professional's benefit, edification or entertainment. While I do not mean to deny a potential beneficial role for the humanities, or for the arts as entertainment and edification, the arts and humanities offer, and are, more than this. An aspect of this wider potential lies in their capacity to engender critique.

The Arts as Dangerous

Rees is critical of the *medical* humanities for being tame. He promotes a more interventionist approach by "refusing the ends given to" the humanities and promoting "ethical questioning" that is "genuinely open-ended." His concern is that:

> Literature, art, poetry, music, film, are. too often engaged as if they are non-critical resources which can be deployed in the service of the ends determined by the medical and medical ethical powers that be.[12]

He argues that there is an "ethical imperative" to positively reform the medical humanities. As an example he advocates an "existential reflection" about "caring for persons" – the predominant rationale of all the health professions – and proposes that the humanities advocate "caring for nothing" in order to address ultimate meaninglessness. This is an idea akin to Buddhist *sunya*: a recognition that at the core of any experience of being is a void or no-thing-ness (although Rees makes no direct reference to Buddhism).[12] He acknowledges that this is a 'radical' proposition. However, it may be *too* radical to be taken seriously as it attacks a core value of the healthcare professions and of many working within the humanities. In any case, there is no obvious reason for positioning "caring for persons" and reflections on "ultimate meaninglessness" as being in opposition to each other.

This should not, however, deflect us from his cogent critique of the medical humanities. Rees's central argument is that conceptions of the arts as *non-critical resources* belittle the roles of the arts and artists. It is to treat the medical humanities as a "tool of medicine and medical ethics." "Portentously elided", he writes, "is the possibility that medical humanities is also dangerous."[12] Rees believes that the humanities have gained entré into medical education by adopting the ends of medicine and medical ethics and the result is to "defang all the potential criticisms. that literary and other sources can generate." To illustrate the point he writes that:

> One reads Shakespeare or Emily Dickenson, watches *Lorenzo's Oil* or *Wit*, considers the late paintings of DeKooning or Rembrandt, in order to become a better doctor or improve the work of doctors, and not to question the work of doctors and the associated administration of medicine as an ethical profession.[12]

In this manner lions from the Serengeti become domesticated cats for a warm place in front of the fire. Left to themselves, and appreciated in an appropriate setting, the arts may be challenging, but in this context they are pacified. In my view, however, this is a pedagogical issue to do with the manner in which the arts are employed by each humanities teacher. There is no inherent reason that the films, paintings and literature Rees refers to might not lead to "question[ing] the work of doctors and the associated administration of medicine as an ethical profession." Nevertheless, there may be more general societal perceptions of the value of the humanities that incline teachers to present a subdued and limited account of these materials.

At the nub of this issue is a perception of the humanities as marginalised in relation to science-based knowledge. In a medical context, rather than confronting this marginalisation, the response has been to emphasise the utility of the humanities. Slouka, however, decries this tendency and mounts a muscular defence:

> The humanities, done right, are the crucible within which our evolving notions of what it means to be fully human are put to the test ... They are thus, inescapably, political. Why? Because they complicate our vision, pull our most cherished notions out by the roots, flay our pieties. Because they grow uncertainty. Because they expand the reach of our understanding (and therefore our compassion), even as they force us to draw and redraw the borders of tolerance.. The humanities, in short, are a superb delivery mechanism for what we might call democratic values. There is no better that I am aware of.[26]

In a similar vein, Bleakley *et al* wrote that "One of the primary functions of art is surely to challenge the basis upon which we are civil. Art often sets out to shock our sensibilities and question our limits to taste."[27] This is to draw "attention to the transgressive nature of art" and artists who "challenge societal norms working with and against the boundaries of taste and expectation."[28] The role of the humanities is *not* therefore to "tiptoe through the minefield, leaving the mines intact and loaded" but to accept that provocation and discomfort (if not explosions) play a valuable role in learning. There is something antithetical about treating the arts as a mere resource for a specified purpose when their strength lies (in part) in their capacity to break bounds and to lead to unanticipated freedom of thought and appreciation.

The Medical Humanities as Critique

One of the more compelling arguments for a role for the humanities in medicine is to provide critical reflection on assumptions and predominant 'taken-for-granted' metaphors of medicine and the healthcare professions more generally. However, the medical humanities have shied away from this role. Bishop is critical of the medical humanities for acting as a "compensatory mechanism for the mechanical thinking that has dominated and continues to dominate medicine." His point is that the very attempt to humanise medicine in an instrumental way, has served to reinforce and perpetuate a dualism that already exists between the humanities and medicine, a dualism that is founded on an erroneous distinction. More importantly, it misses the possibility of the arts finding "human being at the margins of what it is always a struggle to say."[6] Davis and Morris also challenge a "science/humanities, facts/ values divide" by refusing to accept any "hard and fast boundary" between "biology" and "culture."[29] To put this in the positive, as Davis and Morris do in their 'Biocultures manifesto,' "[s]cience and humanities are incomplete without each other." As a consequence, "the biological without the cultural, or the cultural without the biological, is doomed to be reductionist at best and inaccurate at worst."[29] The essence of these criticisms is that medicine, with the connivance of bioethics, assumes a dubious distinction between fact and value as if medicine is about fact (and aligned with science) and ethics and the humanities are about questions of value.

Shapiro *et al* raise the "problem of how certain biomedical narratives are privileged."[1] Of particular concern are the "prevailing metaphors" which are "mechanistic (the body as machine), linear (find the root cause and create and effect) and hierarchical (doctor as expert)" and the "dominant narrative" which is a "story of restitution" in which the "patient becomes ill; patient is cured by physician expert; patient is restored to preillness state."[1] Anyone engaged (as I am each year) in interviewing incoming medical students will know that the 'body-as- machine' and a 'story of restitution' are dominant narratives of students even before entry into a medical course. As many of my clinician colleagues acknowledge, these are inaccurate and misleading portrayals of medical practice, yet the metaphors have been remarkably resilient. One of their effects is to marginalise the humanities. On the hopeful side, however, as Shapiro *et al* note, there are "many reflective physicians and medical educators" who support "an expanded vision of medicine and medical education."[1] For this expanded vision to have any effect, it needs to be "nurtured and enlarged" and displace (or at least be taken as a serious challenge to) the preeminent biomedical model in medical education.[1]

Provocative Art as Critique

As one of the ways to explore and question assumptions of medicine, including the metaphor of the 'body-as-machine', I examine the work of two leading international performance artists, the Australian Stelarc and the French artist Orlan, who have subjected their bodies to modifications and extensions. Their work deliberately challenges conceptions of the body, along with medicine's relationship with technology in a number of ways. What their projects have in common is technological or surgical augmentation of their bodies. Both of them intentionally confront the notion that individual corporeality is intrinsic to identity.

Stelarc for example, in performances of THIRD ARM, has allowed internet audiences to activate electrodes in his body to effect movements of an additional prosthetic arm. In MOVATAR, the machine itself prompted movements of his body. He has described himself as "intrigued about identity, the self, free will and agency in these performances" when "his body becomes, or is partly, taken over by an external agency."[32] Unlike science fiction, this is not a thought-experiment but a direct physical experiment with his body incorporating (or being altered to include) technological extensions.

Orlan's face has been surgically sculpted on numerous occasions to embody icons of feminine beauty including "the nose of Diana, the mouth of Boucher's Europa, the chin of Botticelli's Venus, and the eyes of Gerome's Psyche."[33] These operations have been broadcast live to galleries around the world as "baroque theatrical performances. in which she and her medical attendants wore fashion-designer costumes."[28] Poetry reading and music accompanied the surgery, in an operating theatre decorated with large bowls of grapes. There is an apparent intention both to invert the usual power relationship between patient and doctor, and to shock. Jane Goodall has commented that:

> Both artists. are creators of scandal in the original sense of the term as. a trap or stumbling block, metaphorically interpreted as a moral snare causing perplexity and ethical confusion (OED).

> Some forms of risk-taking may be scandalous, but scandal in this sense tests the moral ground and puts morality itself at risk.[34]

She interprets the work of Stelarc and Orlan as "good scandal done which generates complex confusions around high-intensity issues and cannot be resolved through the simple assertion of precepts."[31] For Zylinska, this goodness results "from the impossibility of providing a consistent, totalizing narrative about the events in question."[32] The point I wish to pick up on is this capacity of these works to generate controversy and debate about the mean-ing and implications of the work without "providing a consistent, totalizing narrative."

Both Stelarc and Orlan have positioned their work as speaking of the "posthuman body", the "body as obsolete" and a "post-modern and cyber-cultural body." The idea of our bodies as extensions of technology leads Joan Broadhurst Dixon to describe the human as fluid and in question, and to conclude that "We are losing touch with our bodies, our human physical dimensions, and with it our meaty morality (or ethics)."[35] Indeed there is now a genre of post-human literature of which Stelarc and Orlan's work has become a part.[36-42] However, I am not examining their work as an adherent to a new of canon of thought about post-human beings, but rather, for its capacity to generate controversy and questions. Some of these questions will inevitably be about the value of the works themselves and their underlying presuppositions, and about the relationship between the artists and their medical attendants. Others may relate to the artists' claims about the body as obsolete and the 'cyborg' blending of body and machine. This in turn draws attention, poten-tially, to the assumptions of the 'body-as-machine' within both medicine and art.

Others observing performances of Orlan and Stelarc have not seen an *obsolete* body but are drawn to the meaty and suffering body. For Jones and Sofia, the artists' bodies "in the here and now" are bodies that "bleed and pulsate" and experience "the reality of pain."[43] Both Stelarc and Orlan deny or downplay that pain is a significant element in their projects. However, Jones and Sofia observe that "[d]uring her operations Orlan tries to show no distress, but this doesn't mean that the pain disappears [it] is displaced onto the audience. something she herself acknowledges." They note similarly that "Stelarc asserts that the intrusions he makes on his body are a means to an end and are only coincidentally painful." Yet, for their audiences, "witnessing of pain is an important part of the performance of both artists, and one that not all can endure, especially when surgery is performed." Jones and Sofia consider that there is a "redemptive value from the audience's viewpoint" in that "their bodily suffering spares us the greater agony of having to find out more directly what is entailed in transforming ideals into flesh."[43]

These are just some of the controversies surrounding the work of Orlan and Stelarc. As provocations in the context of medical education, their work raises many questions concerning the role of medicine; whether we are indeed moving to a technologically augmented cyborg body; and ethical questions about whether any of this is ethically acceptable for art, or medicine, and on

what basis.[28] Art is not immune from demands for social and ethical responsibility (Zylinska, p. 149-74).[44,45] Neither the art work itself nor commentaries
by the artists (and others) presuppose any particular answers. The works
themselves, and the commentaries, are however powerful provocations for
students' own enquiry.

Beyond Orlan and Stelarc, there are other potentially challenging possibilities in the work of current artists. Catts and Zurr (from SymbioticA) have
used tissue culture as "an effective methodology to confront the complexities
and to contest dominant ideologies."[45,46] In their installation 'Tissue Culture
& Art (ificial) Wombs (AKA the Semi-Living Worry Dolls)', they cultured
cells on polymer scaffolds as 'worry dolls', in a series from 'A' to 'G', with the
promise that the dolls would take those worries away. Doll 'A', for example,
represents "the worry about Absolute Truths and people who think they hold
them."[47] This artwork is "both 'tongue-in-cheek' and serious in attempting to
draw attention to assumptions and ethical conventions within art, science and
culture and open these up for critique and deeper understanding."[28] Similarly,
Julia Reodica cultivated her own vaginal cells for a 2004 project 'hymeNextTM'
to produce a series of artificial hymens that "aim to confront modern sexual-
ity, and provoke thought on the female body and the emphasis placed on
virginity" (Zylinska, p. 161).[45,48] Eduardo Kac is renowned for his GFP Bunny
Alba, the green fluorescent rabbit made by using transgenic materials (Zylinska, p. 150-2).[45,49] Bioart of this kind raises many questions about the danger
of artists working with biological materials to culture, clone and generate new
life forms, anddmore fundamentallydabout the relationship between science
and art (Zylinska, p. 149-74).[45]

I have focused on the work of artists working 'at the edge' (so to speak) of
their art, and in particular, provocative performance art involving alterations
and extensions of the body, and bioart which makes use of new biological
technologies. Equally, work in other genres of the arts gives rise to controversies. For example, David Foster Wallace's last novel *The Pale King* addresses
the issue of boredom with "little resembling an over-arching narrative," no
plot, just something sketched "here and there" like "shards in the tornado."[50]
Ross, in his *The Rest is Noise*, listens to the 20th century through its music
in a journey into atonality, discordance, and beauty in surprising moments,
glimpsed against the backdrop of the politicians, wars, demagogues, dictators
and genocide.[51]

The point I am endeavouring to make is that recent work in any of the
arts tends to defy easy understanding and resist instrumental application. It
also resists the artist's interpretation (as discussed above in relation to Stelarc

and Orlan) and is resistant to a ready translation into a teaching medium to make a particular point. New art of this kind demands to be taken seriously on its own terms (or not at all).

Another reason for suggesting this approach is that students in the health professions are conspicuously young (obviously so in medicine and dentistry, and true of the majority of students in nursing, social work and psychology). My impression of medical students (in Australia, Singapore and England at least) is that 19th and early 20th century art, literature and music has little interest for many of them. Current and more risqué artwork may be more appealing. Moreover, exploring current art is more likely to be a genuinely shared enquiry between the teacher and student, both of whom may experience similar responses. Using material that we as teachers are struggling to make sense of is not as conspicuously manipulative as drawing on classics to make particular (pre-determined) points about issued whether about medicine, or death, or living in poverty. We are comfortable with the classics – and have views about them – in a way in which we may not be with recent film, art, music or literature from artists who are playing with and against the boundaries of their own genre.

A further reason is that, rightly or wrongly, medicine and the health professions are projected and perceived as gung-ho, heroic, unlocking nature's secrets with promises of laboratory grown organs from our own cells, pushing the limits of human finitude, and rendering the secret codes of our genes open to scientific code breakers who promise to eradicate cystic fibrosis and diseases of old age. These ideas are strong provocations in themselves. They need to be met with equally strong images and responses from the arts.

However, I am not proposing that this should be the only approach. My underlying concern is with a manipulative and clumsy use of the humanities and the arts as instruments to achieve a specific purpose. This occurs when students are expected to read a novel to gain a particular understanding—where the teacher has a prescribed agenda in mind. The value of the arts and humanities is in their open-ended support of questioning, and their potential to "enliven and animate and develop new forms of engagement that allow for participation and discovery through enactment and embodiment and not just through abstraction or theory."[28] It derives (in part) from a capacity of art to generate controversy and debate about the meaning and implications of the work and the subjects referred to. This is still an instrumental use of the arts, I acknowledge. The difference is that art is used *not merely* as a means, but with respect for each work of art in and of itself. The same respect can be extended to the classics—and is by good teachers. Even when familiar, the classics need to be read for the surprise, the delight, or listened to attentively for that exquisite or devastating moment. They too resist easy translation. They can be discussed as works open to many interpretations. Art needs to be allowed its own impact and not be exploited solely, or predominantly, for some other purpose.

The Humanities, Arts, and Healthcare Education

If art and the humanities are to play a more critical role, rather than "attempting to 'produce' humanistic attributes widget- fashion" (to use Shapiro *et al*'s term), it raises the question of how this may be possible in healthcare education.[1] For reasons of space I am constrained to offer the barest sketch of an answer to this question.

There is a good argument for offering humanities *electives* to medical students. However, arguments based on the "intrinsic *value* in their own right" of the humanities and their being "essential components of the educated mind" (Macnaughton, p. 192)[4] are insufficient to substantiate *compulsory* courses in the humanities in my view. These arguments only have cogency if we accept as valid medicine's place as an *elite* profession and a concomitant need for "the 'gentleman-physician' well versed in the classic liberal arts."[23] Little is correct, I believe, in observing that there are many competent clinicians indifferent to aesthetics and that the arts only influence those already open to them.[8,17] It may be counterproductive to insist on teaching the humanities to those not interested, at least in the context of traditional medical courses.

In my view there needs to be a shift in the foundational assumptions of medicine and the metaphors by which medicine is taught if the arts and humanities are to contribute more fully to medical (and other healthcare) education. To persist with a metaphor of 'body as a machine' and 'medicine as a science' offers little space in which the arts and humanities can contribute in an appropriate way, other than as electives for those students with a special interest. The metaphors and myths of biomedical medicine are obviously limited, but like many such simplifications they have been effective in medical education for the last century. I claim, however, that the discontinuities and disjunctions have become too many and too great to persevere with these oversimplified models.

Shapiro *et al* go some of the way toward this conclusion in suggesting that there needs to be a lessening of the "ubiquitous divide between scientific/ clinical medicine" and recontextualising of medicine to place the "medical humanities close to the core rather than on the periphery of the profession."[1]

At the Peninsula Medical School in the UK, Bleakey *et al* describe a more far-reaching shift of the kind I am suggesting, where the medical humanities have been adopted as "an explicit theme in the core undergraduate curriculum" as well as being represented in elective study units. As they report them, these changes represent a significant expansion of the underlying conceptions of medicine.[27] My sense is that, for the arts and humanities to play an effective role within medical (or other health professional) curricula, there needs to be a similar broadening of understanding. From my experience of teaching ethics in medicine, I am aware that a change, toward recognising ethics as underpinning medical practice, was required before it became accepted and integrated within medical education. For years, even after being adopted as a required course in many schools of medicine, ethics struggled as an add-on, an adornment in the school brochure, but not taken seriously by faculty.

Short of re-conceiving foundational metaphors in medical education, it still remains open to individual teachers to introduce elements of the humanities or arts in their teaching in any course within medicine, or for a medical school to introduce a substantial strand that has integrated the humanities (such as the personal and professional development modules in some medical schools). In skilful hands I believe this can work. However, teaching the humanities is a challenge within a medical course founded on the traditional biomedical model.

Conclusion

In this paper I have discussed different approaches to the arts and humanities in medicine and the healthcare professions. These include the humanities as providing instrumental benefits so as to make physicians more understanding of people and more effective physicians;[8] the humanities as enriching the lives of healthcare professionals; the humanities as a source of critique in medicine and the health professions; and the importance of addressing the arts and humanities on their own terms. This has led to questioning "a humanities curriculum ... injected into, or grafted onto, a medicine curriculum as compensation, complement or supplement"[27] and to an exploration of the need for a fundamental realignment of medical curricula to address the fictions of the biomedical model and its concomitant fiction of clinical practice as science. It is in the context of a shift in conception of medicine of this kind, that the arts and humanities may find their place within healthcare professional education.

Whether or not this occurs, it is a mistake to treat the arts and humanities as benign and passive additions to healthcare education. The intention of this paper has been to underscore the strength of the arts and humanities as supports for open enquiry. The paper is also proposing that the scope of the arts and humanities be more broadly encompassing to include material at the edge of the humanities *oeuvre*—such as the performance art of Stelarc and Orlan. Such material may have a special attraction and power for the relatively short time it remains challenging and difficult. Its potency will also diminish and it too will be seen as a quaint relic of concerns that are passé. However, as we turn that corner, artists will be creating yet another genre, and further challenging works with layers of meaning, because that is the nature of art.

References

1   Shapiro J, Coulehan J, Wear D, *et al*. Medical humanities and their discontents: definitions, critiques, and implications. *Acad Med* 2009;84:192-8.

2   Greaves D. The nature and role of the medical humanities. In: Evans M, Finlay IG, eds. *Medical Humanities*. London: BMJ Books, 2001:13-22.

3   Gillon R. Welcome to the medical humanitiesdand why (editorial). *J Med Ethics* 2000;26:23-30.

4   Macnaughton J. Why medical humanities now? In: Evans M, Finlay IG, eds. *Medical Humanities*. London: BMJ Books, 2001:187-203.

5   Downie R. Medical humanities: means, ends, and evaluation. In: Evans M, Finlay IG, eds. *Medical Humanities*. London: BMJ Books, 2001:204-16.

6   Bishop JP. Rejecting medical humanism: medical humanities and the metaphysics of medicine. *J Med Humanit* 2008;29:15-25.

7   Petersen A, Bleakley A, Brömer R, *et al*. The medical humanities today: humane health care or tool of governance. *J Med Humanit* 2008;29:1-4.

8   Little M. Does reading poetry make you a better clinician? *Intern Med J* 2001;31:60-1.

9   Wear D. The medical humanities: toward a renewed praxis. *J Med Humanit* 2009;30:209-20.

10 Stokes J. Grief and the performing arts: a brief experiment in humanizing medical education. *J Med Educ* 1980;55:215.

11 Downie RS, Hendry RA, Macnaughton RJ, *et al*. Humanizing medicine: a special study module. *Med Educ* 1997;31:276-80.

12 Rees G. The ethical imperative of medical humanities. *J Med Humanit* 2010;31:267-77.

13 General Medical Council. *Tomorrow's Doctors, 2003*. http://www.gmc-uk.org (ac-

cessed Oct 2011).

14　General Medical Council. *Tomorrow's Doctors, 2009.* http://www.gmc-uk.org (accessed Oct 2011).

15　Perry M, Maffulli N, Willson S, *et al.* The effectiveness of arts-based interventions in medical education: a literature review. *Med Educ* 2011;45:141-8.

16　Chen JY, Salter DJ, Chan LC. Pen, brush and camera: outcomes-based medical humanities. *Med Educ* 2010;44:1139.

17　Little JM. *Humane Medicine.* Cambridge and New York: University of Cambridge, 1995.

18　Gillis CM. Medicine and humanities: voicing connections. *J Med Humanit* 2008;29:5-14.

19　Keizer B. Medicine: tales of empathy. *Threepenny Review* 2003;93:94.

20　Macnaughton J. The dangerous practice of empathy. *Lancet* 2009;373:1940-1.

21　Kant I. *Groundwork of the Metaphysics of Morals.* Gregor M. (ed. & trans). Cambridge: Cambridge University Press, 1997.

22　Downie R, Macnaughton J. Should medical students read Plato? *Med J Aust* 1999;170:125-7.

23　Warner JH. The humanising power of medical history: responses to biomedicine in the 20th century United States. *Med Humanit.* Published Online First: 31 July 2011. doi:10.1136/medhum-2011-010034.

24　Scheper-Hughes N. Medicine and the Humanities: [E]merging Definitions. *Townsend Center for the Humanities: Townsend Center Occasional Papers [listed as Keizer Bert 'Euthanasia Policy in the Netherlands'].* http://townsendcenter.berkeley.edu (accessed Oct 2011).

25　Proust M. *From 'Madame Swann at home,' Remembrance of Things Past.* Vol. 1. Scott Moncrieff CK (trans). New York: Random House, 1961.

26　Slouka M. *'Dehumanized: When Math and Science Rule the School'.* Harper's Magazine, 2009:32-40. http://www.harpers.org/archive/2009/09/0082640 (accessed Oct 2011).

27　Bleakley A, Marshal R, Br¨omer R. Toward an aesthetic medicine: developing a core medical humanities undergraduate curriculum. *J Med Humanit* 2006;7:197-213.

28　Macneill PU, Ferran B. Art and bioethics: shifts in understanding across genres. *J Bioeth Inq* 2011;8:71-85.

29　Davis L, Morris D. Biocultures manifesto. *New Lit Hist* 2008;38:411-18.

30　Stelarc. 2011. http://stelarc.org/_.swf (accessed Oct 2011).

31　Orlan. 2010. http://www.orlan.net/ (accessed Oct 2011).

32　Zylinska J, Hall G. Probings: an interview with Stelarc. In: Zylinska J, ed. *The Cyborg Experiments: The Extensions of the Body in the Media Age.* London & New

York: Continuum, 2002:114-30.

33 Zylinska J. The future . is monstrous. In: Zylinska J, ed. *The Cyborg Experiments.* (Ibid). 2002:214-36.

34 Goodall J. An order of pure decision: un-natural selection in the work of Stelarc and Orlan. In: Featherstone M, ed. *Body Modification.* London: Sage, 2000:149-70.

35 Broadhurst Dixon J. Postscripts: ground zero. In: Broadhurst Dixon J, Cassidy EJ, eds. *Virtual Futures: Cyberotics, Technology and Posthuman Pragmatism.* London and New York: Routledge, 1998:164-6.

36 Badmington N, ed. *Posthumanism.* Bassington & New York: Palgrave, 2000.

37 Badmington N. Theorizing posthumanism. *Cult Critiq* 2003;53:10-27.

38 Bostrom N. A history of transhumanist thought. In: Rectenwald M, Carl L, eds. *Academic Writing Across the Disciplines.* New York: Pearson Longman, 2011.

39 Hayles NK. *How We Became Posthuman: Virtual Bodies in Cybernetics, Literature, and Informatics.* Chicago & London: University Of Chicago Press, 1999.

40 Moreno JD, Hughes J. Human vs. posthuman. *Hastings Cent Rep* 2007;37:4-7.

41 Simon B. Introduction: toward a critique of posthuman futures. *Cult Critiq* 2003;53:1-19.

42 Thacker E. Data made flesh: biotechnology and the discourse of the posthuman. *Cult Critiq* 2003:72-97.

43 Jones M, Sofia Z. Stelarc and Orlan in the middle ages. In: Zylinska J, ed. *The Cyborg Experiments.* (Op. cit.[32]). 2002:56-72.

44 Zylinska J. You killed Barack Obama. *J Vis Cult* 2009;8:190.

45 Zylinska J. *Bioethics in the Age of New Media.* Cambridge Mass, & London: MIT, 2009.

46 Catts O, Zurr I. The ethics of experiential engagement with the manipulation of life. In: da Costa B, Philip K, eds. *Tactical Biopolitics: Art, Activism, and Technoscience.* Cambridge, Massachusetts and London: MIT Press, 2008:125-42.

47 Catts O, Zurr I. Growing semi-living sculptures: the tissue culture and art project. *Leonardo J* 2002;35:365-70.

48 Pasko JM. Bio-artists bridge gap between arts, sciences: use of living organisms is attracting attention and controversy. Associated Press 3/4/2007. http://www. msnbc. msn.com/id/17387568/ns/technology_and_science-science/ (accessed Oct 2011).

49 Kac E. http://www.ekac.org/transgenicindex.html (accessed Oct 2011).

50 Grossman L. Unfinished business: resurrecting David Foster Wallace's last novel. *Time Magazine* 2011;177(15):46-50.

51 Ross A. *The Rest is Noise: Listening to the Twentieth century.* New York: Farrar, Straus and Giroux, 2007.

Index

abduction, 191
abnormal discourse, 196
abnormality, 298
Accreditation Council for Graduate
    Medical Education, 239–240
Ackerknecht, Erwin H., 70–71
ADA. *See* Americans with Disabilities
    Act
affect, 248
aging, 263
ague. *See* malaria
AIDS, 231, 234
Alexandrians, 91
alopecia, 38
altruism, 240
    medical humanities and, 278
    professionalism and, 241
    self-interest and, 246
AMA. *See* American Medical Association
American College of Physicians, 240
American Journal of Cardiology, 82–83
American Medical Association (AMA),
    105
    Code of Ethics, 250
    Council on Medical Education, 3
    panel on Medical Curriculum and
        Human Values, 8
American Society for Bioethics and Hu-
    manities (ASBH), 12, 26
Americans with Disabilities Act (ADA),
    296
Ammonius of Alexandria, 44
analytical reading skills, 175–176
anatomy, 91
"Ancient Medicine," 87
aneurism, 53
anthropology, 102
    medical epistemology and, 199–200

antiseptic method, 66
applied humanities, 284
    scholars, 271
Aquapendente, Fabricius ab, 39, 42
Arabic medicine, classical, 91
Arantius, 39
Aretaeus, 39
Aristotle, 90, 189
    on drama, 197
    on medicine, 190
    on practical reason, 193
Arnold, Matthew, 197
Ar-Rází, Abú Becr Mohammed Ibn
    Zacaríyá, 39
Arrowsmith, 234
Ars Poetica (Horace), 197
art
    bioart, 317
    dangerous nature of, 311–313
    functions of, 313
    history, 199
    medical education and, 318–320
    medicine as, 80–81, 306
    provocative, 314–319
The Art of Fiction (Gardner), 229
ASBH. *See* American Society for Bioeth-
    ics and Humanities
Aspects of the Novel (Forster), 229
Association of American Medical Col-
    leges, 23, 105, 134, 239–240
authority, 156
autism, 300–301
autonomy, 241
    disability and, 298

Bacon, Francis, 294–295
Bacon, Lord, 34
Bad Nauheim, 103

classroom discussion, 260
clinical cases, 194
clinical judgment, 193–194
  bioethics and, 202*n*3
  narrative and, 195
  narrative ethics and, 200–201
  science and, 195–196
clinical relevance, 276–277
Clinton, Clifford, 82
Clouser, C. Danner, 187–188
club foot, 43–44
Cnidians, 88, 98
Code Gray, 182
Cohen, Maynard, 175
Cohnheim, Julius Friedrich, 52
collateral circulation, 53
College of Visual and Performing Arts, 179
Columbus, Realdus, 42
Coma, 184
commercialism, 240, 251
Committee on Human Values in Medicine, 119
community
  medical education and, 129
  service, 250
compassion, 4, 5
  definitions of, 151–153
  human values and, 128
  medical humanities and, 278
  patient and, 155–156
  in professionalism, 245
  psychology and, 156–157
  in student-teacher relationships, 153–155
competence, 131
  cultural, 23
  humanistic, 282–283
  in medical education, 282–283
  narrative, 212, 249
  subcompetencies, 236
Compleat Physician, 152
Comte, Augustus, 158
Conference on Medical Education, 115
confrontation, 114
congenital conditions, 301

"Constructing Normalcy: The Bell Curve, the Novel, and the Invention of the Disabled Body in the Nineteenth Century" (Davis), 298
Copernicus, 39
Cordell, Eugene, 6, 31, 47
  on history, 33
Corynebacterium xerosis, 233
Cos, 87–88
Coulehan, Jack, 22, 24, 236–237, 269
Couser, G. Thomas, 290–291
Cousins, Norman, 172
Creighton University, 11
Crime and Punishment (Dostoyevsky), 25
critical thinking, 160
cross-disciplinary reflection, 280–281
cultural competency, 23
Cunningham, Merle, 108, 115–117
curing, 231
  disability and, 301
Cutting for Stone (Verghese), 224
cynicism
  in medical education, 112–113
  in medicine, 246
cystic fibrosis, 318

"Daffodils" (Wordsworth), 260
Danforth Foundation, 10
danger, 229–230
Daremberg, Charles Victor, 80
Davis, Lennard, 298, 314
Davis, Phil, 170
Dax's Story, 181
The Deadly Deception, 182
Deaf people, 300
death, 112
deformity, 294
dehumanizing process, 106, 150–151, 154
  in medical education, 110–111
  patient in, 111
  rebellion and, 113
  students on, 125
Dekker, Thomas, 95

United Presbyterian Church, 10
United States, medicine in, 240
University of Buffalo, 37
University of California, 9
University of California Berkeley, 258,
    262
University of California San Francisco,
    258
University of Connecticut, 106, 122
University of Maryland, 35
University of Minnesota, 35
University of Pennsylvania, 35
University of Pittsburg, 171
University of Texas Medical Branch, 2
University of Wisconsin, 70

Varolius, 39
vascular system, 53
Vastyan, E. A., 10, 13, 19–20, 131
Verghese, Abraham, 224–225
Vesalius, Andreas, 39, 51, 96
    influence of, 52
Vidaver, Doris, 175
villains, 243–244
Virchow, Rudolf, 51
    on medicine, 78
virtue, 239, 246
Voices From the Front, 182
von Baer, Karl, 51
von Beyer, Adolf, 61
vortex motion, 57

Wallace, David Foster, 317
Warner, J. H., 310
Watts, Malcolm S., 9
Wear, Delese, 23, 24, 224
Welch, William Henry, 47
wellbeing, 269
Wellcome Trust, 2
Western civilization, 75
White, Hayden, 198
White Coat ceremonies, 251
Whose Life Is It Anyway?, 184
Williams, Peter, 245

Williams, William Carlos, 172
witnessing, 241
    narratives, 285
Wolfe, Thomas, 234
women's health, 171
Women's Medical College of Baltimore,
    31
Woolf, Virginia, 169
Wordsworth, William, 260
World War I, 74–75
World War II, 75
    medical history and, 80
A World without Bodies (Mitchell), 300

Zarconi, Joseph, 23
Zurr, I., 317
Zylinska, J., 315

22939631R10222

Made in the USA
Middletown, DE
12 August 2015